ESTROGENERATION

ESTROGENERATION

HOW ESTROGENICS ARE MAKING YOU FAT, SICK, AND INFERTILE

ANTHONY G. JAY, PH.D.

PYRIMIDINE
PUBLISHING

TALLAHASSEE, FLORIDA

Pyrimidine Publishing Company, LLC
155 Office Plaza Drive, Suite A
Tallahassee, FL 32301

All registered trademarks in this book are property of their respective owners.
The publisher is not responsible for websites (or their content) that are not owned by the publisher.
Library of Congress Control Number: 2016962910
ISBN: 978-1-946546-01-2 (HB)
ISBN: 978-1-946546-05-0 (PB)
ISBN: 978-1-946546-02-9 (EB)

PYRIMIDINE
PUBLISHING

WE PUT THE "FUN" IN "FUNCTIONAL"
WWW.PYRIMIDINEPUBLISHING.COM

I dedicate this book to Ave Maria University. I would not be where I am today without the outstanding education I received from Ave. In essence, the culture and people of Ave Maria University championed a "work ethic" that went beyond mere "work" and inspired the pursuit of "ethic". And so what if I never learned to spell Armaggedon. At Ave Maria, I realized this wasn't the end of the world.

Contents

ESTROGENERATION

Our Sobering Situation

PAYPAL CO-FOUNDER PETER THIEL once said, "we wanted flying cars but instead we got 140 characters".

I suggest that we could refurbish Peter Thiel's slogan and similarly say "*we wanted a cure for cancer but instead we got...more cancer*". Not quite as catchy as flying cars, I know, but a true story.

Welcome to the Age of *Personal*ized Science and the Age of *Gene*tics. I'm glad you are here with me. It's the dawn of an exciting day.

But welcome, too, to the Age of *Politic*ized Science and the Age of *Estrogen*ics. What a mess! It has become clear that our current system needs an overhaul or we will no longer even outlast the lifespans of our predecessors.

Specifically, our trust in the current political and medical systems seems to be diminishing, along with our testosterone, our muscle-mass, and our fertility. Meanwhile, rates of obesity, cancer, blood clots, depression, and allergies are on the rise far beyond population increase percentages. Oh, and every single health problem I just listed relates back to these things called "estrogenics" and what I call "*The 7 Deadly Things*", as you'll see.

Within the setting of my life – a little fishing, a little courtship, and a big wedding – this book reveals our current climate of artificial estrogens with sobering "Chagrin". Estrogenics are a clear and present danger and estrogenics relate to *most of our modern health epidemics*. They are destroying us and they are destroying the wildlife around us.

At the same time, the "Tonic" is herein prescribed – how we can reverse this mess or, at the very least, how you and your family can stay out of it. It starts with education and vigilance; the recognition of these artificial estrogens and what to do to carefully avoid them. It's important so let's get started.

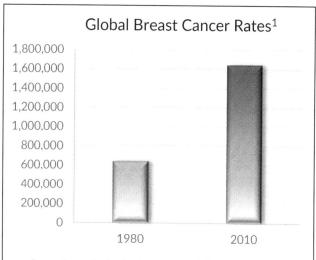

Global Breast Cancer Rates[1]

	1980	2010

A preview of what's to come...global breast cancer rates comparing 1980 to 2010. Are plastic water bottles with pink ribbons the optimal "solution"?

PART

1

INDECENT EXPOSURES

CHAPTER 1

We Are Sterile Contaminated by Estrogenics

Stinklers

WHEN I ARRIVED AT AVE Maria University's campus for the first time, I nervously scanned the sea of unfamiliar faces. I was 18 years old.

I had no idea that, within a few hours, I was about to learn some bizarre information pertaining to artificial estrogens. This new estrogenic information would shake me to the core. It would change my outlook on what goes *into* my body and *onto* my body. In fact, what I was about to discover would one day inspire this very book.

"Don't worry, I'll hold your stuff. You just focus on making friends," my trendy cargo shorts reassured me.

I advanced deeper onto Ave Maria's campus, like a deer stepping out onto a meadow.

This was a new chapter in my life. It was time to "grow up", time to focus on my future, my grades, my...fashion sense.

Looking around, I noticed a handwritten name tag that spelled "Dave". It was scrawled in blue-marker. Above the name tag was a friendly face. I walked up, smiled, and introduced myself. From there it was onward and upward; orientation week at Ave Maria University in the sunshine state of Florida.

On that fateful day at Ave, I felt especially out of place because I had never once visited the campus. I have always had a weakness for impetuosity, so when I had heard that the culture and faculty at Ave Maria University were phenomenal, that had been good enough for me. Well, that and the promise of this rare and peculiar thing called "warmth".

You see, before I free-soloed to Florida for college, Minnesota was my home. Far, far out, rural Minnesota; the grassy county of Stevens.

In case you haven't heard, Minnesota is cold. Sometimes even minus 40 degrees cold – that icy juncture where Daniel Fahrenheit collides with Anders Celsius. In fact, some *crazy* people even drive trucks onto the ice of frozen lakes in Minnesota [hand slowly raising]. Think about that for a second – the ice is thick enough to support a truck. Consult your physician before attempting.

Because of the sheer plethora of ice patches available to motorists, my motherland is actually known as "The Land of 10,000 Lakes". A slightly lesser known fact about Minnesota, however, is that it is also the land of 100,000 fishermen. Now that's 10 fishermen per lake, in case you're doing the math and we're talking about *serious* fishermen – people addicted to fishing. Anyone familiar with this addiction? [hand raising again] It's what usually drives people like me to take trucks onto ice in the first place.

Besides a few of my past college adventures, fish play a central role in this book. They "breathe in" and "soak in" estrogenics day and night. We'll discuss the unfortunate estrogenic burdens within fat, livers, and urine in animals ranging from polar bears to alligators, as well as the resulting health problems from all these exposures, but *fish* will be featured more consistently and more prominently than the rest. Fish are second only to humans in this book. We can learn a lot from the humble and tasty fish. Recent insights into infertility from artificial estrogens, for example, were first discovered in fish.

So, like a fish out of ice-cold water, this Minnesotan migrated to Florida. To Ave Maria.

Shortly after I met Dave and a few other new college classmates, we were all herded into a large auditorium. Lectures and orientation break-out sessions commenced.

Overall, I felt that the orientation presentations were informative but they lacked sparkle and passion. They seemed more like legal "fig-leaves" rather than useful information. One talk, however, broke the mold. Perhaps literally...since mold secretes a substance that acts like estrogen in our bodies, as I would discover later.

The orientation talk began when a smartly dressed speaker stepped up to the lectern and stated: "you probably shouldn't drink the tap water in these parts." Strong words to newly minted freshies! Why not drink the water!? The speaker went on to say that artificial estrogen was present in the water.

Was this person being over-dramatic or over-scrupulous?

Either way, my roommates and I weren't taking any chances. Even beyond that cautionary orientation speech recommendation, my redneck palate – a palate raised on "real" well water especially sensitive to chemical tastes – had already confirmed that the water was indeed full of chemicals.

So, at 3 A.M. that very night, we all drove over to the Naples Wal-Mart and bought a chrome water filter and a yellow whiffle ball bat. I never understood why we bought the whiffle ball bat but the water filter saw heavy use.

The filter worked as a flip attachment to our sink faucet. Mercifully, it successfully removed the nasty chemical flavor that was otherwise in our dorm room's tap water. Done!

Or were we?

The tap-water epiphany set my mind reeling. Are artificial estrogens found in places beyond the water? And how do they impact my health? Asking these very questions over the course of years began to elevate my awareness. And sure enough, I eventually would begin to find estrogenics in places I would have never predicted. Such observations were all due to that initial spark of orientation awareness.

Apparently – we were additionally informed during that memorable Ave orientation lecture – "you shouldn't drink the tap water" because water in that Southernmost region of America contained especially high levels of birth-control hormones. "EE2" it was called. Nobody really explained what EE2 did exactly or why chugging EE2 was bad but it sure sounded odious. "Man boobs?" suggested a classmate after the talk.

The larger story went something like this: "Florida is at sea level. Most water is contaminated by salt, so the municipal water supply needs to be continuously recycled. When people flush hormones out of their bodies in the form of pee, the hormones circle right back through the water supply and don't really come out during that recycling process."

Hormone *concentrate*. Gotcha. "Recycle, reduce, and re-pee". It sounded like a bad dream or a disgusting twist on "going green".

The experts even had a name for the early-stage recycled water. They called it "reclaimed".

Once my mind was scarred by the reclaimed water epiphany, I realized that reclaimed water was all around me in Florida. The little ponds around campus where I would fish for bass with Father Robert Garrity had signs that read: "Catch and Release Fishing Only: Reclaimed Water". Many canals too, similar signage. And could you honestly trust water *without* the signs? Even many *lawns* warned of reclaimed water use around Naples, Florida.

Oh, and the lawns! Those lawns harbored the infamous Florida sprinklers.

Nearly my first day at Ave Maria University, Dave – who turned out to be my roommate – almost immediately christened the sprinklers surrounding our dorm "the stinklers".

Each and every evening, promptly after the sun disappeared, the stinklers automatically hissed into action, and you could smell the skunk-sulfur vapors. They stunk!

Now to be fair, other countries and states beyond Florida all have "treated", "recycled", or "reclaimed" shower, toilet, and sink faucet water in varying degrees. This is true all around the globe.

But just how *directly* is your toilet water 'transformed' into drinking water? Easy. Simply measure how much EE2 is present. And measure other estrogenics while you're at it. If estrogenics are high in the water supply, the water is being recycled too directly.

I am here to testify to you, with gratitude, that these measurements are finally being done.

Without gratitude, however, I can also tell you that the estrogenic levels are higher than you might think. These persistent little fake hormones simply do not want to come out of the water. We will detail many actual numbers related to this water supply issue in Chapter 4, while concomitantly looking into estrogenic contamination in our food. For now, though, you've been warned; it's a mess.

The water issue really "boils" down to this. While living organisms like bacteria and parasites are successfully filtered out or killed by high chemical levels, the smallest molecules, especially the hormones, are generally not removed from drinking water. They certainly can't be "killed" since hormones are not alive.

Furthermore, boiling or cooking does very little to destroy estrogenics.[1] You *must* filter them. Yet, this is harder than it sounds. Some filters do not remove estrogenics. And there are dozens of other things you should be doing to avoid estrogenics...

The good news is that by the time you finish this book, you will have a thorough grasp on the sources of artificial estrogen in your environment *and* you will know how to remove them like a pro. It will change your life, your view of reality, and, most importantly, your health. We'll also revisit Florida, fishing, and introduce a special girl I met at Ave Maria University.

Paradoxically, as I write this many years later, armed with a Ph.D. in Biochemistry from Boston University, I was invited back down to Ave Maria University to speak. The topic: estrogenics, our exposures, and our future. Here is your one-sentence summary: estrogenics are a class of molecule that are structurally similar to estrogen *and* they are trouble. *Serious* trouble. *Family tree* trouble.

And for that recent estrogenics talk, I arrived at the Fort Myers airport late one night in February. Can you guess the first thing I smelled when I stepped out from the automatic sliding doors of the Fort Myers airport – hmmmm – rising into the warm, humid, Florida air? Stinklers. Good to be back.

Your New Vision

Today, I realize that far more than toilet-flushed EE2 birth control chemicals are in our fishing lakes, our seafood oceans, and our drinking water supply. Other estrogenics from plastics, food coloring, herbicides, soaps, and fragrances are lurking there too. And the health problems "stretch" far beyond man boobs.

The good news is that you can remove or avoid estrogenics to great degrees. Especially from your drinking water.

But before spending money on the "perfect filter" or making a single lifestyle change, you really need to be convinced that there is a problem. Not only that, but you also need to be convinced that the problem is immense. That's my job. You won't endure open heart surgery if you believe you are perfectly healthy, as I explain to my high-school religious ed students in Boston. Recognition of a major problem is necessary to motivate a major – and oftentimes inconvenient – change.

So here's the plan. Basically, for your very own "open heart surgery diagnosis", *Part 1: Indecent Exposures* will begin with a simple definition of the term "estrogenic".

On the heels of that definition, we jump right into the all-important list I have researched and created for your benefit. This list is designed to heighten your estrogenic awareness and it revolves around what I believe are the top 10 estrogenic substances found in our daily environment. I dub this list the "IRS 10 List" or the "Ill Reproductive System List" due to impending sexuality issues we will investigate. These issues include something scientists call "male feminization". It also includes infertility.

Still in *Part 1*, after simply listing the estrogenic items, we will explore smoking hot issues within the scientific research. This includes scientific spin, conflicts of interest, and publication bias related to commercialized estrogenic items. Soy will be most prominently featured, comparing all the pros and cons, but the legal status of every single top 10 estrogenic item will be featured. Overall, this discussion is designed to sharpen your vision into the modern estrogenic research scene from an "insiders" vantage.

Next, in *Part 2: Rising Disease*, severe health problems arising from eating or drinking estrogen-like items will be unveiled. These are health problems on the very cutting-edge of scientific discovery and you will see how the problems impact both humans and unbelievable numbers of wildlife species.

More specifically, the estrogenic health problems we focus on in *Part 2* will be common elements that basically all estrogenic substances share. I call these health problems "*The 7 Deadly Things*" because they are seven *collective* concerns that unite all the individual estrogenic substances.

Finally, in *Part 3: Today and Tomorrow*, we discuss how estrogenic-induced infertility, obesity, and cancer can be *passed on* to future generations. This inheritance of infertility, obesity, and cancer is called "transgenerational" impact and a special focus will be given to infertility since I view this as the largest, most lasting problem.

Of course, I prefer not to leave you on an emotional low at the end of the book. "We're all going to die and future generations are becoming fat, sick, and infertile" is not my idea of a compelling call to action.

After we discuss the long-armed reach of estrogenics, we explore specific, simple, and practical solutions to all your estrogenic problems. These solutions will be presented as a 3-tiered system of *"Gold"*, *"Silver"*, and *"Bronze" Estrogenic Avoidance Plans*. Of these 3 plans, the single plan that best suits your situation and needs will hopefully emerge within the context of your health and your performance goals.

Put another way, my intention in writing this book is to build an enlightening and overwhelming case against estrogenics based on the hard work of hundreds of top scientists. I've seen how damaging these chemicals are and I want you to see this, too. The case will grow Bigger, Faster, Stronger[i], and – bam! – this case will close with practical, realistic guidance. Ultimately, *you* will need to make a decision: how extreme do you want to be within the final chapter's specific *Gold, Silver,* or *Bronze Level Estrogenic Avoidance Plans*?

If you are a "financially-challenged" college student, for instance, you may decide to tolerate some light estrogenic exposures. You might go *Bronze Level* and choose things with the biggest payoffs toward overall health and convenience. I don't recommend this approach but I empathize and we can still be friends.

If you are a professional athlete or military operative, on the other hand, you may want to be zealous about avoiding estrogenics. Many athletes and operatives are already benefiting from this meticulous *Gold Level* estrogenic avoidance approach and it's a winning approach. Many of your competition will overlook artificial estrogen avoidance so *Gold Level* avoidance will give you a huge competitive advantage if this describes you.

Similarly, if you have a genetic predisposition to breast cancer, you need to strongly consider being *Gold Level* aggressive. Similar, too, if you struggle with depression, obesity, or infertility. Extreme estrogenic

---

[i] A documentary worth watching.

avoidance may be accompanied by some new challenges but your efforts will pay off. In the end, going "Estrogenic-Free" will become part of your bright and cherished legacy.

"Tuning Into" the Definition of Estrogenics

Ok. So let's blast right into defining "estrogenics" as I promised. "Estrogenics" sounds like a cross between "estrogen" and "genetics" but what does it mean?

A good definition of an "estrogenic" – and the one I will be using throughout this book – is "something that binds or 'sticks' to estrogen receptors in your body". Simple.

But, wait. Estrogen receptor? Let's define "estrogen receptor" and look at the 80/20 Principle to understand how an estrogen receptor works.

Estrogen and estrogenics function within the steroid hormone system. I parallel this steroid hormone system to a radio broadcasting system.

Radio broadcasting works like this: a radio tower sends out a signal. For this example, let's say the song is "I'm Gonna Miss Her" by Brad Paisley on Gator Country, 101.9 FM. A current Florida radio station *and* a fishing song. Perfect.

If you tune-in to 101.9 at the proper time, you'll pick-up that broadcast and hear Paisley's piece. By tuning-in, you act as a receptor. Really, your radio acts as the receptor. And "I'm Gonna Miss Her" is the estrogen or hormone in this example.

Again: it's all very simple. The song is sent out from one location and picked up at another location. That is the essence of the hormone concept: your body creates hormones in one place and sends them out into your blood. They – the hormones – are picked up by receptors in other locations. The key phrase here is "other locations".

For a fun, real-life example, let's look at a hormone named "leptin". Your body creates and secretes this snazzy hormone every day within your fat cells.

We interrupt this broadcast to give you a quick side-story and trivia winner. Since fat cells secrete leptin hormone, this means fat cells are scientifically classified as an "endocrine organ" – an organ that secretes hormones. Therefore, people's skin, in certain cases, is <u>not</u> their largest "organ". Fat is.

Fat being the largest "organ" is contrary to what most people think. For example, here is a scene from the TV show, The Office:

Michael Scott: We think a lot alike [Dwight]. Sometimes you will think something and I will say what you're thinking.

Dwight Schrute: OK, what am I thinking right now?

Michael Scott: Umm, nacho chips.

Dwight Schrute: No... How skin is the largest organ of the body.

Sorry, Dwight - this is science. There are always exceptions. And, by the way, did I just get nerdier than Dwight Schrute? Daaang.

The truth is, with the current rate of obesity over 30% throughout America and rising, many people have more fat cell volume than skin cell volume. Of course, we'll just keep that factoid quietly to ourselves and try to fix the underlying issues. Oh, and we will spend almost an entire chapter – Chapter 5 – talking about how estrogenics are literally stored for years inside your fat cells and how they are also causing your body to create more fat cells! Yuck. There is even a correlation between rising rates of obesity and rising rates of estrogenics in our global environment but we'll arrive there soon.

So, let's get back to the hormone leptin. Understanding leptin will help you understand all other hormones.

When leptin hormone enters your bloodstream, all the cells throughout your body that have a "leptin receptor" will be affected by leptins. Those cells will snatch out the leptin from your blood and the leptins will change those cells.

Take your brain, for instance. Your brain is an organ with leptin receptors. So when leptin is in your blood, coursing around, leptin enters the brain and binds receptors and "tells" you to stop eating. "You are full," it signals. Leptin, therefore, is known as the communicator of the feeling of satiety (in your brain) or fullness.

On the other hand, your tongue apparently has no leptin receptors. Therefore, leptin just comes and goes in blood circulating around your tongue. It carries no lingual impact. Weird thought but a true story.

So in essence, no radio = no 101.9 FM tunes. No receptor = no hormonal actions at that particular location in your body. This is a key concept. If organs/tissues in your body have receptors, they can pick up the hormone. Conversely, no receptors equal no response from your body.

Why is this information so darned important? Well, because the *estrogen* receptors are pretty much spread *all throughout* your body. They are far more prevalent than leptin and most other hormone receptors. In fact, estrogen receptors are practically in every cell of your body! So, when you tamper with your body's estrogen levels by "using" *estrogenics* (even if it is not on purpose – I realize that you are not "injecting" estrogenics), this causes problems *all throughout your body*. Estrogenics will not *just* change your brain, not *just* change your fat, not *just* change your muscles, not *just* change your reproductive organs, not *just*.... well, you get the point. Estrogenics change most of your cells because most of your cells have estrogen receptors. This is similar in wild mammals and in fish, too, by the way. This is why artificial estrogenics – those items we discuss throughout this book – can cause such diverse problems and such major problems. Estrogenics act all throughout your body, systemically, on estrogen receptors that are...all throughout your body.

Where Are Estrogen Receptors Found?[2]

- ✓ prostate
- ✓ breast
- ✓ uterus
- ✓ ovary
- ✓ esophagus
- ✓ skin
- ✓ trachea
- ✓ lung
- ✓ liver
- ✓ bladder
- ✓ kidney
- ✓ skeletal muscle

- ✓ thyroid
- ✓ pituitary
- ✓ spleen
- ✓ lymph node
- ✓ tonsils
- ✓ hematopoietic stem cell
- ✓ adipocyte [fat cell]
- ✓ macrophage [immune cell]
- ✓ monocyte [immune cell]
- ✓ dendritic [immune cell]
- ✓ T-cells [immune cell]
- ✓ B-cells [immune cell]

Scientists have found estrogen receptors – the units that receive estrogen (or <u>estrogenics</u>) and carry out actions in your body – all throughout the human body.

Good. So now we're on the same page, or the same song, with the receptor concept. But before we move on to my estrogenic Top 10 List, there is one final detail that is important regarding hormones like estrogen or artificial estrogens: the consideration of speed versus longevity. How quickly do estrogenics act and how sustained are estrogenic effects on your body?

Well, our bodies have two major ways of "internal" communication: nerves and hormones. These are each extremely different.

First, think about your nerves. Nerves carry that lightning fast, electrical signaling; the speedy communication. Electrical "hares".

Hormones, on the other hand, are the "tortoises". Unlike electricity, hormones travel slowly.

And this is where the Brad Paisley radio and receptor analogy falls short. Hormones are not like sound waves or electrical currents. They are physically derived from cholesterol. At least "sex hormones" are derived from cholesterol. And the "sex hormone" category includes estrogen and testosterone.

So these sex hormones are created, secreted into your blood, and then they slowly move along throughout your body. This happens physically, not electrically.

Put another way, hormones travel at the "speed of blood". Blood can transport hormones anywhere blood goes. Hormones don't use an electrical nerve "wire".

And once those little rascals arrive, hormones have a more sustained impact on your body than your nerves could ever dream of having. This is good. If nerves sustained a long-lasting impact like hormones, you would be convulsing with electricity all the time. Envision a permanent seizure and you can see why this would be bad.

Electricity is literally lightning fast. Hormonal impacts, on the other hand, can last beyond a few minutes. They often last hours or days. In fact, hormonal impacts, we are now discovering, can even be *genetic*. Since DNA and genes are passed on, it doesn't get any more "long-term" than this.

Sustained impact from hormones – and estrogenics that activate the estrogen hormone response – will become a very key concept we will revisit in the final chapters, especially Chapter 9. "Epigenetics" – marks on our DNA – will be included in that discussion but I don't want to get ahead of myself.

The Estrogenic Top 10 List

Now that you understand what I mean when I say, "estrogenics are things that bind or 'stick' to estrogen receptors in your body" and some of the potential *long-term* ramifications from that binding, let's move along and specify the most common estrogenics. These are estrogenics – artificial estrogens – that you are probably lathering on, munching on, sniffing, and drinking every day. Be aware that there is also a handy summary for future reference in this book's Appendix.

Here and throughout this book, I will be calling this list the "Ill Reproductive System List", or "IRS List". As mentioned, this list is so named because I believe reproductive infertility is the most significant tragedy relating to these artificial substances.

Finally, the IRS List is exactly 10 items long, so I often refer to it as the "IRS 10 List".

The Ill Reproductive System (IRS) 10 List

1. **PHYTOESTROGENS**
   The "Plant Estrogenics"
   Found at high levels in plants like soy, flax, lavender, and cannabis

2. **MYCOESTROGENS**
   The "Fungus Estrogenic"
   Arising from fungal contaminations, especially seen in grains

3. **ATRAZINE**
   The "Herbicide Estrogenic"
   The common herbicide you have probably never heard of

4. **TRICLOSAN & APEs [Alkylphenols]**
   The "Soap Estrogenics"
   Hidden in soaps and other cleaning products

5. **BP & 4-MBC [Benzophenone & 4-Methylbenzylidene Camphor]**
   The "Sunscreen Estrogenics"
   Found in most cheap sunblock lotions and hand-soaps

6. **RED NUMBERS 3 & 40**
   The "Artificial Food Color Estrogenics"
   Found in red colored processed foods and beverages

7. **PARABENS**
   The "Fragrance Estrogenics"
   Hidden in cosmetics, especially where under the word "fragrance"

8. **PHTHALATES**
   The "Plastic Additive Estrogenics"
   Extremely common plastic "conditioners" plus fragrances

9. **BPA & BPS [Bisphenol A & S]**
   The "Plastic Ingredient Estrogenics"
   Estrogenic plastic ingredients

10. **EE2 [17α-Ethinylestradiol]**
    The "Birth Control Estrogenic"
    Oral contraceptive ingredient that mimics natural estrogen

As you move forward, realize that the IRS 10 List is the "spine" of this book, the backbone. In other words, everything revolves around this list. Some items on the IRS 10 List are more problematic to your health than others but all the items are bad.

And as you might suspect, the Ill Reproductive System List is not exhaustive. The IRS 10 List only covers estrogenics I find to be pervasive. These items made the cut because people are frequently exposed to them on a *daily* basis.

There are a number of other substances that are also estrogenic but are not included because our exposure frequency is low. The reason for this, in essence, is because I want to remove planks before we start looking for specks. The major items are the ones harming your health. After you finish this book, you may want to go out and investigate the "specks" but it's not necessary.

In addition, other common or daily-used chemicals may be found out to be estrogenic in the near future. Unfortunately, we are *surrounded* by artificial chemicals and many are barely studied. It's only a matter of time before new estrogenics arise in our "daily bread".

For the less common estrogenics as well as for the newly emerging estrogenics, I keep an updated list on my website.[3] I also appreciate assistance in finding new and emerging estrogenic items *provided* they are shown to be estrogenic by good scientific sources. The proofs laid out in the next chapter serve as first-rate scientific source examples. Let's move forward and begin that audit of each IRS 10 List estrogenic.

CHAPTER 2

Estrogenic Proofs, Laws, and Features

Laws in Order

YOU WILL REMEMBER I MENTIONED the addicted fisherman earlier and held up my hand. From experience, I can tell you that the true fisherman – the addicted fisherman – seeks the opiate of accomplishment. The bigger, prettier, or rarer the fish, the better. We discover, we pursue, and we conquer.

When I moved to Florida for college, I instinctively knew I needed to prioritize my life and eliminate distractions. Decisions I made as a freshman, I realized, would immeasurably impact my future. All my choices had to be carefully calculated.

To this end, I put pen to paper and organized some ideas. I strategically outlined major life changes. Yet, despite being well intentioned during this process, I made a fundamental mistake.

Specifically, in Minnesota before college, I had been fishing on days of the week ending in "Y". It might be fair to say I had been fishing for fish and fishing for girls, too. It was a tough life. During college orientation, I resolved to drastically change and go fishing-free.

"Who needs girls and who needs fish," I thought, sitting in my sunny dorm suite with visions of perfect grades dancing in my head. *I had come to college as a student and study is what I would do.* "Deny yourself, take up your cross daily, and follow me," was auto-looping in my head and the emphasis was on "deny yourself".

The problem was that girls were around 60% of the college population. Avoiding involvement with girls would be a challenge. And for gill-bearing aquatic vertebrates with fins, the ocean was only a few short minutes away.

It didn't take long before my restrictions quickly became draining. Undoubtedly, they even diminished the quality of my studies.

In essence, in the process of trying to improve, I had overlooked the importance of balance. Having a balanced social life is healthy. Similarly, the meditative aspects of outdoor pursuits are restorative and counterbalance the stresses of intense studying. Removing these key facets from my life was not only inconvenient but it was counterproductive.

In a similar manner regarding the IRS 10 estrogenics, a key question is whether total elimination too extreme. These items are all around us on a daily basis so is it really worth the effort to avoid them? Will avoidance simply distract us from prioritizing other healthy pursuits?

To answer these questions, we first need to know whether each item is truly estrogenic. Do the IRS items all act on the same receptor, the estrogen receptor? Do they act like estrogen in our bodies in some artificial and twisted way? If the answer to these questions is "yes" then elimination of the IRS 10 estrogenics emerges as a viable and scientifically sound health option rather than an extremist position. Artificially activating your estrogen receptor basically guarantees that health dysfunctions will follow....

This chapter, therefore, begins by setting out short "Proofs" of each item's estrogenicity. This is scientific validation of estrogenic behaviors.

But this chapter goes much further.

Gaining mastery over estrogenics demands that we view the full panorama of problems. Proving estrogenic status is not enough. Soy, after all, is still viewed by some as a "health food" despite common acceptance that it is an estrogenic item.

Accordingly, "Unique Features" specific to each estrogenic will also be included in this chapter's estrogenic panorama. "Unique Features" are clues of lurking health problems even beyond *The 7 Deadly Things* we will connect later. Glimpsing various solitary health problems is eye-opening in itself, even though these "Features" are really just a minor slice of the overall health problem pie.

Finally, each estrogenic item will also include information about the legal status of each item, or "what everybody else is doing". We will ask:

where do various government regulatory boards stand? And every estrogenic item will be investigated.

Throughout this process of investigation, I believe you will find shocking answers to these questions that hold vital health clues for you to consider. Let's dig into the list.

Estrogenic #1.

PHYTOESTROGENS
The "Plant Estrogenics"

First on the Ill Reproductive System (IRS) 10 List, are the phytoestrogens. These are basically the plant 'roids. "Phyto-" simply means "plant", so we're talking about plant estrogenics, or estrogenic substances that certain plants actually create and use for their own growth.

Proof of Estrogenic Behavior

Unlike most other estrogenics on the IRS 10 List, I don't feel obligated to prove to you that phyto*estrogens* are, indeed, estrogenic. Estrogen is built into the name.

Legal Status of The Plant Estrogenics

Phytoestrogens are legal in all forms all around the globe, even though soy can bind the opioid receptor via the opioid peptide "soymorphin".[1]

What is this opioid receptor that soy can activate? The opioid receptor is the same sort of receptor that binds other addictive substances like morphine, heroin, and endorphins. I will not be discussing these addictive properties within this book but they are interesting to note.

Unique Features of The Plant Estrogenics

Phytoestrogens are created by plants and, therefore, are in different plants at different levels.

This raises an important question. How many plants should you be watching out for? A long and complicated list? Plants with the equivalent of "huge muscles" or "curves"?

Looking at actual numbers will give us a comparative sense. And, thankfully, one study has done most of the work for us. I'm happy to announce that some hard-working researchers analyzed over 100 food plants for phytoestrogen content in a single study.[2]

Before I reveal the results from that massive study, however, I first want to mention two extra items this particular study failed to include: marijuana and lavender.

While many people are not exposed everyday to marijuana or lavender, there is a chance you might be, so I included them. Lavender, after all, is currently legal in many American states. And you will find lavender in astonishingly diverse numbers of organic beauty products.

Not a vast amount of research has been done on the estrogenic nature of lavender or cannabis but there is enough. There are now more than 10 scientific studies of "lavender + estrogen" and around 100 total studies with either "cannabis + estrogen" or "marijuana + estrogen". One of the latter searches yields this title: "*Estrogenic effects of marijuana smoke condensate*".[3]

I specifically appreciate this paper title because it hints at two rather unique aspects of these phytoestrogens: "smoke" and "condensate".

Either smoking marijuana or "incensing" with lavender essential-oils result in: (1) condensing the estrogenics that are present in the plants and (2) breathing them in via the smoke. Obvious enough, right?

In other words, inhaling estrogenics directly through your lungs into your bloodstream is a clear way to dose heavily on estrogenics and concentrating the estrogenic levels is a problem, compared to – say – what you might find if you actually would "stop and smell the lavender" out in nature.

Since lavender and cannabis are estrogenic, you should realize that they are extremely likely to engender all the estrogenic problems we will go through later in this book, *The 7 Deadly Things*. Keep that in the back of your mind if you are frequent "user" of lavender or cannabis smoke.

And despite especially limited studies with lavender – only 10 compared to 100 cannabis studies – lavender has already given rise to many cases of prepubertal gynecomastia from chronic exposure in personal care products.[4] Multiple studies.[5] For those of you not already familiar, gynecomastia means man boobs.

How are people "chronically exposed"? Through soap, usually. That's what scientific researchers were looking at in the above study. People are also chronically exposed via aromatherapy diffusers.

Ok. So let's move along to that big plant study I promised – the one with over 100 plants compared for phytoestrogen content. In this study, the researchers used units for each item of micrograms [µg] of phytoestrogen per 100 grams [g] of the food, but you should just focus on the actual numbers. Getting lost in the units would be a travesty.

The top two phytoestrogenic items found in the study were flaxseed at **379,380**µg and soy beans at **103,920**µg. In other words, soy and flax each produce huge estrogenic payloads. Hundreds of thousands of micrograms. Nothing else even came close.

And, yes, it is true that "other types of beans or legumes have phytoestrogens", as some people sometimes patronizingly explain to me. I won't argue with that. The researchers in this study tested white beans, red beans, mung beans, lima beans, kidney beans, broad beans, black beans, and baked beans.

Black beans had **9**µg and chick peas had **5**µg, for example. Those were on the "high" end.

What this essentially means is that you need to eat 10,000 cups of black beans, and...well, you haven't quite eaten the amount of phytoestrogens you get from 1 cup of soy beans. Hmmm. And you need to eat 20,000 cups of chick peas to reach phytoestrogen levels from 1 cup of soy beans. Yeeeaaaah. And flax is almost 4-times worse than soy, in case you want to run with this math.

One other interesting thing from this same study is that they found soy *protein* has a whopping **8,840**µg of phytoestrogen. In case you wonder, this is way too much phytoestrogen. In fact, basically anything with *processed* soy has too much estrogenic load. Often, *processed* foods are worse than the plain plant items because processing condenses or thickens the phytoestrogen content. Sound familiar? The cannabis/lavender "smoke condensate" example ringing any bells?

Let me give you a specific case revealing how food processing condenses phytoestrogens. Let's go back to the black beans. As I said, black beans have 9µg of phytoestrogen per 100g of beans. Really, nothing to worry about. But black bean *sauce*? Well, that has **5,330μg** of phytoestrogen.[2] That escalated quickly, yes?

In fact, the only other "raw", unprocessed plant-food item over 1,000 in the big phytoestrogen study was sesame seeds at **8,008μg**. And I doubt you would eat 100 grams of sesame seeds in one sitting but I suppose it's still a good factoid to know. Maybe people enjoy eating some processed sesame product that I'm not yet aware of.

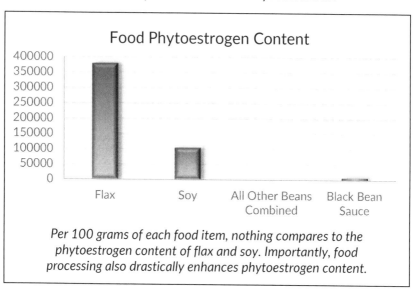

Food Phytoestrogen Content

Per 100 grams of each food item, nothing compares to the phytoestrogen content of flax and soy. Importantly, food processing also drastically enhances phytoestrogen content.

Surprisingly, black licorice almost cleared 1,000μg of phytoestrogens so that, too, was noteworthy. Especially since I actually know certain people that might actually eat a few hundred grams of licorice in a single sitting, given the chance. We know who we are.

Beyond those few items and processed foods, you really needn't worry about phytoestrogen. Great. Simple.

One final thing: it *is* important to note that this massive food study looked at specific types of phytoestrogens. These specific types were coumestan, isoflavones, and lignans. Sounds boring but stay with me, it's not.

Interestingly, soy phytoestrogen is almost entirely isoflavone. Conversely, flax is almost entirely lignans. And when I say "almost entirely", I mean it. Of the 103,920μg of phytoestrogen in soy, for example, 103,649µg is isoflavone (99.7%). And of the 379,380µg of phytoestrogen in flax, 379,012µg is lignan (99.9%). And, frankly, coumestan is so low in actual food and plant items that were studied, it isn't even worth mentioning again, so I won't.

In the next chapter, we'll zoom in on soy isoflavone research, including a discussion about research bias and spin. But what about lignans? Flax is clearly loaded with estrogenic lignan.

First of all, I personally avoid consuming high amounts of flax. It is powerfully estrogenic and that is enough for me.

But it is important for you to know that lignans entertain an interesting "secret" that makes them "less bad".

What is this "secret"?

Your gut bacteria.

In the 1980's, scientists found that lignans decrease free testosterone but they were more specifically investigating "enterolactone", a break-down product of lignan.[6]

Thankfully for us, it seems, good bacteria in our intestines have adapted to break lignans down into various units. Enterolactone is one such unit. Breaking down estrogenic lignan diminishes some of the estrogen-disrupting or estrogenic problems we will later observe in this book.

In other words, since lignans are one of the few *natural* estrogenics, our bodies have somewhat adapted to deal with them. Our probiotic gut bacteria have adapted, more specifically. It is not natural to drink processed flax oil but eating a small amount of flax seeds is well-managed by our bodies. At least this is what the current evidence suggests. Our intestinal bacteria, it seems – the gut bacteria, the good probiotics – break down lignans into all sorts of products with long, complicated names.[7]

As an aside, this is what I think of as the "Paleo Principle": we've been exposed for eons, so we've adapted.

Why have we been exposed? We've been exposed because lignans are created by plants as a protective measure more so than a growth factor.

When an insect eats plants with high levels of lignans, for example, the insect will become sick or die. That is certainly "protective"! It's nature's home-defense!

Lignans are actually being studied as a potential anti-cancer therapy because of this cell-killing ability. Those studies are being performed only in dishes with cells at this point but are still interesting. (There are a number of studies but this [8] review is good if you are interested in reading more about lignans killing cancer cells.)

Finally, to be fair, there are a lot of published papers that find a few isolated *positive* benefits from lignans. Mainly, this has to do with improvements in blood lipid profiles and apparent decreases in inflammation.

These lignan benefits, however, nearly always focus on isolated metabolites of lignans – pieces of lignans that are broken down by bacteria in our gut. They generally do not focus on the lignan itself.[9]

In addition, positive studies about flax and lignan bring out an important factor to consider we will reintroduce later: spin and bias.

For example, I find science journal titles like this: *"Dietary lignans: physiology and* **potential** *for cardiovascular disease risk reduction"*[10] [emphasis mine here and throughout the entire book in quotations].

Having the "potential" for a healthier heart from eating lignans sounds exciting...until you read further into the paper. You find quotes like this: "The associations between lignans and decreased risk of cardiovascular disease are promising, but they are yet *not well established*". Interesting. Let's just leave the jury open on this for now and revisit it in Chapter 3.

Estrogenic #2.

MYCOESTROGEN [zearalenone]
The "Fungus Estrogenic"

The prefix "myco-" means fungi. When we discuss mycoestrogen, therefore, we are talking about "fungi-estrogen".

The fungi kingdom, importantly, includes molds and yeasts. Mycoestrogen-secreting molds and yeasts are found predominantly on food items such as grains, but stay sharp. Coffee, chocolate, and other food products are also susceptible to mold sporulation during processing and storage. Dark and damp basements are potential hotspots for mold, too.

Proof of Estrogenic Behavior

Like phytoestrogen, myco*estrogen* is obviously considered estrogenic by scientists. It's, once again, built into the name. However, unlike the various plant estrogenics, "zearalenone (ZEA) is the *only known mycoestrogen*."[11]   Knowing that zearalenone, or ZEA, is the sole mycoestrogen makes life easier. We can more easily and precisely search and sum up key studies involving ZEA knowing this is the sole mycoestrogen.

ZEA – according to the same study above – is also one of "the most *common* mycotoxins". Mycotoxins are "fungus" (e.g. mold) toxins, so that's bad. ZEA is pervasive but plenty of clear and informative research has been done.

Legal Status of The Fungus Estrogenic

A number of countries have established legal limits for ZEA levels. This, I think, is a further indicator that ZEA is strongly estrogenic and deadly for your health.

Russia, for example, does not legally allow more than 1,000 micrograms (µg) per kilogram (kg) of ZEA in relevant food products. This law in Russia has been in place since 2001.[12]

Next, Europe's allowable ZEA levels range between 20 – 350 µg/kg [micrograms per kilogram], depending on whether you are looking at items like baby food items (20 µg/kg) or unprocessed corn for animal feed (350 µg/kg).[13]

In total, 16 countries worldwide have ZEA limits.[14]

America? Nope – the USA is not on the list of countries with ZEA limits.

Unique Features of The Fungus Estrogenic

First, quotations about ZEA as the "only known mycoestrogen" and "the most common mold toxin" come from a science paper titled: "*Developmental toxicity and estrogenic potency of zearalenone [ZEA] in zebrafish [Danio rerio]*". When I found this paper, all I needed to see was the phrase "developmental toxicity" and I wondered: why is nobody talking about ZEA?

Yet the bad news gets worse. "The mycoestrogen zearalenone (ZEA) is found worldwide as a contaminant in cereals and grains, including maize [corn] and soybeans."[15]

Soy! Wheat! So maybe it's not just the gluten and the pesticides in America's wheat that are causing so many health problems for astute observers today? ZEA is a "growing" factor. And just wait until you see the connection with ZEA and estrogenics to our immune systems when we discuss "The 7 Deadly Things". It's a bombshell.

But let's keep the spotlight on unique side-effects of ZEA.

One thing I appreciate about the mold estrogenic, ZEA, is that scientists are not afraid to investigate and call-out *negative* estrogenic effects. No cautious politics here, in other words. Scientists find ZEA filthy and they dig right in. They tear ZEA apart.

Scientists show that ZEA causes liver tumor-formations, [16,17] brain problems,[19] and impairment of *male* reproductive systems.[20] And, among other things, researchers find it to be hepatotoxic, haematotoxic, immunotoxic and genotoxic.[21] If you don't know what this all means, who cares. That's a lot of "toxic"!

I especially appreciate that researchers aren't afraid to even refer to ZEA as a "toxin"[22] – something you will never find with soy, even if parallel studies are done showing similar health problems.

There is even *more than one* review paper published on ZEA within *pet foods*. These scientific review papers highlight "worldwide prevalence and preventative strategies"[23,24] against ZEA in pet foods, and, of course, I have no problem with that. But let's improve our own food, shall we? *Gratias.*

One final thing, a serious issue. Despite all the toxic effects that have been discovered pertaining to ZEA, some researchers as recent as 2012 propose that ZEA should be *given* to postmenopausal women as hormonal replacement therapy![25]

Please pass on taking that drug if it is offered to you in some back alley or in some blinking, fluorescently lit medical office. Of course, α-ZEA is the specific version of ZEA that is recommended in this paper...the version of ZEA with US patent protection. Oop, there it is!

Estrogenic #3.

ATRAZINE
The "Herbicide Estrogenic"

When I was visiting Minnesota last summer, I stopped by a local farm that I know and love. I had once worked on this specific farm.

As I took the kids up the ladder and inside a goliath-green tractor, I asked about atrazine over the din of the engine. My buddy had turned the tractor on for my kids.

"Farmers still use atrazine, that's for sure" my friend vociferated, "they are just more careful about spraying near ponds and destroying the frog populations." My wife held up the camera to take a picture. She had to crab walk sideways to avoid catching a nearby boom sprayer in the face.

<u>Proof of Estrogenic Behavior</u>

Because of all the lawsuits and allegations of fraud perpetually "cropping up" with the Monsanto® Corporation and the weed killer glyphosate (Roundup®), most people have heard of glyphosate. Television documentaries even highlight Monsanto® and glyphosate. Atrazine, meanwhile, has snuck under the radar. Until today, that is [applause].

Proving that atrazine is estrogenic begins with a paper titled "Atrazine interaction with estrogen expression systems" published in 2008. This paper explains that over 40 other publications have described results of atrazine responses in "estrogen-dependent systems" yet this particular review calls into question the estrogenic effects.[26] The authors basically say that many of the atrazine "estrogenic effects" are not directly estrogenic.

This is surprising. Let's investigate the authors of that paper a bit.

The authors of this particular paper – the most positive paper about estrogenic atrazine that I could find – were located in Dr. Charles Breckenridge's lab. Where might Dr. Breckenridge work? Syngenta®!!

According to all-knowing Wikipedia, Syngenta® is a "Swiss agribusiness that produces agrochemicals and seeds". Syngenta®, in other words, is a biotech and chemical company. And, as of 2014, Syngenta® was the world's largest crop-chemical producer.

I'll trust the 40 other publications that find atrazine is estrogenic.

Legal Status of The Herbicide Estrogenic

Europe, too, has recognized that atrazine herbicide is estrogenic for many years. This is why atrazine has been completely banned by the European Union since 2004.[27]

It is not banned in the USA and we'll talk more about specific water-supply numbers in a later chapter.

Unique Features of The Herbicide Estrogenic

While atrazine may be illegal in Europe, it is currently the second most used herbicide in America (second only to glyphosate). This means you are almost certainly exposed.

To give some historical context, in the 1990's, Americans used about 10 million pounds of glyphosate each year. Today, that number has bloated to over 300 million pounds each year for glyphosate.[28]

Atrazine, not far behind glyphosate, is currently at 80 million pounds per year.[28] And these are only the numbers for use in America. They are extremely "super-sized" numbers, considering we're talking about a chemical illegal in Europe.

In fact, the outrageous atrazine loads in America have led the Center for Biological Diversity to drum-up a lawsuit against the EPA for atrazine annual tonnage and resulting environmental damages. The EPA's response? They have committed to creating an "Assessment Report" by June of the year 2020.[28] A report! Whew – what a relief.

I did the math and if use of atrazine weed killer continue to rise at the current rates, atrazine use will go over 2 billion pounds per year by the time the 2020 EPA report comes out. This is sarcastic because atrazine use likely won't arise to such extreme heights, but the atrazine-use "use curves" have been excessive. Especially for a chemical that can and should be illegal.

Here is my more probable prediction: the 2020 EPA atrazine "Assessment Report" will be slightly "positive". It may even be published by Dr. Charles Breckenridge. At that point, new lawsuits will be launched against the EPA for the new record-breaking levels of herbicides being used by American farmers in 2020. The levels might not be in the billions of pounds but they will certainly be higher than current levels.

Next, for that pending lawsuit, another EPA "Assessment Report" will be recommended. Maybe it will be due in 2030. I expect of course [with an even heavier dose of sarcasm], that the 2030 Atrazine Report will really "stick it to the man".

"Atrazine," says Brett Hartl, a director at the Center for Biological Diversity leading the atrazine legal charge, "chemically castrates frogs even in tiny doses, is an endocrine disruptor, and likely causes birth defects in people. The EPA should have banned this years ago."[28]

But – frankly – there is too much money, or, I mean, "food availability" – at stake, with atrazine. Can we really make this stuff illegal?

Let's have a look at a small sliver of the science research and see if Brett Hartl is onto something. We'll focus on unique attributes and reveal the rest later. Keep in mind the Center for Biological Diversity receives substantial monies from these EPA lawsuits – and they spawn a lot of lawsuits – so they may be exaggerating and may not have pure intentions. Money interests work in both directions. Let's see.

Low doses of atrazine, maintain authors of one research paper, cause developmental toxicity in mouse embryos.[29] The study uses the word "cause" – a strong word for scientists – and they especially found high numbers of embryonic death. These types of deaths are often called "chemical abortions" so this is a grave result. Especially when you consider that mice are more similar to humans than frogs.

There is also good evidence that suggests atrazine increases rates of specific types of hernias in exposed human fetuses.[30] Unfortunately, no direct studies have been done looking at "historical rates of hernias" or "rates of hernias in 'developed' versus 'undeveloped' countries", but I hope a study will come out on this in the future and incorporate all estrogenics, not just atrazine.

Estrogenic #4.

TRICLOSAN & APEs [Alkylphenols]
The "Soap Estrogenics"

We'll talk about estrogenic "transfer" from soaps through your skin in the coming chapter on fat and estrogenic fat-gains. For now, let's simply prove these soap chemicals are estrogenic and identify unique health risks.

First, while you've probably heard various things about weed killers and their adverse effects on health, I realize that you have probably not heard about alkylphenols (APEs[i]). Today, however, we live on a planet of the APEs.

Technically, APEs are "surfactants", which means they cause the delightful suds in soaps. Mainly, therefore, we are exposed to APEs from standard American detergents or soaps, although APEs are sometimes even used as starting material for the chemical production of antioxidants.

An enabling feature of APEs is they are capable of being produced en masse very cheaply.

The singular reason most people have never heard of APEs is they are absent from ingredient labels. There are no legal ramifications so why would anyone want to reveal that their soap contains APEs? APEs, therefore, have become one big, unhealthy secret.

Triclosan, unfortunately, is also often found in many soaps. Even some toothpastes. It is more of a germ-killing agent than a soap but it's added to many soaps so I'm including it here. Fortunately, at least triclosan must be added to the "active ingredient" list if it is present, so you can at least identify triclosan presence and avoid buying triclosan soaps.

Proof of Estrogenic Behavior

Let's begin with triclosan. While the triclosan-estrogenic link is a fairly new discovery, I find that it has become accepted by most research scientists. For example, here is one representative 2015 paper about fertility problems that compares triclosan to BPA (bisphenol A – an item we will discuss shortly) and casually notes that "they both have estrogenic properties and similar chemical structures and pharmacokinetic features and have been detected in human fluids and tissues."[31] That's a long sentence but the similarity of triclosan to BPA is communicated, loud and

---

[i] APE usually refers to "alkylphenol ethoxylates" but I simply use if for all alkylphenols for simplicity and to help you (and me) remember the term.

clear. So does the estrogenic nature of triclosan. Many other studies reveal similar statements so let's move on to APEs.

Like monkeys, there are many different breeds or varieties of APEs. In other words, we're talking about an entire family of molecules.

But while hundreds of variants of APE family members exist,[32] they are all fairly similar.

Of course, the existence of so many different varieties of APEs makes scientific research, and my own investigations, annoyingly laborious. For instance, while some people are finding that APEs have "strongly estrogenic properties,"[33] others are finding "weakly estrogenic properties."[34] Everybody seems to study and use different APEs.

Simply searching "estrogen + nonylphenol" – nonylphenol is probably the most popular APE – yields over 1,000 professional scientific publications (on PubMed). That's probably the most powerful indicator of an estrogenic substance that you can get – more than 1,000 considerations – so we'll leave it at that.

Actually, even looking specifically at "estrogenic" and "nonylphenol" where both terms are exclusively in the title yields over 2 dozen studies. That's just for that one single APE.

Legal Status of The Soap Estrogenics

Since APEs are estrogenic, what is their legal status? Well, here's something I was shocked to find: China added certain APEs to their list of severely restricted toxic substances in 2011.[35] China. And, similar to atrazine, the European Union has entirely banned them – both for use and production.[36]

Meanwhile, in America...you guessed it. Crickets.

Thankfully, triclosan has better news. Triclosan has recently undergone some favorable legal changes in America. While it is already illegal for use in germ-killing products in EU,[37] after more than 40 years of triclosan being declared "generally recognized as safe" in the USA, triclosan will soon be "not generally recognized as safe" starting September 2017.[38] At that time, it will be removed from germ-killing care products. But don't wait. If your soap has triclosan, show it to the nearest trash bin.

Unique Features of The Soap Estrogenics

Harken back, for a second, to atrazine. Remember how low doses caused chemical abortions in mice? Despite the widespread use of triclosan, it has similar deadly impacts. This 2015 paper, for example, was published by the Nature Publishing Group, and the title is: "Triclosan causes spontaneous abortion accompanied by decline of estrogen sulfotransferase activity in humans and mice".[39] Chemical abortion, once again. Due to estrogenic properties. Other health problems with triclosan will turn up later.

How about the prevalent little APEs? Well, let's look to nature for one telling sign. A little caterpillar-like creature called a velvet worm, actually secretes APEs...for defense.[40] The velvet worm secretes APEs to protect themselves against predators eating them. This is similar to lignans that are found in flax. Of course, caterpillar secretion for defense might simply mean the stuff tastes nasty. Are APEs actually bad?

You decide. Check out this 2014 paper titled: "Estrogenic effects of nonylphenol [an APE] and octylphenol [another APE] isomers in vitro by recombinant yeast assay (RYA) and in vivo with early life stages of zebrafish".[41] In this scientific study, the researchers basically found developmental genetic changes due to APEs simply by exposing the fish embryos to APEs for a single day. After this one-day exposure, the scientists waited and checked for genetic changes 2 weeks later. They found numerous altered genes from the APEs. Two weeks later...after one day of exposure to these fish. Let that "sink" in.

Additionally, APEs transfer from the mother to babies in utero above "tolerable" daily limits.[42] This in utero transfer can lead to "implantation failure, pregnancy loss, or other complications".[43] But here I catch myself getting into *The 7 Deadly Things* collectively found in estrogenics. Let's charge on.

Estrogenic #5.

BP & 4-MBC [Benzophenone & 4-Methylbenzylidene Camphor]
The "Sunscreen Estrogenics"

Still on the subject of soap, I recently was shocked to find benzophenone (BP) in my own liquid hand soap. I still cannot believe this, frankly. I had just gotten rid of all my lavender hand soap and now BP. What is up, America?

Proof of Estrogenic Behavior

Estrogenic proofs for BP and 4-MBC begin with the chemistry.

As you know, chemistry terms are daunting, so here is a tip. Anytime you find the word "*phen-*", as in alkylphenols (APEs) or benzophenone (BP), you should be wary. The chemical is probably estrogenic. It doesn't matter if "phen-" is a suffix, a prefix, or wherever; if it's in a word, be wary.

It follows, then, that scientific studies support the idea that BP is estrogenic.[44]

The same is also true of "*benz-*", as in 4-methylbenzylidene camphor (4-MBC)[45] or Benzyl Washington. Ok, I made that last one up, but if Benzyl Washington was a real chemistry molecule, it would probably be estrogenic. Strongly estrogenic.

Unfortunately, as of 2013, researchers claim very "few studies on the occurrence and fate" of 4-MBC in humans.[46] Nevertheless, these same researchers acknowledge that 4-MBC is estrogenic and they show data to support this.

And just so I don't receive irate emails here, "oxybenzone" is also found in sunscreens and is also estrogenic. Indeed. Science publications show this clearly.[47] And see that "*benz-*"? It's the quick tip-off. Oxybenzone is a type of BP. Steering clearing of BP includes steering clear of "oxy". Simple.

Also, throughout the book I'll generally only use abbreviations for BP and 4-MBC and other IRS 10 items but food or personal care product ingredient lists will usually include fully spelled chemical names. Just something to keep in mind as you scurry around your house checking ingredient labels.

Legal Status of The Sunscreen Estrogenics

Despite being recently named the "Allergen of the Year" by the American Contact Dermatitis Society,[48] BP remains legal both in America and Europe.

4-MBC, on the other hand, was banned in Europe in 2015.[49]

In America...not only is 4-MBC legal but corporations even own profitable patents on 4-MBC formulations.[50]

Unique Features of The Sunscreen Estrogenics

When I was discussing the sunscreen estrogenics with a professional organic chemist – a Ph.D. scientist friend of mine – he raised a fascinating point. He told me that 4-MBC and BP bind or stick to estrogen receptors, just like any other estrogenic substance. This is because they pose as natural estrogen and tell the body to do estrogenic acts just like other estrogenics. This is not new news.

When these sunscreen estrogenics stick to the receptor, he went on to explain, ultraviolet light from the sun is capable of fully fusing 4-MBC or BP to estrogen receptors. I know this sounds complicated or technical but "stick" with me.

The UV light from the sun is essentially capable of "gluing" the sunscreen estrogenics to the estrogen receptor. If or when this chemical reaction occurs, the estrogen receptor would be stuck in the "on" position. Biochemists call this a "constitutively active receptor".

Like a light switch or, more accurately, a "sun-light switch", having 4-MBC or BP stuck to the estrogen receptor would then be capable of causing longer-term damage. Longer-term estrogenic actions. This is because the receptor "switch" would be turned "on" far longer than nature ever intended.

Using the radio analogy from earlier, "gluing" 4-MBC or BP onto your estrogen receptor would be like breaking the on/off dial on the radio. The radio would stay on until the speakers or the radio itself broke.

Sun-thing to keep in mind.

Especially since scientific animal studies are done in artificially lit rooms and do not test ultraviolet sunlight fusion effects.

In terms of additional unique health attributes, 4-MBC "causes pituitary effects comparable to hypothyroidism" even while it has "strong anti-osteoporotic effects".[45] BP is also associated with endometriosis[51] and the list goes on. Like the other estrogenics, BP will rear its ugly head later in the book. Get out your samurai sword.

RED NUMBERS 3 & 40

The "Artificial Red Food Color Estrogenics"

Not long ago, I was shopping. Saying that I "dislike" shopping is a huge understatement. Shopping – the antithesis of the outdoors – is basically my kryptonite.

On this particular trip, shopping was worse than normal. I was feeling faint. I hadn't eaten all day and it was about 3 P.M. I had just arrived at the store so, foolishly, I made a hasty decision to buy something with refined sugar. I picked out the first bright brand of berry zen "fruit" juice I stumbled across and I headed for the check-out counter.

After I earned my freedom from the checkout counter, I whiffled outside to crack and drink my juice. I took one long, committed, gulp and then I realized the juice had a nasty chemical aftertaste.

Like a true health pro, it was at this point I checked the label. The liquescent solution was listed as having "Red No. 40" [Red Number 40]. Estrogenic Red No. 40! I threw it out immediately and went back through the checkout line, hugging a box of OatMega® protein bars. Those were a solid win and I receive no endorsement check for saying so!

Once you start looking, the red "food" coloring dyes seem to be everywhere. It wouldn't be so bad if it was just the "junk" foods like soda, candies, or gelatin desserts (like Jell-O®), but I even find Red No. 40 in foods ranging from salad dressings to salmon fillets. In fact, at least in one US grocery store, 40% of all food items were found to contain Red No. 40, while 78% of the candies contained this nasty red dye.[52] I'll say it again: what is up, America?

Proof of Estrogenic Behavior

After researching this topic extensively, I have concluded that essentially all the red artificial "food" coloring dyes are questionable. I advise that you just avoid them all and don't stress about distinguishing individual red dye names.

I encourage abstinence of the reds because, first and foremost, good studies are sparse. Shamefully sparse. This in itself is a problem.

For example, 93% of scientists from a committee voted that "additional studies are needed".[53] This was a committee commissioned by the FDA in 2011 to investigate artificial red food colorings.

We need further studies because artificial chemicals should not be something we assume are good until proven bad. This happens frequently today and it's far from wise.

Next, mediocre studies are frequently cited as an excuse to justify the use of red dyes. "Satisfactory" or "safe" health outcomes can be shown for just about anything using poor studies but don't accept this.

For instance, a 1959 rat study titled "Screening of some food colors for estrogenic activity" found that "no estrogenic activity" was found in tests of Red No. 3 [Red Number 3]. The study – which required me to use my Ph.D. credentials in order to even access and read the actual text – was terribly designed. Scientists injected rats for 3 days with various food dyes. Next, they measured the resulting...uterine weights. Yes: they literally cut out a uterus from each rat and put it on a scale. And this was the only measurement they made! Then they concluded that no weight changes in each uterus meant no estrogenic activity. Expert food scientists are buying this?

Conversely, there was a more thorough study done in 1997 also on Red No. 3. Just check out the title: "Estrogenic and DNA-damaging activity of Red No. 3 in human breast cancer cells".[54] Once again, the title says it all. Today, Red No. 3 is recognized as both estrogenic and DNA-damaging. And this study is not an isolated piece of work, although I would prefer to see hundreds of studies on estrogenic properties, not merely a few.

Speaking of study numbers, this is a confusing topic because food color dyes have numerous names for the same thing. Take "Red Number 17" or "Red Number 40" or "Allura Red AC" or "6-hydroxy-5-[(2-methoxy-5-methyl-4-sulfophenyl)azo]-2-naphthalenesulfonate". All of those names refer to the exact same dye. Tricky.

And remember how I encouraged you to be skeptical or wary about items that contain the word "pheno-"? Phenothiazine – and phenosulfothiazine, for that matter – are artificial, estrogenic,[55] red dyes.

<u>Legal Status of The Artificial Red Food Color Estrogenic</u>

Chances are, you've almost certainly ingested both Red No. 3 and Red No. 40 recently. These red dyes remain legal and are extremely pervasive. Let's have a peek at the broader legal context.

First, Red No. 40 is legal in the US, UK, and Europe. In both Europe and the UK, however, products containing Red No. 40 must be labeled with the words "[this item] may have an adverse effect on activity and attention in children". [56,57]

No such warning label is found on American products.

In addition, prior to the formation of the European Union, Red No. 40 was banned in Denmark, Belgium, France, Germany, Sweden, Austria, Norway, and Switzerland.[58] With the formation of the EU, however, these bans dissolved. Except Switzerland, which held out,[59] Red No. 40 is now legal in the EU.

Red No. 40 is also banned in Japan.[60]

Regarding Red No. 3, the legal story is more complicated. First, Red No. 3 is legal in the US and Europe.[61] Well, except one exception, which I'll mention under "Unique Attributes".

But in America, Red No. 1 was banned in 1961, and No. 2 and No. 4 were banned in the 70's. Red No. 3? Why was Red No. 3 skipped?

It wasn't for lack of trying. By 1985, the FDA had postponed action on banning Red No. 3 a total of 26 times.[62] Probably a financially motivated delay, in case you wonder, but motive would be hard to prove.

What I can tell you is that food processing plants rely heavily on artificial dyes to make all their ensuing brown mush look delectable. Especially to children, vulnerable, or undereducated individuals...

<u>Unique Features of The Artificial Red Food Color Estrogenic</u>

Let's investigate why 26 attempts were made to ban Red No. 3 by 1985. Unique health problems are prominently featured in this discussion. Other health problems more emblematic of estrogenic impacts also occur but we'll put a hold on those.

Long before 1985, Red No. 3 was found to have "major toxic manifestations". These toxicities were said to be "indicative of central nervous system depression."[63] That was 1977.

What is depression of central nervous system, again? Depression of the brain and spinal cord, the central origin of our bodily controls. We certainly don't want to "depress" that system to make our "strawberry" "fruit" "snacks" look appealing. But we carried on without a Red No. 3 ban in 1977.

More "colorful" studies emerged. Researchers found Red No. 3 "inhibits dopamine uptake into brain synaptosomal preparations" in 1980.[64] This discovery caused the researchers of this study to suggest that Red No. 3 may explain childhood hyperactivity – before childhood hyperactivity was really even the big "thing" it is today.

Contemporary follow-up studies confirmed the hyperactivity finding.[65] So did a 2007 randomized, double-blinded, placebo-controlled, crossover trial, performed in the UK.[66] Now the product label warning should make more sense: "[this item] may have an adverse effect on activity and attention in children".

In fact, the 2007 UK study concluded that: "Artificial colors [multiple varieties of red dyes] or a sodium benzoate preservative (or both) in the diet result in increased hyperactivity in 3-year-old and 8/9-year-old children in the general population". That's a conclusion that hauntingly reverberates in the head.

How does the Red No. 3 story end?

Well, the New York Times wrote a piece about Red No. 3 in 1990 that temporarily spiked awareness.[67] Some readers may even vaguely remember this article and its short-lived impact.

The public outcry – what else? – finally motivated a "partial ban" for Red No. 3 in the US in 1990 that is still in place as I write this.[68] Realize that this partial ban was ten years late. It came more than 10 years after studies suggested that we should clearly implement a total and complete ban of Red No. 3, especially since Red No. 3 cannot be said to be an important ingredient for anything but marketing.

And the ban was "partial"? Yes. Red No. 3 can still be used in food and drink, just not in cosmetic products.[68] This is why I still find Red No. 3 in various syrups and things I accidentally buy as recent as last year. And, like the "fruit" juice I bought while feeling ill, I go beyond buyers-remorse when I see Red No. 3 or Red No. 40 on my food labels at home. I slam dunk those mistakes into the nearest trash can.

Estrogenic #7.

PARABENS

The "Fragrance Estrogenics"

Up to this point on the IRS List, you may be feeling that you've done well in life. You've successfully dodged many IRS items we've seen thus far plus you've probably raised your awareness to new heights for improved product selections. You, therefore, are rewarding yourself with a "Soy-Free" snack as you read smugly along.

Sorry to burst your soapy "Estrogen-Free" bubble but the next two IRS 10 List items are so pervasive they are virtually impossible to avoid. These are the nasty "pee-words": parabens and phthalates (the "p" sound is silent in phthalate, in case you were wondering ["thalates"]).

From an avoidance perspective, I personally do the best I can, especially for my kids, but I realize that some revolting "pee" exposure is inescapable. Unless you have taken the "Benedict Option" or have committed to becoming a sealskin-wearing Eskimo, you are getting body pollution from parabens and phthalates. Let's start with parabens.

<u>Proof of Estrogenic Behavior</u>

Parabens are generally agreed upon by the scientific community to be only "weakly estrogenic".[69] This means that parabens bind the estrogen receptor – yes – but not too tightly. This gives less of an estrogenic effect.

Of course, parabens are nevertheless estrogenic.

And, like the annoying APEs, parabens are an entire class of molecule, so a large number of slightly different versions exist. This means estrogenic powers vary. For example, one paraben called "isobutylparaben" has comparable estrogenic effects to BPA.[70]

"Benzylparaben" is another paraben example. Remember the "benz-"? Of course you do. "Phenylparaben" is yet another. "Phen-" ringing any bells? That's what I thought.

<u>Legal Status of The Fragrance Estrogenics</u>

Another thing that may not surprise you at this point is that the European Union has banned both benzylparaben and phenylparaben from cosmetic products, along with 3 other parabens.[71]

Do I even need to tell you where the US stands on the legality of all these 5 parabens?

<u>Unique Features of The Fragrance Estrogenics</u>

Because certain parabens family members are not strongly estrogenic, they have fewer health repercussions. Parabens do, however, alter thyroid hormone levels during pregnancy.[72] That, alone, is a considerable problem.

Furthermore, a recent study identified that "paraben may, to some extent, either cause or contribute to the brain physiopathology in autism spectrum disorder".[73] This study was done by testing brain "markers" in an "autistic like rat model" and it certainly raises some scientific eyebrows. Especially since 2 additional studies found similar results.[74,75]

Another fairly recent study in rats found parabens increased anxiety.[76]

Estrogenic #8.

PHTHALATES
The "Plastic Additive Estrogenics"

There was once a team of stumped scientists in Atlanta, Georgia. They were at a loss because they couldn't find anyone without phthalates in their blood. Yet these scientists needed a "Phthalate-Free" group of people to compare with "Phthalate-Exposed" people for their American lab research study. What could they do?

Well, the situation was grim. Investigators earlier that same year had revealed that US infants far exceeded the EPA's maximum threshold phthalate levels in blood tests.[77] That was 2014.

Furthermore, phthalates had been found in literally in every single US food group scientists tested, which further explained the phthalate exposure prevalence.[77]

In fact, especially hazardous phthalate levels, in that study, were found in cooking oils and dairy products. This makes me wonder whether various health problems related to oils and dairy are actually from those products or from the estrogenics in those products.

Anyway, one day, one of the Georgia researchers had an idea: they could recruit remote Alaskan natives for their phthalate study. Remote Alaskan natives were tested and – bingo! – they were "Phthalate-Free".

The rest was easy. They compared the health of Alaskan natives to non-Alaskan Americans, comparing all the phthalate urine levels. The scientists discovered an association existed between phthalate levels in urine and breast cancer.[78] Not good news but great ingenuity.

This story highlights a frustrating aspect of phthalates besides the spelling of the word: phthalates are virtually everywhere from all the plastics and perfumes. In your new car? Check "yes" for those emissions.[78] Your contact lenses? Yes.[79] Your food containers? Check. Levels, of course, rise as you microwave or heat your food in plastics.[79]

Phthalates, you see, are chemicals sometimes used in perfumes but mainly used as "plasticizers". During the process of making plastics, phthalates are strategically added to increase plastic clarity, flexibility, and durability. Mostly, they make plastic look better by making it appear less cloudy.

Since we all associate cloudy plastic with inferior quality plastic – because in nature cloudiness usually denotes contamination – we actually prefer this chemical contaminant. In other words, we tend to purchase phthalate-containing plastics over cloudy plastics. "Clear" irony.

Importantly, phthalates are not the main ingredients in plastics. Instead, they sit in "molecular cracks" similar to salt added to food or something like glitter. And, like glitter, you can't seem to get rid of phthalates. They release into liquids or food upon contact.

Come to think of it, I can't even think of a single modern processed food that doesn't come into contact with plastic at one time or other.

Often, foods are heated or pasteurized and added into plastic even while the foods or liquids are scalding hot. That's a serious problem.

This further tells me that "health" studies of cooking oils and dairy products are all skewed because differing phthalate levels will influence or bias results in such studies.

The worst irony, though, I think, is that phthalates are used in numerous medical devices.[80] Scientists express concern about this issue and they should. We want to call it health "care"...

Proof of Estrogenic Behavior

Like APEs and parabens, phthalate chemicals come in a variety of different constructs. This is why scientific journals make declarations like this: "[Phthalates] have different degrees of estrogenic modes of action".[81] Phthalate family members act on estrogen receptors in varying degrees. They have slightly different shapes. This tends to complicate scientific research.

For example, using "recombinant yeast screening" in the 1990's, some phthalate family members were said to be "weakly estrogenic".[82] Similar to parabens. Also, similar to parabens, however, more recent studies using better technology have updated the status of phthalates. Now they are considered significantly estrogenic. At least certain phthalates.[83]

That was 2014. Even in 2013, quotes like this one can be found in toxicology journal articles: "In the last years the concern about the negative effects of phthalates on reproduction significantly increased".[84]

Hmm. We will discuss why the research and "estrogenic impact" claims flux so drastically but that needs to wait until the next chapter.

Legal Status of The Plastic Additive Estrogenics

In 2015, a number of phthalates were added to the European Union's "restricted substance" list.[85] Each EU member state was charged with implementing and enforcing the ban. Meanwhile, Denmark was saying "WHAT?!"

In 2014, you see, Denmark just caved to EU pressure. Denmark finally scrapped the comprehensive phthalate ban they had in place.[86]

Meanwhile, the EU ban went into effect on the last day of the year 2016...except for medical equipment. Somehow, medical device companies convinced the European Parliament to give them a grace period for medical devices until July of 2021.

There is no such phthalate ban in the USA, of course, despite recognition by the FDA that phthalates are rampant.[87] Put frankly, the FDA downplays phthalate health concerns that scientists are finding.

America does "restrict" phthalate presence in children's toys. Some phthalate types but not all types. However, even the "restricted" phthalates are allowed up to 0.1% in the children's toy plastics.[88]

That phthalate "restriction" law was put into place under President Bush in 2008. It is worth noting that the EU had this identical children's toy law in place back in 1999.[89]

Unique Features of The Plastic Additive Estrogenics

With this chapter nearly complete, *The 7 Deadly Things* are coming soon. Here is a preview, summarized by this single line from a professional scientific journal: "phthalates have been associated with a number of serious health problems, including infertility, testicular dysgenesis, obesity, asthma, and allergies."[90]

"But that is not all. Oh, no. That is not all..." to quote the "Cat and the Hat" by the late, great, Dr. Seuss.

Similar to the artificial red "food" colorings, phthalates are associated with "long-term attention deficit" in children.[91] This attention deficit may be due to phthalate induction of neurotoxicity, discovered in 2016.[92] Or perhaps it is due to phthalates derailing aspects of brain development (such as brain-derived neurotrophic factor [BDNF]).[93] This finding also came to light in 2016.

Meanwhile, phthalates alter thyroid function,[94] reflecting data on soy and the sunscreen estrogenics.

And remember how sunscreen estrogenics are more likely to permanently fuse with the estrogen receptor, due to UV light? There are now concerns that radiation from things like medical x-rays are increasing phthalate problems due to similar effects. A 2016 paper delves into this subject. It is titled: "Interaction between Ionizing Radiation and Phthalates: An Unrecognized Risk for Human Health?"[95] Let's not keep this one "unrecognized". After all, pregnant women using perfume have been found to have 167% higher urine concentration of phthalates than those women off "the juice".[96] Like parabens, then, phthalates are as common as perfume.

Estrogenic #9.

BPA & BPS [Bisphenol A & S]
The "Plastic Ingredient Estrogenics"

It is imperative to recognize that "BPA-Free" does not mean "BPS-Free". Yet these plastic ingredients act virtually the same in your body! So if you buy a "BPA-Free" bottle, it might be made from BPS (bisphenol S) or something similar.

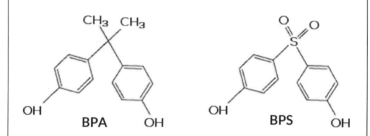

Chemical Structures Comparing BPA and BPS

BPA   **BPS**

Bisphenol A (BPA) and bisphenol S (BPS) are extremely similar. Both are estrogenic and hazardous to your health. Yet plastics made using BPS can technically be labeled "BPA-Free".

Veiled versions of BPA are correspondingly unhealthy. Here is a quote, for instance, from the Environmental Science & Technology journal: "BPAF, BPB, BPF, and BPS have been shown to exhibit antiandrogenic and/or estrogenic activities similar to or even greater than that of BPA."[96] BPAF, BPB, and BPF, of course, are also camouflage chemical versions of BPA. Chemically, these could be called "BPA brothers". Literally. For simplicity, I have only included BPA and BPS as "Estrogenic #9" (of 10) but this is all good information for you to know.

Furthermore, because BPA and BPS act so analogously, I'll simply be looking at studies regarding BPA throughout the rest of the book. That will simplify everything by eliminating the need to constantly refer to "BPA and BPS" every time I mention research studies.

Now: you need to be careful not to confuse phthalates with the plastic ingredient BPA. These items are uniquely distinct even though phthalates and BPA cause many of the same human health disorders and they are all plastic estrogenics.

Let's go back to a food analogy to highlight the differences of BPA and phthalates. This will be better than describing the chemical creation of plastics.

It's simple. Think about making a corn tortilla. BPA would be more like corn mush or some other "main ingredient". Phthalates are like the salt or some other "seasoning". You can't make a tortilla out of pure salt any more than you can make plastic out of pure phthalates. You can, however, make plastic out of BPA.

If you want to get technical, BPA actually needs to link up with other BPA molecules in order to form a plastic. If all the BPA was "linked up" this would be all good. Unfortunately, there are always "unlinked" BPA molecules in plastics, so it leaches out.

Furthermore, BPA is "lipophilic" or "fat-loving" so things like oil that are stored in BPA are more of a problem than water-based solutions. This principle is actually true of all estrogenics. We'll circle back to it later.

Proof of Estrogenic Behavior

Like many estrogenics we've seen, the estrogenic status of BPA has undergone numerous ups and downs. In other words, some scientists have argued that BPA is weakly estrogenic and some have argued it is strongly estrogenic. There is still ongoing debate.

In this case, there are no family members. We are only talking about BPA. Yet discrepancies about estrogenic status still exist. Why?

Well, scientists have difficulties in these studies because of estrogenic "fat-loving" properties. Estrogenics like BPA float on water and stick to everything during scientific experiments. They even stick to the tools, called "pipettes", used to add BPA to dishes or containers.

I learned such research tribulations when I studied fat during my Ph.D. work. Whenever I "added" fat to an experiment mixture, in the form of fatty acids, I discovered that the fats stuck to everything. How much was I actually testing? It was difficult to say.

This means that experimental results about substances like fats or BPA or estrogenics can be way off. Scientists can completely underestimate an effect or a problem. This leads to debate whether something acts strongly or weakly estrogenic.

A study about the "Binding and solubility of oleic acid to laboratory materials", for example, revealed that up to 95% of oleic acid – a fat found in high levels in canola oil[97] and in even higher levels in avocados depending on fruit ripeness[98] – was lost by "dissolving [this fatty acid] in plastic and adsorption to glass or metal."[99] Up to 95% was lost! That will drastically skew a study! What that means is you add only 5% of the fat you thought you added and this loss is generally not accounted for or considered.

Despite these important qualifiers, BPA is strongly estrogenic, even at extremely low doses.[100] Done.

<u>Legal Status of The Plastic Ingredient Estrogenics</u>

Even though things like phthalates are equally destructive to our health, BPA has recently become scientifically shunned. In this regard, it is similar to ZEA from fungus.

What I appreciate about all the BPA scapegoating and attention is this has led to the substantial negative effects of BPA finding daylight and media attention. This is one example of how public opinion and politics impact both the scientific culture and your own health. In fact, as I write this, phthalates and parabens each have just over 2,000 scientific publications to their names. BPA has about 10,000. This BPA study number doesn't even include BPS or other BPA analogues.

And one thing we have learned from such a massive number of studies is that more studies uncovers more health problems. The health problems were always present, we have just discovered more as studies have piled up.

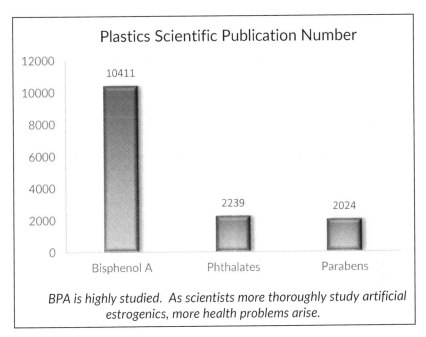

BPA is highly studied. As scientists more thoroughly study artificial estrogenics, more health problems arise.

From over 10,000 BPA studies, how has the legal status of BPA evolved?

Well, first, we apparently have learned enough for the FDA to begin "reassessments" of BPA. In 2012 the FDA banned BPA from baby bottles but, even though the FDA never really executed their ban, they are reassessing it anyway.

Due to the FDA's sluggishness regarding BPA, individual states are stepping in and making anti-BPA laws; 13 states to be exact. Most of the state BPA laws involve items "designed to be used by a child less than 3 years of age" similar to the original federal ban.[101]

Will the FDA reassessment of BPA mean a stronger ban? No. The FDA is clear about that. The FDA is currently declaring certain levels of BPA in canned foods, baby items, etc. as perfectly acceptable.[102]

It's important to realize that a ban on some of these estrogenics isn't sufficient. BPA is the perfect example. When states ban BPA, for example, many corporations turn around and slightly modify BPA and continue producing a product just as unhealthy or worse than their original product. Like BPS. Or BPAF, BPB, or BPF. This is why transparency here is key.

Moving along to other countries, the EU has recently improved their position on BPA. They cut the "allowable limits" more than 10-fold in the last few years due to increasingly negative research findings. Environmental research is especially a strong factor. Still, they haven't banned BPA, much to the dismay of places like France and Denmark – countries that originally had BPA bans in place.[102, 103]

Denmark is especially worth highlighting. Danes originally declared they would stand strong against the EU's lack of judgement regarding the allowance of BPA to be manufactured and used in products. Specifically, Danes said they would not lift their own BPA ban.[102] More than 5 years later, however, when political push came to shove, Denmark is now allowing "EU approved" BPA levels while complaining that "the safe levels need work".[104] This, you might have already noticed, is the Denmark and EU phthalate story all over again.[86]

<u>Unique Features of The Plastic Ingredient Estrogenics</u>

Hyperactivity in children, once again, is connected to BPA exposure.[105] This emerging pattern actually makes me suspicious that estrogenics in general are involved in hyperactivity disorders but, unfortunately, the hyperactivity topic has not been thoroughly investigated with most other estrogenics. Frankly, I hope this book inspires such studies.

Now let's flip to something positive. There is evidence that suggests estrogen – natural, God-given, estrogen – is slightly protective against aging and it may even protect the brain from aging.[106] Again, this effect is slight but real.

The irony here, though, is that estrogenics – these artificial estrogens that bind the estrogen receptor – might have the opposite effect. At least BPA does. BPA appears to accelerate aging by out-competing natural estrogen. Another thing we should be researching related to all IRS 10 estrogenics.

In this study of worms, for example, BPA shortened worm lifespan.[107] Why worms, you ask? Well, for one, they are easy to grow in large numbers and worms reproduce quickly. Like fruit flies.

And while fruit fly lifespan has not been tested using BPA exposure, estrogenic *parabens* were tested and parabens were also found to shorten fruit fly lifespan.[108]   Seeing a pattern?   Another thing to investigate.

On the topic of lifespan, what would really be ironic is if sunscreen estrogenics 4-MBC and BP accelerate aging. The paraben and BPA findings make this a good hypothesis. "Protecting" against the skin aging-effects of sunshine while causing aging from the use of 4-MBC and BP would be just too much. This seems like an obvious thing to study, but, alas, research has not been done here either.

Aspects of aging and estrogenics is really an untapped field, as I write this. Only a few studies have been performed and they hint at future bad news to come. Probably, it will take about 20 years.

Estrogenic #10.

EE2 [17α-Ethinylestradiol]
The "Birth Control Estrogenic"

Over 100 million women worldwide – over 60% of all married women on our planet – are currently on chemical contraceptives containing EE2 (17α–ethinylestradiol).[109] Legions of people globally are involved with these drugs on many levels.

Proof of Estrogenic Behavior
EE2 is estrogenic. EE2 was intentionally designed to mimic estrogen, activate the estrogen receptor, and stay in the body longer than natural estrogen.

Legal Status of The Birth Control Estrogenics
It has become clear that Europe has maintained higher legal standards pertaining to estrogenics than America. However, EE2 is where Europe falls short. Here is where they dropped the balls [sic]. In a few pages, I even show you a remote Swiss mountain lake with high levels of EE2.

Meanwhile, in America, not only is EE2 legal but over 20 states allow minors "consent to contraception".[110] Certain states have programs that pay for these drugs, so legal documents generally use this phrase "consent to contraception" rather than saying "minors may buy contraception drugs".

<u>Unique Features of The Birth Control Estrogenic</u>

Despite the fact that drug sheets are readily available, most people don't read them. Especially minors. The drug sheets are a lot of work to sift through, tiresomely technical, and pedantic.

But drug sheets are worth reading, especially for contraceptives. The health problems are substantial. For instance, I include [below] the "adverse reactions" to Alesse® oral contraception, which contains EE2. These "adverse reactions" are listed on pages 18 – 20 of the drug sheet. They are not headlined, to say the least.

Oral Contraception Adverse Reactions

✓ Acne
✓ Amenorrhea
✓ Anaphylactic reactions
✓ Breast changes
✓ Budd-Chiari syndrome
✓ Cervical erosion
✓ Cholestatic jaundice
✓ Exacerbation of chorea
✓ Colitis
✓ Intolerance to contact lenses
✓ Corneal curvature steepening)
✓ Dizziness
✓ Edema/fluid retention
✓ Erythema nodosum
✓ Abdominal pain, bloating
✓ Hirsutism
✓ Infertility after discontinuation
✓ Diminution of lactation
✓ Decreased libido
✓ Melasma/chloasma
✓ Changes in menstrual flow
✓ Mood changes, depression

✓ Nausea
✓ Nervousness
✓ Pancreatitis
✓ Exacerbation of porphyria
✓ Rash (allergic)
✓ Loss of scalp hair
✓ Decrease in serum folate levels
✓ Spotting
✓ Exacerbation of systemic lupus
✓ Unscheduled bleeding
✓ Vaginitis, including candidiasis
✓ Aggravation of varicose veins
✓ Vomiting
✓ Changes in weight or appetite
✓ Cataracts
✓ Cystitis-like syndrome
✓ Dysmenorrhea
✓ Hemolytic uremic syndrome
✓ Hemorrhagic eruption
✓ Optic neuritis and loss of vision
✓ Premenstrual syndrome
✓ Impaired renal function

Adverse reactions from users of oral contraception are rarely communicated in full, especially for minors.

All other EE2 containing oral contraception drugs have a similar "Adverse Reactions" list.[111] Most are very low likelihood occurrences but the chance of acquiring one or two of these health issues when taking oral contraception is much more likely. Overall, it's a gamble. Just don't gamble blindly. At least know the list exists and what is on it.

Also, you might compare this list with the "Where Are Estrogen Receptors Found?" list in the previous chapter. You will observe many similarities. Did I mention that over 100 million women worldwide – over 60% of all married women on our planet – are currently on chemical contraceptives containing EE2?[109]

CHAPTER 3

The Roots of
Our Estrogenic Tree

The "Nature" of Our Problem

POST-ORIENTATION AND BACK ON THE Ave Maria campus, I had settled in nicely. Despite my making a few counterproductive decisions, college life proved to be fun and I found my classes engaging.

An additional blessing was my college roommate Dave. Dave and I discovered we had a lot in common and we became timeless friends. Furthermore, I will always be grateful to Dave because he redirected me back to my roots, back to nature, back to fishing.

In my early semesters of college, I undertook work in a science lab. For me, the lab was another good fit and working in the lab would kindle a different sort of redirection. In lab, my story began with an understanding of scientific funding but ultimately ended in the arms of a pretty girl...but let's start with Dave.

Dave was a former Second Class Petty Officer of the US Navy and he was second to none with his winning character, eidetic memory, and spasms of spontaneity. Dave had mid-length blonde-brown hair, alternating variations of facial hair of that same color, and the best scrunch-faced falsetto imitation of Guns N' Roses songs you could imagine. Brilliant. We remain friends to this day.

To better introduce Dave, let me give you one true story example.

It began in our 2nd story dorm room, where a perfectly placid Dave was sprawled on the couch. The couch was located in our spacious sunroom and Dave was catching up on his homework. Specifically, he was reading *Oedipus Rex*, a book written by the famous Greek tragedian Sophocles, and Dave was totally engrossed.

At that same time, I happened to be in the same room, sitting at a desk overlooking a window. I was butchering math equations on some scratch paper and finding it to be a fairly normal day.

Suddenly and without warning, Dave burst to his feet with a bloodcurdling scream. He employed the full capacity of his Navy-seasoned lungs. I searched wildly for the nearest exit, just in case. Was the window too high?

As Dave jumped from the couch, he pitched his book upward and it bounced off the high ceiling. The book came crashing down onto our cheap desk lamp with a crunch and a clang.

From the bowels of our dorm suite, another roommate – Jon – charged out to the rescue.

"What was that?" exclaimed Jon.

"I'm not reading ever again!" declared a ruffled Dave, eyes flashing.

"What!? - You're not *reading*?"

"The main character in this story just gouged his eyes out!"

"Daaaave!"

During the same year that Dave was boycotting reading, I founded the "Ice Skating Club". Dave, with all his newfound free time, became the Vice President. Actually, Dave had a lot on his plate that year – he was elected Student Government President by a popular vote, for example – but the Skating Club workload was light.

In essence, our Skating Club duties entailed renting the Germain Arena ice rink in Fort Myers a number of times each semester and showing up to ice skate.

Each skating event was exclusive for Ave Maria students and everyone had fun. For me, however, these endeavors reminded me what ice looked like and kept my repressed Minnesota Spirit alive. They brought back some of that missing balance for me. At Germain Arena, we were reduced to skating around in circles and none of us were about to make the "Minnesota All Hockey Hair Team"[i] but we nevertheless kept coming back and packed the rink on each outing.

Meanwhile, I avoided dating and outdoor adventure as I had vowed. Then my freshman year was over in a flash.

---

[i] A low-budget YouTube annual series sensation.

Next, I began my second year at Ave Maria University. Along with my usual college affairs, I started working longer hours in the lab doing scientific research.

Specifically, I began work in the lab of a well-respected senior scientist named Dr. James Peliska. In the Peliska lab, I learned how to investigate and even create drugs against HIV (human immunodeficiency virus).

Dr. Peliska is a Ph.D. organic chemist and an HIV expert. He had even worked with Pfizer on some major HIV drug tests.[1] Preeminently, however, Dr. Peliska is a phenomenal teacher and a fun character.

My involvement in the Peliska lab made me recognize one of the under-appreciated benefits of going to a relatively small college: you really get to know your professors, see how they conduct their affairs, and ascertain how the system as a whole operates.

In addition, at a smaller school, you really get to know your classmates.

For me, one such classmate was a pretty and positively energetic girl with irresistibly curly hair. I'm talking about curls like those tiny ribbons you find hanging in bunches taped to gifts. This girl's name was Allison.

Allison was also a biology major and, again like me, she had dedicated herself to working in the lab. Allison, I further observed, had a contagiously fun habit of simpering and shrugging her shoulders two or three times when she was excited – like when she was off to go fishing.

Allison, I soon discovered, came from a fishy – I mean fishing – family. This made sense because she was also from Minnesota. Had all the stars aligned?

Either way, around the time I met Allison, my roommate Dave decided we should stop talking about fishing and just do it. I agreed. I found time to introduce fish back into my life. At 5 A.M. After staying up until 2 A.M.

On that fateful beach trip, I immediately realized that I should never have abandoned these sorts of adventures. Dolphins were wave-riding and little terns were diving for minnows. It was fun and healthy. For me, it was also a better antidote to the stresses of college life than ice skating. I decided to found a University Fishing Club.

And Allison? It wasn't long before I became "hooked" in more ways than one.

Let's spend some time talking about the influence of money on estrogenic products and how this might impact you and your health. Working in the lab of Dr. Peliska is where I began my early education into scientific funding, so let's begin there.

What quickly became clear to me in the Peliska lab was our unique financial circumstances. At Ave Maria University, especially in those early days of the university, we received basically all our lab money from private donations.

Most notably, the main philanthropist of Ave Maria was Mr. Thomas Monaghan, Ave Maria's founder. Mr. Monaghan had also founded Domino's Pizza and owned the Detroit Tigers baseball team prior to founding Ave Maria University, so he had a prodigious résumé.

It didn't take long for me to further learn that our donated lab money was not the status quo.

In the USA, most money that goes into scientific research at universities originates from corporations or grants from the US government.

Again: ours did not.

Because money entered our lab from private sources, we enjoyed incredible freedom and flexibility in our lab work. Even while our budgets were undoubtedly tighter, we were able to pursue basically whatever we felt most passionate about researching and solving.

Most places do not have this freedom.

Most American research labs obtain money one of two ways: either they investigate things that the government wants and commissions or they investigate things that a large corporation wants and commissions.

And government and corporate "wants" often align, sometimes for better and sometimes for worse.

Money, you see, is a tremendous stressor and influence within professional scientific research. No money equals no research.

And money is the elephant in the estrogenic room because selling estrogenics generates massive profits. Lucrative items include soy, weed-killers, plastics, fragrances, and birth control drugs. This would not be a problem if these items were healthy or at least not harmful but that's just it. They are relentlessly harmful, as you'll further see. Even beyond one generation.

Now, from a "bottom-line" perspective, consider how much cheaper it is to use estrogenics in soaps, deodorants, and perfumes, rather than expensive ingredients that are healthy. Many estrogenics are ultimately derived from petroleum products, for instance.

Or consider how much money is made selling pills to "hack" fertility rather than promoting "natural family planning" (NFP), which is free.

Or consider how the addition of estrogenics increases sales of processed foods. Why else would you find Red No. 40 in things like salad dressings? Examples go on and on.

Basically, when the dust of unbridled competition settles, the "best" corporations emerge selling estrogenics. Consumers even "demand" it. Remember the example of clear versus cloudy plastic? Plus, we want things to be cheap, right?

Overall, estrogenic items are leading the profit margin category. Next, these same companies remain at the corporate "pinnacle" by championing money-based incentives and implementing political influences to safeguard the same estrogenics they are peddling. In other words, estrogenics are safeguarded by the very profits that they produce. Kind of a vicious circle of bad health, don't you think?

So, as you can imagine, corporate and government influences can be directed away from caution and watchfulness regarding unnatural substances – particularly remunerative artificial estrogenic substances – and swayed in the direction of the money flowage.

But how might *university* science be adulterated by the estrogenic monies?

Easy. Most university lab directors need to continuously write grants to stay afloat. They constantly implore government-commissioned committees to "grant" them money. In fact, begging for money is literally a 40-hour per week job for many scientists – I kid you not – which, by the way, was another benefit of private funding at Ave Maria University. With the private funding, there was far less money "begging" and more actual lab research being performed.

Anyway, the end result of all the money begging at the typical university is problematic. Even *beyond* wasting millions of expertly-trained-scientist-man-hours every year in a frustrating liturgy of paper pushing.

Government grants – the primary money source for most labs around America – have a way of forcing people to investigate topics that government funding committees *deem important.* Basically, "study this topic or else you will have no funding" is the dark cloud hanging over scientist's heads. The important topics are decided by a current government "ethos", which is often strangled by corporate interests.

That is the trifecta of estrogenic influence: alignment of corporate, government, and university interests.

So that's where the bias originates within the *types* of studies that are funded. A funding bias. Done.

Publication Bias

Before we move on, we unfortunately need to red flag one more scientific bias that will also reemerge throughout this book. This one is more direct: it's *publication* bias.

Publications are important because (1) if you publish more papers you win more grants and (2) people and policies are influenced by results communicated through scientific publications. Science papers have a powerful influence.

Here's the problem: lay people often believe that scientific journals are "pure" – unbiased and impartial. It's cool if you do. Many students acquiring various degrees in science even believe this too. Alternatively, you may be one of those people who really doesn't know *what* to think about the scientific publication process. It might be a sort-of black box or mystery to you, as it is for most non-scientists.

Let's briefly go through it and simplify the scientific publication process. The potential issues will highlight themselves.

The dominant scientific publication process is called "peer-review". Peer-review goes as follows:

You run a lab. You perform some experiments and you write a paper about those experiments and the results you found. Publishing your paper, as I said, will help you secure future grant money. So, you submit your paper to a journal. During the online paper submission application process, you *select* other scientific buddies, termed "experts" or "colleagues" – usually people you have met at conferences and have befriended over the years – and these buds take on the duty of reviewing your paper. In other words, *you* tell the science journal who should peer review your paper. It is a required line on most scientific online website submission forms. True story.

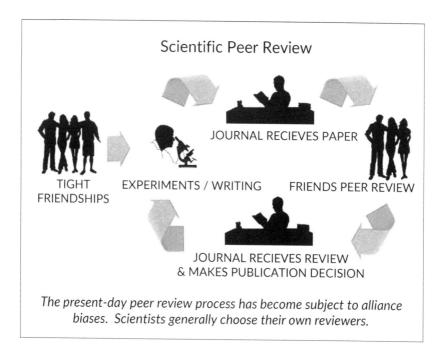

Scientific Peer Review

TIGHT FRIENDSHIPS

EXPERIMENTS / WRITING

JOURNAL RECIEVES PAPER

FRIENDS PEER REVIEW

JOURNAL RECIEVES REVIEW & MAKES PUBLICATION DECISION

The present-day peer review process has become subject to alliance biases. Scientists generally choose their own reviewers.

It sounds like I'm fabricating this, so let me repeat that last part: you literally tell the scientific journal your top choices – who should review your paper – and they generally use *your* choices! Don't be surprised if you've never heard this before because most medical doctors I know aren't even aware of this. It's a dirty "little" lab research industry secret.

Teleport yourself back into your scientific career. It is competitive. Everybody wants more money. You realize that every time another grant of yours is funded, you get a pay raise – yes, a pay raise – so you study specific topics that the government deems important and you write grants and publish papers on those same "important" topics.

One gloriously sunny day, you are indoors on your computer. You are finalizing some edits and you decide you are ready to publish a paper. Naturally, then, you go online and submit the paper to a top science journal and you carefully select your buddies to review the paper as you submit it. With your career on the line, you certainly wouldn't want to leave your paper publishing to random chance or genuine criticism.

Next week, the scientific journal emails your buddies – usually 2 or 3, from the choices you've given them – and the journal gives them your research paper. The journal also bestows on them the professional "honor" of reviewing your paper (for free, of course).

After reading your paper, your buddies may (1) recommend that your paper is published or (2) they may recommend that it needs modifications or (3) they may recommend that it should be outright rejected.

Oh, and – yes – they see that *you* are the author of this paper as they read and review it. Sound unbiased and immune to politics?

Now, not only are scientific papers subject to this "peer review" procedure but scientific grants, too. And the sheer number of how many papers you have published is a huge consideration in winning grants.

Overall, the "peer review process" could be accurately compared to high school or college essay writing. When you wrote a high school essay, the teachers grading your essay noted your name at the top of your essay. If the teacher harbored any grudge against you, look out – that grudge will undoubtedly influence how they think as they read the paper. This is simply how we are wired as humans: we make associations and extrapolations.

Now, I've been taught during my Ph.D. studies that seeing the name on the cover page of prospective science papers or grant applications is deemed "necessary". It is critical, supposedly, because the reader "needs to be able to recognize lab history and credentials".

In essence, while reading anything scientific and even throughout this book you can see why I want you to remain skeptical – in a healthy way – of published scientific articles and funded studies. People often discover positive benefits that they are already looking for and these benefits are easily published without much nod toward adverse effects.

Next, be wary of the ensuing media spin added on top of the professional scientific spin. If a scientist is publishing papers that contain a biased spin, media may add further spin. Professional scientists are certainly skeptical, so you should be too.

Dr. Marcia Angell, the ex-editor-in-chief of the New England Journal of Medicine, recently stepped away from the New England Journal of Medicine for precisely this reason – the rampant corruption and spin. In Dr. Angell's own words:

> I witnessed firsthand the **influence of the industry** on medical research during my **two decades at the New England Journal of Medicine**. The staple of the journal is research about causes of and treatments for disease. Increasingly, this **work is sponsored** by drug companies. I saw companies begin to exercise **a level of control** over the way research is done that was **unheard of when I first came** to the journal, and the **aim was clearly to load the dice to make sure their [products] looked good**. [...] This is an industry that in some ways is like the Wizard of Oz – still full of bluster but now being exposed as **something far different from its image**. Instead of being an engine of innovation, it is a **vast marketing machine**.[2]

Ironically, she did her postgraduate training at Boston University School of Medicine (the same place as Yours Truly).

Anyway, don't hate this process – it is not hopeless or evil – but do be cautious and skeptical. It has gotten messier.

A good *Principle for Evaluating Estrogenics* that I developed for screening science papers and a *Principle* I recommend to you is this:

1.

Principle for Evaluating Estrogenics: *If a scientific study is favorable and positive regarding something that could be bought and sold, be wary!*

In essence, journals generally do a respectable job publishing decent scientific work. But everybody – and I mean everybody – has an agenda when writing scientific work.

This is true of most things that are *competitive*: the winner's selection is vulnerable to arbitrary, political, and subjective influences.

And, naturally, mega biotech corporations – usually run by Ph.D. scientists – know this process intimately. They game the system frequently. I'll show you a specific instance soon – in this very chapter in fact – where a chemical herbicide company *literally* employs scientists that publish "pro-atrazine herbicide" research papers. Yeaah.

In the backdrop of our current funding bias and publication bias, you should also recognize the prevalence of conflict-of-interest, a close relative of the funding and publication biases.

How do you begin to spot conflict-of-interest? Where do you look?

Well, once again, you start by looking for a strong spin. You look for science articles that "cherry pick", gloss-over, or ignore major contradictory publications and data. These manage to get published more often than we would like.

For that, we will highlight an example shortly, where one estrogenic item – soy – is said to "improve bone density". The study, meanwhile, ignores the fact that this same estrogenic item increases cancer, allergies, blood clots, etc. Yes: conflict and agenda are often hitched-up tight, dragging close behind the money wagon.

First, to introduce conflict of interest is to introduce Dr. Marion Nestle. In a good way. Dr. Nestle is more passionate about finding and revealing agenda-driven and direct conflict-of-interest studies than anyone I know. I recommend you check her work out.

She has no relation, by the way, to the Nestlé® food company, which ironically funds many food-related studies. The Nestlé food company supports research that could certainly be viewed as "promotional" or well within the category of "conflict-of-interest". Footnoted here[3] is one such study *funded* by the Nestlé food company, promoting the "healthy nature" of whole-grains. Don't they sell whole-grains?

Anyway, Dr. Marion Nestle is a professor at New York University and has a Ph.D. in Molecular Biology. She is legit. Dr. Nestle was even the chair of the Department of Nutrition, Food Studies, and Public Health for 15 years (1988 – 2003) and is still a prolific author. Since March of 2015 – not that long ago, at the time of this writing – Dr. Nestle has been actively collecting professional scientific studies *that include conspicuous conflicts-of-interest*. She found a large number. And, for each study, she includes highly professional analyses on the bias or conflict.

In the short time Dr. Nestle has searched, she has found 168 corporate-funded studies. And guess what? Only 12 of those 168 studies find results that are "unfavorable" toward the company products – 156 are "favorable". [4]

In other words, when a corporation *funds* a study, the "findings" are nearly always highly positive toward their particular product. Shocker, right?

You see why I am wary of published articles promoting or favoring estrogenics? And why you should be too? You should at least demand to see *multiple* studies before accepting anything that sounds promotional regarding estrogenics, especially when a study creates an entire field of straw-men.

Like the legal status of estrogenics, some countries, of course, are worse than others.

I'll put two article quotes side by side and you tell me which is from an American journal and which one is from a Chinese journal.

Here goes the first one, from 2008:

> Parabens [...] produced a positive uterotrophic response in vivo. They also damaged the late stages of spermatogenesis, altered proportion of [mouse] pups born alive, and body weight of offspring. They reduced the number of sperm in the epididymis, and the sperm motile activity in male offspring.[5]

"Uterotrophic", by the way, means that there is an effect on the uterus. And "in vivo" means "in live animals". Also, damage to "spermatogenesis" is simply damage to sperm formation. Lots of code, lots of damage.

Next, I present to you, this gem:

Over the years, some activist groups have targeted cosmetics as possible human health threats, claiming that cosmetic ingredients are not adequately tested for safety and may pose risks to consumers. The groups allege that industry practices related to safety testing are flawed, that there is little government oversight, and that cosmetics contain cancer-causing chemicals and other toxicants [...] The health-related allegations involving specific chemicals (e.g., phthalates, parabens, and 1,3-butadiene) fail to consider important scientific studies and recent regulatory conclusions about these chemicals, which have found that they are not hazardous. Animal and human physiology differ in crucial ways, further invalidating simplistic attempts to extrapolate rodent testing to human health risks.[6]

Ok, you win. You knew the second rambler was American. But did you realize this particular American medical research journal article was titled "A Position Paper of the American Council on Science and Health"? It came directly from the American Council on Science and Health. You may not have guessed that. It is written in such a defensive way it reads like a political debate transcript.

Errors

One final cautionary word before we "dig" into soy and then leave all this behind for greener Pasteur's [sic]. Scientific *errors* are increasingly common in our competitive and fast-paced scientific publish-or-perish system. And even if the errors are caught, it is generally too little, too late.

One author, Pascal-Emmanuel Gobry, points out an important example in his article titled *"Big Science Is Broken"*.

Gobry writes:

Steven Levitt, of *Freakonomics* fame, largely built his career on a paper arguing that abortion led to lower crime rates 20 years later because the aborted babies were disproportionately future criminals. Two economists went through the painstaking work of recoding Levitt's statistical analysis — and **found a basic arithmetic error.**[7]

As I said, a lot is at stake. Laws are often passed that are based on *errors* such as Levitt's. Unfortunately, most people who read *Freakonomics* – including myself until I read this article by P.E. Gobry – never find out about these errors.

"Then there is outright fraud," P.E. Gobry continues. "In a 2011 survey of 2,000 research psychologists, *over half* admitted to *selectively* reporting those experiments that gave the result *they were after*". Wow.

P.E. Gobry also recommends that you check out the well-respected intellectual journal *First Things* and the article called "Scientific Regress".[8] This *First Things* article tells of large numbers of psychology experiments that *nobody* is able to repeat or confirm, even with exact imitation of the original studies.

Now, if you are like me, you might be thinking, "Ok, so *psychology* studies frequently live in Sketchville but major research science journals like *Nature*, *Cell*, and *Science* are safe, right?"

No, not exactly. The big research journals may be better than psych journals but they are not immune to scientific error, sloppy work, or outright fraud.

For example, not long ago, I was eating lunch with a top executive from a huge biotech and pharma company. He shall remain nameless. This exec told me "whenever people within our [drug] company read something in a science journal about an amazing new drug or treatment, we *first* attempt to repeat that research in our own labs. Even if the paper was published in a top science journal, we first repeat it. Without replicating the experiments 'in house', we would otherwise waste millions of dollars trying to create a drug based entirely on a faulty experiment published in a journal. I estimate," he went on, "that *over 50% of the time,* we cannot repeat published study findings." He was referring to *professionally* published scientific research studies!

And actual studies confirm this. For example, a study performed by a group of researchers at Bayer® investigated the reproducibility of scientific studies. A study about studies. They found that the medical and science journal's *published studies* "do not match up with their in-house attempts to replicate"...more than 75% of the time![8]

So, basically, science is drowning in bad studies.

Now you're probably saying: "Well, can I trust *anything*?"

Great question! Yes!

The trick is to use the *Principle for Evaluating Estrogenics* and look at *numerous* articles rather than merely one isolated science research paper. I'll add another helpful *Principle* soon, as well.

If you want to get an *overall* sense of the positive and negative aspects in each scientific area, you need to pierce through the agendas and faulty science. Basically, while reading science, you should *always* think about the *possible* agendas. Ask yourself who might benefit from the outcome or profit from a certain result. That is the best approach.

Trusting Your Soy Mate

Now, let's get back to splashing in that pool of estrogenics. Pour yourself a piping hot, soy-milk, red-velvet latte into a #7-plastic mug and let's go.

First on the Ill Reproductive System (IRS) 10 list were the phytoestrogens. We saw a panoramic view of the "phyto-" category already but I want to include another word about soy. Actually, about 1,000 words, but potato/patato, right? This is important.

Soy is estrogenic. And like other estrogenics, soy glaringly reveals some of the 3-tier influences of money in scientific work we've been discussing: corporate, government, and academic. For this reason, I'll use soy as THE representative example of the influence of money in scientific work while showcasing genuine health issues arising from soy. Other estrogenics *could* be highlighted in ways analogous to soy but "soy isolate" will do just fine. Especially since we are all familiar with soy.

Now, growing up, my home was surrounded by soy bean fields. And as a teenager, I used to work on 3 different Minnesota monoculture farms that raised both corn and soy beans. All 3 of these farms were massive – one was about 30,000 acres, for example.

Every other year like clockwork, the farmers all planted soy where the corn had grown the previous season and vice-versa. What heartland farmers all knew was that soy beans are important because they are legumes – they replenish the soil's vital nitrogen supply. Every other year, corn gluttonously devours the vital nitrogen bequeathed by the beans and the cycle begins anew.

While soy is estrogenic, other beans that we commonly eat are *not* estrogenic. Like pinto beans or black beans. Yet other beans are also legumes. So why do US farmers continue to almost exclusively grow estrogenic soy rather than other beans?

For one, soy beans – the actual beans – are round in shape and they practically fall out of their shells once the beans become dry and hard. The plants grow nice and straight, too. Furthermore, soy bean varieties are often patent-protected for various practical purposes like chemical herbicide resistance. In other words, soy beans are ideal for large-scale, corporate, farming. And corporate farming/processing is the sort of thing that suckles powerful lobbies.

From the farm to the store, here is how this works. The US government subsidizes soy crops in numerous ways, essentially encouraging farmers to grow excess soy beans over and above other crop types. This overgrowth *enables* "food" companies. Really, I'm not talking about "food" companies but rather "chemical processing companies". That's why I add quotation marks around the word "food". These processing companies become *fiscally addicted* to buying soy beans cheaply.

Next, the chemical processing companies pulverize the soy into mostly non-perishable by-products and sell these products as "food" packaged into different shapes and sizes. Of course, the soy products then need to be promoted as "healthy" with numerous "low calorie options", so "science" is employed here to "prove" health benefits. And... here comes the smoke and mirrors.

As recent as 1999, you can find quotes like this in professional scientific journals. I am including the entire 79-word abstract from this paper because it is so short and overly saccharine. It states:

Recent research demonstrates that consuming **soy is beneficial** for women but **how much** and from what foods are **still undetermined**. This article looks at the broad range of research relating to women's health and soy consumption and **makes recommendations for including soy** in a woman's daily diet. Additionally, it's **important for practitioners to be aware of the potential benefits of soy** as many of their patients will be asking about alternative therapies for hormone replacement therapy, such as soy consumption.[9]

"Soy is beneficial for women" is the clear message here. It's not even subtle. And, of course, your recommended daily consumption is given the old "undetermined" status.

Since a relatively small amount of processed soy can be bad for you (you usually buy it in processed form), it would actually be a legal disaster to recommend lots of soy, so what is going on?

First, everyone reacts uniquely and individually to diets, so you could almost make this type of statement about eating anything. "Exactly how much lead paint you should eat is undetermined".

And speaking of law and legal ballet, this particular paper was carefully titled *"Considering Soy: Its Estrogenic Effects May Protect Women"*. Most people reading this paper would not realize that this title was written conservatively – once again – by *legal necessity*. Even in 1999, there were truckloads of dirt coming out on soy.

Interestingly, when I looked up the two authors of this paper, one was a Shirley Lindsay. I found that Lindsay had presented this paper pre-publication (in 1998) to the "SoyInfo Center". The sidebar of Lindsay's SoyInfo Center presentation reads: "Lindsay has been a near vegetarian for two years, using soy protein as her main protein source [...] Lindsay has successfully eliminated 90% of her menopausal symptoms."[10]

So, now we see personal bias. Lindsay is definitely "soy convinced" after using soy to treat her menopausal symptoms, so she is favoring the positive aspects in her lab research and writing. This can be ok. Menopausal symptoms are possibly the only time soy might be viewed as permissible, if the risks are completely acknowledged. But Lindsay is not including an honest declaration of soy risks. She won't get sued because she is taking a favorable corporate stance but she ignores risks. More on risks soon.

Before moving into important "soy negatives" – the rest of the story – there is one more footnote to Lindsay's story. Because the facts about soy have become much bleaker since 1999, I contacted one of the two founders of the SoyInfo Center. Her name is Akiko Aoyagi Shurtleff. In essence, Akiko told me that they are very much still strongly promoting soy. The SoyInfo Center "Mission Statement" hopes to promote "new industrial uses" of soy,[11] so I was already skeptical about the neutrality of the SoyInfo Center's intentions but now it was confirmed.

Speaking of questionable motives, soy is the gift that keeps on giving. Unless soy truly is healthy, of course...

A recent – 2015 – paper in the *American Journal of Clinical Nutrition* discovered that soy isoflavones (the major *estrogenic* component of soy beans by 99.7%) are somewhat effective in preserving the bones of postmenopausal women.[12] In other words, isoflavones are acting in place of estrogen – again, a clear indication that they are estrogenic – therefore this particular positive impact, namely, a postmenopausal improvement, shouldn't surprise anyone.

It is an honest finding, even though the "effectiveness" was tiny. Mathematically "significant", yes, but tiny.

Non-scientists are often thrown off by this term "significant" – it basically just means "noticeable" in science papers.

Yet despite this "significant but tiny" positive impact from soy regarding bone preservation, this 2015 paper took a strongly positive stance on soy *overall*. What's up with that?

Well, one of the authors from *this* study is on the advisory board of a company called Pharmavite – the maker of SoyJoy® energy bars. Aaannnd, it gets worse. Another author on the study has a USA *patent* on a unique formulation of estrogenic soy isoflavones. In other words, they presumably plan to sell this particular soy estrogenic.

SoyJoy bars probably sold like wild after this 2015 paper, too. Headlines in newspapers based on this paper undoubtedly were glowing. Headlines like "Add Soy to Your Diet",[13] an actual article published in "Harvard Men's Health Watch". *Trusted advice for a healthier life* is their motto, by the way, which successfully sows seeds of permanent confusion.

Shoot: you, personally, might even be seriously considering hustling to the store right now. You may want to buy yourself a box of SoyJoy bars to begin your own "Joy in 7 days" Pure SoyJoy® Bar Diet. After all, soy "preserves women's bones" – at least for postmenopausal women – and I've now shown you 2 very positive soy'tastic papers and a Harvard Health Publication article.

Science journal spin leads to influential media spin, as we saw before. This happens all the time. Where is the harm here? Isoflavones *are* "antioxidants" so they *must* be good for you, right?

Well, I can think of several antioxidants that are toxic (APEs[14] for one), so this isn't necessarily good logic. And regarding postmenopausal-bone-preservation, isoflavones may indeed be good. Let's check.

Here. I have a paper you should consider. This 2002 paper[15] takes a more broad look at isoflavones in soy. It says disturbing things like, "Soy is known to produce estrogenic isoflavones. Here, we briefly review the evidence for [...] developmental toxicity, and estrogen developmental carcinogenesis in rats [...] and human studies suggesting a link between soy consumption and goiter". Yikes! Carcinogenesis, by the way, means "cancer formation". So, to hell with thinner bones – now we're talking about cancer and goiter?

And if rats can get cancer and goiter from soy it is likely that we can too. The stomach of a rat is practically a garbage-disposal. They eat the nastiest things. Here, Templeton the rat in Charlotte's Web comes to mind. Templeton collected disgusting foods like rotten eggs and, in this sense, was a true representative of real-life rats.

Rats are used all the time to test for toxicity but are probably not a great choice. If you find toxicity, fine – you've probably found something very toxic to humans. On the other hand, if there is an absence of toxicity in rats, that doesn't mean much relating to humans.

So, we should check out human studies, just to confirm. Good call.

First, note that the above soy "toxicity" paper was written in 2002, long before the favorable 2015 isoflavones-strengthen-your-bones paper (American Journal of Clinical Nutrition). Can you already see the

SoyJoy influence and spin? Cancer formation and other problems were already known but ignored.

None of the problems with soy were groundbreaking even by 2002, however. In 1960, for example, problems with goiter in human infants were already being attributed to soy.[16] I even found a 1961 paper frankly titled, "Soybean-induced goiter,"[17] probably written as a follow up to that 1960 study. And research about soy having an effect on "tumor growth" was coming out even earlier: try 1955.[18]

By 2015, therefore, the scientific community probably shouldn't be suggesting that we eat soy to preserve our bones. Even for a limited "postmenopausal women" cohort, there are better ways to strengthen your bones than consuming a substance that increases developmental toxicity, cancer (carcinogenesis), and sick thyroid glands (goiter). Seriously.

Frankly, basically any big-picture health study looking at soy will find that consuming even small amounts of soy is associated with multiple harmful effects that outweigh the benefits.

Let's skim one more research article from 2014 and then move along. Maybe the 1950's, 1960's, and 2002 paper that I've selected (showing developmental defects, goiter, and cancer) are just "old" research or flukes.

This 2014 science paper is a review[19] – an overview of research on this topic. The paper is titled: "*Soy foods and supplementation: a review of commonly perceived health benefits and risks*." In this paper, the authors "only" focus on 5 health risks from eating soy products, namely, "increased risk of breast cancer, male hormonal and fertility problems, hypothyroidism, antinutrient content, and harmful processing by-products." Later, they also sneak-in a 6th risk: additional problems with thyroid function from eating soy products. Again, this was 2014. Things have gotten bleaker, not better, in agenda-free soy research between 2002 and 2014. It's a mess.

Our food and water is also a mess. Let's move on to the final chapter of *Part 1* and investigate estrogenic levels in our food and water sources.

CHAPTER 4

Estrogenics by Air, Land, and Sea

The Mercury Rises

EARLY ON, IT WAS MORE Guns than Roses for Allison and me. Then fish and divine providence intervened.

One of Allison's earliest memories of me, and one she loves to relay to her friends, was the memory of being my lab partner. Actually, to say we were "partners" is being generous. Allison recalls that I worked too fast, too independently, and I didn't explain what I was doing during the pre-fabricated college lab experiments. Guilty as charged.

In fact, at the time, Allison even made up her mind not to be my partner in the future.

But then came a citrusy twist. Allison and I were both awarded competitive lab grants that required us to stay in Florida at Ave Maria's campus over the summer and work side-by-side. Our grants included free room, board, meals, and a $2,500 stipend. My roommate Dave was also staying the summer, working in the I.T. department, so it was an easy "yes" for me to stay.

"Living in Florida for just one summer can't be that bad," I told my skeptical family members back in Minnesota. "And, anyway, I'll learn some incredible scientific skills first-hand."

At that point, I had never experienced a summer of Florida heat, so ignorance was still bliss.

Of course, then it happened. Nearly the first day of my full-time lab job, a heat wave swaggered in, exhaling uncomfortable breaths of humidity, enough to fog my glasses. Wow.

To adapt, Dave and I became regulars at the beach that summer. We would smoke aromatic tobacco from briar-wood pipes in our right hands while holding fishing poles in our lefts. As we learned to consistently catch small ocean fish, we became more and more serious about our Fishing Club. It didn't take long and we began dreaming of catching a shark, a huge shark.

Sharks, you see, could never be ignored. Not only have I had them bump my leg while I was wading deep into the water on a full moon night, but nearly every trip to the beach, something large and powerful would snap our fishing line. *It had to be sharks.* In fact, on more than one occasion, we would be reeling in a smaller snook fish and the snook would get chomped in half on its journey to our ice chest. Brutal!

Despite these aggressive strikes, our early sharking attempts were a struggle. My Minnesota fishing skills proved non-transferable for the truly monster fish because these fish outmatched us. And even after Dave and I upgraded to stronger, 80-pound test, fishing line, *that* wasn't "cutting it". Giant mystery fish were still breaking off, presumably because of their razor-sharp teeth...presumably sharks.

With our minds "reeling" with new ideas, we bought pre-fabricated foot-long steel leaders and tied those to the ends of our lines. This led to another new and unexpected problem: the crimped connections on the leaders would break during battles with giant fish. Plus, even when the crimps didn't break, the 12 inches of steel proved to be too short. Our lines were getting bit *above* the steel. Were we hooking sharks or sea monsters? We sometimes wondered.

Then it happened.

One day, after all this trial and even more error, I caught my first shark. The shark was a little 3-foot-long bull. I was fishing with Dave and another friend named Trey, in Trey's boat, and catching the shark left me truly ecstatic. It was small but still a trophy to me. It represented a tremendous accomplishment and so much hard work.

Back on campus I began bragging about my first shark. Interestingly, people would commonly warn me: "don't eat the big sharks – they retain high levels of mercury." "Seriously?"

This advice, I later verified, is true.

In fact, when you look at the lake-by-lake "fish consumption" guidelines around the USA (e.g. Minnesota's[1]), things look bleak. Whether you inspect lakes, rivers, or oceans, you quickly ascertain that mercury abounds. Not all tests are updated nor are all waters tested but plenty of data exists.

The good news is that mercury levels in our water have improved. Awareness has been raised and measures have been taken.

Even so, however, the number of "unacceptable" lakes is astonishing. Due to mercury, "only eat fish from this lake once per month" is an extremely common dietary recommendation in government handbooks. The slogan "do not eat" – no serving sizes, nothing – is also commonly stamped on numerous bodies of water.

Obviously, these guidelines are only based on mercury levels rather than estrogenic levels in the water but let's consider this for a minute.

Mercury levels in water have risen because traces of mercury are often added as *preservatives* to herbicides/fungicides/pesticides. Mercury kills bacteria, fungus, and other microorganisms, just like it kills your brain cells. Therefore, wherever herbicides are sprayed, mercury usually ends up in the water.

Of course, when the mercury ends up in the water, so, too, does the actual herbicide chemical. At least, that seems likely and logical.

And, here, I'm thinking especially and specifically about estrogenic atrazine. Remember atrazine? The second most used herbicide in America that is totally illegal in Europe? Yeaah.

In other words, high mercury levels – and high levels are prevalent throughout the USA – indirectly might indicate high estrogenic levels. This is likely, if atrazine and other chemicals have long shelf-lives. We'll look at actual numbers soon but, so far, this is all common-sense logic: mercury is likely indicative of artificial estrogen presence.

Next, let's go one step further. Chemical companies are steadily diminishing mercury levels from "food-grade" herbicides. These corporations are developing other preservatives and getting better at removing trace amounts of residual mercury. Good.

Meanwhile, however, atrazine and other dangerous chemical levels continue to rise in usage, as we saw with the lawsuits in Chapter 2; sometimes rising dramatically.

Therefore, as we find less mercury in our water and fish, this leads to a false sense of security. Finding less mercury – as our current standards are set – leads to an increased "edible allowance" for fish even as the *true* toxicity of the fish meat is likely *increasing*. The estrogenic toxicity is becoming a larger health issue while being downplayed.

In the end, this all requires a lot of ridiculous deliberation. Can I eat this wild-caught bass? What about a large tuna? Maybe we should just stick with fast-foods??

Actually, as a side bar, fast-food estrogenic levels are finally officially being "unwrapped" in a 2016 lab study.[2]   And it probably won't surprise you that the study found high levels of Ill Reproductive System (IRS) List estrogenics in the fast food. Specifically, this study found that eating representative fast-foods ("for research") increased certain estrogenics in the blood by over 50% in some cases – and by over 40% in *most* cases. In other words, fast-food is *impregnating* us with estrogenics!

Keep in mind that many children and teens are eating what qualifies as "fast-food" in school cafeterias *everyday* around America so this is *big* news. Over the long-term, this actually leads to an impregnated phenotype or impregnated appearance but we'll save that discussion for the next chapter.

Why are estrogenics in fast-food at levels high enough to spike our blood? Where are the sources of all these estrogenics? And what are the specific numbers in the water supply?

Estrogenic C-Level

Let's begin at the beginning. In America, we are *annually* spraying 80 million pounds of weed-killing atrazine onto our fields, especially corn. Remember that number for a minute: 80 million. And this is *only* in America, where we dream as big as we want to (lyrics from a Brooks & Dunn song). Many other countries, of course, are also not exactly rationing their chemical-crop-sprays.

And why should we be thinking about other countries? Well, aside from oceanic pollution, we import ship-loads of food from these countries.

Take Brazil, for example. Brazil is estimated to use a whopping 100,000 pounds per year of atrazine.[3]   Yet Brazil is #3 in global corn production. America and *China* take the top 2 spots.[4]

So, what about China? Well, as with all things Chinese, data on atrazine use is difficult to find. What I can tell you, however, is that Chinese farmers unloaded a hefty 10 million pounds of atrazine onto their fields in 2012 – the most recent data I could find – and the Chinese have been increasing atrazine usage every year since 1980.[5] Not as bad as the US (80 million), but bad. This all assumes honest atrazine number reporting, of course.

When the chem dust settles, where are all these millions of pounds of atrazine ending up? The results are in, folks: a tremendous amount is being washed into our lakes, rivers, and oceans.

And atrazine is remaining there. Let's start there.

Atrazine, similar to most estrogenics from the IRS 10 List, has a long shelf-life and does not readily break-down.

This long shelf-life is by design, by the way. Rapidly expiring estrogenic products would bleed corporate money – a dilemma also encountered in the processed "food" industry.

So, what might be the time frame for atrazine shelf-life? Weeks? Months? The answer appears to be *years*. The actual product information from one fact sheet I found says atrazine in water is "very stable over several years". That's not unusual.

But, "objection," you might say, "farm dirt contains bacteria." Agreed. Bacteria are able to break down man-made chemicals like atrazine, meaning that soil "persistence" is important to investigate.

How long does atrazine last in dirt? Thankfully, scientists have done this exact study. According to researchers, the *half-life* of atrazine at 77 degrees Fahrenheit – a fairly hot testing temperature – was 315 days in red soil, 165 days in brown soil, and 248 days in black soil.[6] That's a long time for *half-life* of anything in dirt!

In fact, based on this information, let's say you filled a sippy-cup with atrazine and poured it into a lake. It is likely that this atrazine would *literally* take longer to break-down and degrade than the oil from that 2010 BP Deepwater Horizon oil spill that occurred in the Gulf of Mexico.[7] All 600 million liters of that oil!

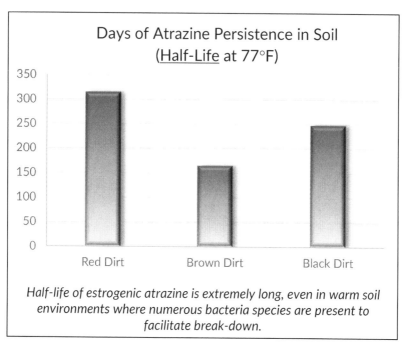

Days of Atrazine Persistence in Soil
(Half-Life at 77°F)

Half-life of estrogenic atrazine is extremely long, even in warm soil environments where numerous bacteria species are present to facilitate break-down.

With the immensity of atrazine crop spraying and its slow breakdown, you might expect to find atrazine in many lakes. You might also expect atrazine is being circulated by rivers and oceans.

Indeed, this is the case.

Many Brazilian waterways, for instance, easily top their own maximum allowed atrazine levels, which is 2,000 ng/L (nanograms [ng] per liter [L]). Brazilians commonly find atrazine levels more than 4-times over this particular "maximum allowable limit".[8] The authors of this Brazilian water study concede that this is indicative of a clear and present "health risk".

And, just to inject another layer of reality here, these "maximum allowable limits" are subjective.

As you know by now, for example, atrazine is downright illegal in Europe. Zero is the allowable limit there, in other words. Brazil might say 1,999 ng/L is not harmful for your health but Europe enforces a maximum limit of 1,000 ng/L for *any pesticides in any type of water.*[8]

Meanwhile, in the USA, 3,000 ng/L is the maximum allowable limit for atrazine in *drinking water*.[9] Care to guess what I think about that? The allowable limits are subjective but it doesn't change the health impacts we'll see later.

It's also important here to note that 200 ng/L of atrazine – not 2,000 but *200* ng/L – has been demonstrated to cause "reproductive abnormalities" in frogs.[10] Those poor creatures are absorbing it through their skin, not to mention the raw eggs sitting in estrogenic cess.

Anyway, let's check out atrazine amounts in a couple other representative water sources – sources closer to home – and then move beyond atrazine to other infamous IRS List estrogenics. Caution: the overall picture is grim.

A study of lakes in western Texas found about 80% of them contained high levels of atrazine.[11] And let's remember, Texas is extremely dry. This means rain is less likely to wash atrazine into Texan lakes and rivers. The slow breakdown of atrazine in dirt is clearly a major factor in that outcome.

Next, and somewhat predictably, the Mid-West of America was discovered to have worse estrogenic loads than Texas. In a study that spanned Illinois, Iowa, and Minnesota, atrazine was found present in 94% of those tested water bodies.[12]

Even a bunch of "preserved" wetlands, investigated in a different study, were found to have a "median concentration of atrazine in surface water at 200 ng/L"[10]. Wetlands! The wetland study even revealed that atrazine was present, at least in the cases investigated, because *subsurface* tile drainage waters were flowing into these pristine wetland ponds.

Overall, the more you "surf" the scientific research, the "clearer" it becomes that atrazine is ubiquitous in American waters. It is also heavily dosing waters from countries we import many foods and drinks.

Ok. Let's move beyond atrazine. Other estrogenics also are becoming concentrated in our lakes, our planet's river arteries, and, of course, our oceans, so let's "dive in".

Researchers investigating zooplankton in the Baltic Sea above Poland recently made a whale-of-a-discovery. Their study, published in 2016, found high levels of both BPA [bisphenol A] and APEs [alkylphenols] in the zooplankton. I don't know about you, but I envision the Baltic Sea as virtually "virgin-water" compared to the waters in and around the US and China, but these waters were found contaminated.

These oceanic researchers further reminded us that zooplankton are "susceptible to *accumulating* endocrine disrupting compounds,"[13] making the problem much worse.

This accumulation is another nod toward *fat* storage of BPA and APEs and other estrogenics, so keep that in the back of your mind.

This also means these chemical loads likely impact the denizen sea life, including whales, sharks, cod, etc., with possibly profound impacts.

This impact occurs because zooplankton are at the very bottom of the food chain. When scientists discover zooplankton are accumulating estrogenics, the estrogenic load is expected to correspondingly increase as you move up the food chain. Again, this is due to the fat storage issue that we will "breach" in the next chapter.

The moral of the Poland zooplankton study is that globally, nobody seems to have escaped the estrogenic water problem.

To reinforce this idea, a different study discovered that APE and BPA estrogenics "are ubiquitous in sediments from Northeast Wetlands of Iran, contaminating the aquatic habitats in this area."[14] Iran!

I have further found that APEs from so-called "food-grade plastics" are killing off remote coral reef species.[15,16] As a certified scuba diver, I find studies like this heartbreaking. Everybody, everything, everywhere seems to be touched by our new "estrogeneration" water problem.

And while estrogenics *from plastics* certainly include APEs and BPA from the IRS 10 List, even more they encompass phthalates and parabens. Keep in mind that phthalates and parabens are found in "BPA-Free" plastics, as well as all sorts of fragrances.

"Phthalates" says one scientific study, "are the most common chemicals that humans are in contact with daily."[17] That is an ominous start. The authors explain their reasoning by noting that production of phthalates reaches 300 *billion* pounds *per year*, globally. This number makes the 100's of millions of pounds of atrazine seem measly.

Why the high number? Perfumes and plastics? Well, these same scientists cite phthalate presence in this naughty-list: "*PVC products, building materials (paint, adhesive, wall covering), personal-care products (perfume, eye shadow, moisturizer, nail polish, deodorizer, liquid soap, and hair spray), medical devices, detergents and surfactants, packaging, children's toys, printing inks and coatings, pharmaceuticals and food products, textiles, household applications such as shower curtains, floor tiles, food containers and wrappers, and cleaning materials."* Is that all? No wonder they argue phthalates are the most common chemical we are in contact with daily.

Actually, this same phthalate study included a chart about phthalate levels in *air-dust*. One dozen countries are cited as problematic for phthalate air-dust, including the US and China. Now you can see exactly why I said earlier that "phthalates are like glitter because you can't get rid of them".

Overall, this data tells us that phthalates and possibly other estrogenics advance a three-fold attack. They (1) easily become airborne, (2) swiftly leach into food/drink, and (3) are present in fragrances that people use daily.

But wait. Phthalate water transfer from plastic contact and fragrance are easy to imagine. But phthalate exhaust in the air? Seriously?

"The general public and those with allergies," says one study in the *Annals of Asthma, Allergy, and Immunology*, "are exposed to significant levels of phthalates via diet, pharmaceuticals, phthalate-containing products, and *ambient indoor environment via air and dust*."[18]

Trust me, we'll revisit those allergies!

But the ability of estrogenics, especially phthalates, to become airborne is disconcerting. Plastics are everywhere. In fact, there is even a recent, eye-opening scientific report on bad phthalate "emissions" from vinyl flooring and crib mattresses.[19] If this isn't a concern for parents I don't know what is. And specific guidance will be provided in the last chapter, in case you wonder.

Furthermore, think of all the plastics in the modern indoor child "care" facilities. Check out this study, for example, showing that phthalate exposure in child "care" facilities "exceeded cancer benchmarks" before the age of 2 years in California[20]...the same California, where warm weather abounds and children could simply play outdoors. But real grass? Dirt? Some people would prefer your children play on "chemgrass" or some other artificial cushioning material...which contains phthalates.[20]

Ironically, speaking of playing outdoors, landscape companies sometimes spray atrazine on grass. This is especially common in the southern states with grasses such as bermudagrass or St. Augustine grass. Be watchful for that, if you have children and if you outsource your landscaping.

Now, one final word about air quality.

Recently, I was introduced to a professional science journal article which begins: "Benzophenone-3 (BP-3) is a widespread environmental contaminant and an estrogenic compound. Very little is known with regard to the *occurrence in indoor air* and the inhalation exposure of humans to BP-3."

Very little is known.

But the authors go on: "In this study, 81 indoor air samples were collected from various locations in Albany, New York, USA, in 2014 and analyzed for BP-3."[20] Things heat up with the punchline-conclusion that "BP was found in *all* indoor air samples [...] the highest concentrations were found in cars, followed by barber shops > public places > homes > offices > garages."

This was the first ever survey of BP in indoor air. In 2015. Hopefully more will come soon but this preliminary data does not look promising.

Naturally, I've sleuthed around for supporting studies to answer why there is so much BP in city air and, so far, I haven't found any. I can only speculate. I expect that BP is probably not only added to sunscreen but BP is also added to various plastics to prevent sun damage. I suspect BP is even a factor in that "new car smell" along with the parabens and phthalates and this is why cars were found to have the highest BP air concentration.

Alternatively, high levels in air could simply be the result of BP in hair products. Like my BP-containing hand soap that was escorted to the nearest trash can in Chapter 2, BP is frequently added to hair products to protect against sun-damage. Argh.

Now, after realizing that phthalates and BP are in our air-dust, wouldn't it actually be shocking if both BP and phthalates weren't being concentrated in our waterways? They are.[17]

Parabens, you should know, are also manufactured in huge loads. Annual production may even reach phthalate proportions. Unfortunately, it is difficult to put an exact number on paraben manufacturing quantities because there is such a variety of different parabens.

However, we have some idea of paraben burden. According to one assessment of parabens performed by the "Danish Ministry of the Environment", China and India produce the most parabens but they refused to reveal their production numbers.[21] The good news is that although the Danish government couldn't get the numbers, I did. Just kidding.

The USA, however, was included in this Danish Ministry assessment and we participated: the USA produces about 2 million pounds of parabens each year. That's not overwhelming but I consider this quite high since most of America's paraben production is outsourced overseas.

Beyond the lack of transparency in paraben manufacturing, a 2015 science article captured the essence of this newly emerging problem. The article states: "The *widespread exposure* of humans to parabens present in personal care products is *well-known*. *Little is known about the accumulation* of parabens in marine organisms."[22] Nevertheless, for the first time, these scientists uncovered paraben accumulation in all the organisms they investigated.

Now, I normally don't include lengthy abstracts from science papers because they are generally boring. However, I found this rare winner below. Most importantly, it applies to *all four* of the plastic estrogenics we've been investigating, namely BPA, APEs, phthalates, and parabens and gives a sobering view of reality from genuine experts. It says:

> **Plastics are cheap**, strong, and durable and offer considerable benefits to humanity. They potentially can enhance the benefits that both medical and scientific technology will bestow to humankind. However, it has now been several decades since the **use of plastics exploded**, and we have evidence that our current approach to production, use, transport and disposal of plastic materials has caused, and is still **causing serious effects on wildlife, and is not sustainable**. Because of

frequent inappropriate waste management practices, or irresponsible human behavior, large masses of plastic items have been released into the environment, and thereby **have entered the world's oceans**. Moreover, **this process continues**, and in some places is **even increasing**. Most plastic debris that now exists in the marine environment originated from ocean-based sources such as the fishing industry. **Plastics accumulate in coastal areas, at the ocean surface and on the seabed. Because 70% of all plastics are known to eventually sink, it is suspected that ever increasing amounts of plastic items are accumulating in seabed sediments. Plastics do not biodegrade, although, under the influence of solar UV radiations, plastics do degrade and fragment into small particles, termed microplastics**. Our oceans eventually serve as a sink for these small plastic particles and in one estimate, it is thought that 200,000 microplastics per km^2 of the ocean's surface commonly exist. The impact of plastic debris has been studied since the beginning of the 1960's. To date, **more than 267 species in the marine environment** are known to have been affected by plastic entanglement or ingestion. Marine mammals are among those species that are most affected by entanglement in plastic debris. By contrast, marine birds suffer the most from ingestion of plastics. Organisms can also be absorbed by floating plastic debris, or the contaminants may derive from plastic additives that are leached to the environment. Recent studies emphasize the important role of **microplastics as they are easily ingestible by small organisms, such as plankton species, and form a pathway for contaminants to enter the food web**. Contaminants leached from plastics tend to bioaccumulate in those organisms that absorb them, and chemical concentrations are often higher at higher trophic levels. This causes **a threat to the basis of every food web and can have serious and**

> far-reaching effects, even on nonmarine species such as polar bears and humans, who consume marine-grown food.[23]

Polar bears? Seriously? Either way, this is genuinely dire. In fact, once again this abstract doesn't even sound like a professional science article. It sounds like a radical environmentalist pamphlet. The problem is simply too formidable for word mincing. At least for these concerned authors.

Like these authors, when you start to think of the *additive* effects from all four of these plastic components *together*, you really begin to grasp the tentacles of the current estrogenic water problem.

One final estrogenic to add before we inspect actual "purified" drinking water: EE2 [17α-ethinylestradiol].

Unlike atrazine, EE2 has not yet been found in restored wetlands.

Unlike BPA, APEs, phthalates, and parabens, EE2 is not universally found in the *open* oceans...yet.

Where EE2 is emerging, however, is in water sources closer to home.

For instance, one study of the South China Sea, concluded that, "*high* [EE2] estrogenic risks were *in coastal waters* and low [EE2] estrogenic risks were in the open sea."[24]

The same appears to be true within the USA. In the Gulf of Mexico, for example, sediment "core" samples – mud layers collected using a hollow metal tube pushed deep into the Mississippi Sound – revealed that EE2 was only "detected occasionally".[25] But how about our "drinking" water? That's a different story.

Drinking Estrogenics

When I first discovered that estrogenic atrazine levels in pristine *wetlands* cause "frog reproductive abnormalities" – levels over 200 ng/L – I immediately wondered: what is the condition of our *drinking water*? Are we successfully removing that concerning dose of atrazine?

Well, according to one thorough investigation of America's largest water databases – including the nationwide *Safe Drinking Water Act Data* and the *Syngenta® Voluntary Monitoring Program* – researchers found that 5% of all *raw water* in the USA has atrazine levels at 4,800 ng/L and 1% of our raw water was at 34,000 ng/L.[26] Wow!

That means 1% of our raw water supply has atrazine at 170-times the levels that destroy a frog's private parts!

But, wait, you might say, that's just the raw water. What about the "good" stuff? The stuff that impacts humans? What about faucet water? We all know people who drink directly from their kitchen taps.

That same massive study reveals that 5% of *drinking water* in America is at 2,700 ng/L for atrazine and 1% is at 22,700 ng/L. The "Wow!" is clearly still in play here. Not good.

In essence, rather than 170-fold levels, 1% of our drinking water has 114-times the level of atrazine that causes frog reproductive abnormalities.

Is *your* city in that top 1%? Probably not.

You might make top 10%, though. And how can you be sure? There isn't much transparency for non-scientists on these issues, even when the studies are done and paid for by tax dollars. For example, does your town have a simple and clear website where you can look up estrogenic numbers in your drinking water?

 "Recent estimates in the USA," notes another scientific study done in 2013, "showed that between *2 and 3 million people* are annually exposed to atrazine present in drinking water."[27]

"What levels?" you ask. "Around 200 ng/L", the researchers reveal.

Put another way, 2-3 million of us are exposed to "frog reproductive abnormality levels" in our *drinking* water! And if it sounds like I am obsessed with that phrase about frog reproductive abnormalities, I kind of am. It's fittingly graphic for this "sickening" situation.

Of course, one limitation within this type of research is that scientists generally only test *average* levels. This is a true shortcoming because estrogenic levels can change drastically from season-to-season, city-to-city, and year-to-year. Especially atrazine levels.

What is most worrisome about estrogenic usage – as we saw in the previous chapter – is usage has continued to *rise* each of the past 20 years. Hence, the "frog reproductive abnormality" doses drunk by 2-3 million people in 2013 has undoubtedly risen and is probably increasing annually. Consider that most of this stuff virtually doesn't break down in water, too.

So, here's my conclusion based on the scientific studies: *atrazine is not filtered out of your city's drinking water supply effectively.* Raw water and drinking water numbers are far too similar.

Sadly, this is also true of the other IRS 10 estrogenics. Once they get in, they barely come out. My college orientation lecturer was correct. "Recycle, reduce, and re-pee" appears to be a reality. The current municipal filtration systems are not getting the job done.

So what do you do? You need to take matters into your own hands, for now. The data is emphatically *not* murky. Levels at 170-times above those that "turn male frogs into princesses" – the level *prior* to municipal treatment – is really not too much better than levels 114-times – the level *after* muni treatment. The treatments aren't effective enough and zero is ideal, of course. We'll address all of this in *Part 3* of this book but it's a ticking time bomb unless you act.

Similar to our discussion about lakes and oceans and other "raw" water, let's move beyond atrazine. Phthalates, parabens, BPA, and APEs are worth investigating, the plastic and perfume estrogenics, because they round out the final picture.

First of all, I personally cringe when I see people properly filtering their drinking water...and then storing it in plastic. "BPA-Free" plastic is only a red herring as you have begun to see.

My cringe deepens when people set plastic bottles in the sunlight or in a hot vehicle.

As one study reminds us: "Health risks from the consumption of bottled water increase after UV [sunlight] exposure."[28] These are "risks" that are easy to sidestep so why gamble?!

This is also true of microwaving any type of plastics and pouring hot coffee into a plastic-lined mug: STOP. Would you trust a few studies that say phthalates levels in your water are ok, when 100's or even 1,000's of other studies suggest otherwise? This is another place you will find spin.

"The knowledge-base of bottled water leachate," says the same author as the UV review paper, "is highly contradictory due to varying methodologies and limited multi-elemental and/or molecular analyses."[28]

Honestly, that is usually another way of professionally saying "data on this topic is littered with spin".

Spin by whom?

People selling you plastics for food and drink storage. I suggest research may be "highly contradictory" because there is a lot of money in plastics, not merely because "analyses vary". Of course, the issue of properly measuring and experimenting with these fat-like substances does play a role in the discrepancies but the health dangers being discovered don't disappear because of a few flawed studies.

Anyway, since you already realize how much atrazine journeys from "raw" water into the drinking water, you probably don't need much convincing that phthalates, parabens, BPA, and APEs are also traveling through municipal filters into your noodle soup.[i]

And here, for a nice change of pace, BPA offers some isolated good news. While the other estrogenics appear to be leveling-up, estrogenic BPA levels in drinking water are currently dropping.

Further, since BPA is comprehensively studied, I think this is especially reliable information.

Lowering BPA in our drinking water is predominantly due to widespread concern and public outcry. This is one way you can take action. So, good job public and keep up the good work.

To give some sense of the actual numbers, the *upper* levels of BPA discovered in drinking water were 10 ng/L in America, 10 ng/L in Europe, and 320 ng/L in China, at least in one particular study's selected locations.[28] Not bad.

Phthalates, as you might expect, are a different story. You might even remember this quote from before: "Phthalates are *the most common chemicals* that humans are in contact with daily."[17] And, here again, levels just keep going up.

What is surprising is that despite our heavy usage of phthalate chemicals and the vast recognition of health harms due to phthalates, published scientific studies of phthalates in *drinking* water are surprisingly

---

[i] Skip to the next subsection titled "Eating Estrogenics" if you need no further convincing or if you are not interested in additional specific numbers.

sparse. Or the studies are regionally limited. Or limited in other ways. Or even untrustworthy...

Limitations to scientific studies are old news but what about "untrustworthy" studies? Well, for an example that relates to phthalates, let's inspect one published study done on various New Jersey drinking water sources.[29]

As a disclaimer, while the university researchers who conducted this study looked for chemicals in the water, they never measured *amounts* of chemicals. The only measured chemical "presence".

Anyway, the researchers in this "Jersey-Shore Study" – my name, not theirs – found that 38% of tested "raw" water samples contained phthalates. This is a fairly high percentage.

But at least there was 0% in the drinking water, right?

Of course not! They found 29% of the drinking water samples contained phthalates. Not even 10% less after city "filtration". And, not surprisingly, this finding mirrors my previous conclusion: city water "treatment plants" are *not effectively removing estrogenics*. From Florida to New Jersey...from birth control to atrazine and beyond.

But for me, there is something even *more* disturbing than the lack of studies on phthalates in drinking water. At least in this case.

This same "Jersey-Shore Study" compared their findings to those of the Environmental Protection Agency (EPA).

The EPA found phthalates in only 3% of raw water samples in that *same area*. Compare that 3% to the 38% found by the Jersey-Shore-Study scientists. This is what I mean by "untrustworthy".

Further, the EPA claimed that only 2% of the *drinking water* samples contained phthalates. The Jersey-Shore Study found 29%. These are serious discrepancies and unreliable, indeed.

Ironically, the "Jersey-Shore Study" was funded by the National Institute for Environmental Health Sciences and also the New Jersey Dept. of Environmental Protection.[29] Government funds finding government flaws; are you catching this?

And, predictably due the connection between the scientists and the funding source here, these authors danced around the discrepancy between their data and that of the EPA. They didn't even write a full "Discussion" section in the paper – the Discussion section is usually 1 of about 5 major components of virtually every scientific research paper. They meshed the Discussion into the Results section.

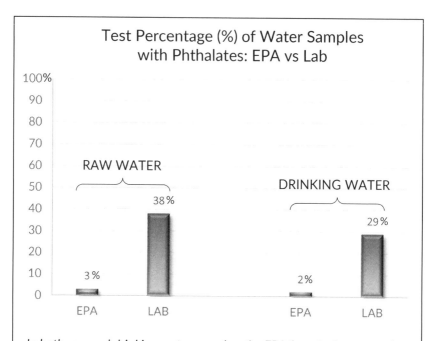

Test Percentage (%) of Water Samples with Phthalates: EPA vs Lab

In both raw and drinking water samples, the EPA found a lower number of estrogenic-positive samples than a university lab. The testing locations were similar.

Using common sense, we also know that a "cocktail" of estrogenics in drinking water is likely to amplify estrogenic problems that we will see later (hint: *The 7 Deadly Things*). So, let's move on to APEs [alkylphenols].

We already found APEs in fairly remote Polish zooplankton at disturbing levels but how about APEs in drinking water?

Well, one APE study discovered reasonably high levels. This same study, in fact, also acts as a good example of the arbitrary limits that are created for "allowable" estrogenic levels so let's check it out.

Rather than New Jersey, this study came from the Great Lakes region. Certain samples of water measuring APE concentrations found APE *below* "water quality criteria" for the United States. In other words, they found "safe" APE levels. However, the authors acknowledged that those *same samples* exceeded the *Canadian* guidelines.[30] So you can now add Canada to the list of countries that are stingier about certain estrogenic levels than America.

As an interesting sidebar, this same Great Lakes study found *pharmaceutical drugs* present in 34% of surface water samples. This is noteworthy because no guidelines are set for how much Prozac you can legally drink or what the legal drinking age should be. And, joking aside, the other drugs should be raising additions questions and concern.

Moving away from the faucet, people enjoy drinking from plastic bottles. Let's consider those a source of drinking water.

It probably won't surprise you that DEHP, a phthalate used to make plastic more flexible, was found at 1,680ng/L in bottled water.[31] This is the same bottled water many people purchase by the case in the grocery store. Have I mentioned yet that the *atrazine* "frog-limit" was 200 ng/L and that the European Union doesn't allow *any* pesticides above 1,000 ng from any water source? Yum.

And we really can't forget about the frogs and other wildlife. This study was titled "A critical analysis of the *biological impacts* of plasticizers on wildlife" and the scientist authors used the paper to remind us that "detrimental" biological effects occur in mollusks, crustaceans and amphibians that appear at exposures "in the low ng/L to µg/L range."[32] This means 1,680 ng/L easily makes the "detrimental" cut for environmental harm and that's only the water inside one plastic bottle.

This bottled water study also mentions a noteworthy scandal called the *Taiwan Food Scandal*. Apparently, in both 2011 and 2014, not just one but multiple Taiwanese food processing and packaging companies were caught illegally adding DEHP into sport drinks, fruit juice, tea beverages, fruit jam, bread, and food powder *as a filler*. They were adding this phthalate because it is cheaper than using oil. Wrap your head around that for a second.

This *Taiwan Food Scandal* story also reminds me of the Subway and McDonalds "yoga mat material" ingredient, azodicarbonamide. Subway, McDonalds, and other places were (are?) adding yoga mat materials to their bread as a filler. They claim the stuff is added as a "conditioner" but let's call a spade a spade. Yet, "at least" in this case, the yoga mat ingredient is perfectly legal – er, at least in the US. Azodicarbonamide is not legal in Europe...

But let's go back to "drink up, hydration is healthy", the Dasani® plastic bottled water slogan.

Estrogenic beverage transfer is due to molecular interactions. It is similar to how soap washes oil off your hands. Once plastics come in contract with water or other liquids, estrogenics leach into that drink.

In addition, oils, fats, alcohol, and other substances in beverages can make the estrogenic leaching problem worse. The added substances "draw out" more estrogenic chemicals.

For a parallel example of this molecular "drawing out" of plastic estrogenics, think about caffeine. A recent study showed that caffeine-containing coffee caused over 20% more BPA "migration" into coffee compared to caffeine-free coffee.[33] The experiment was done by simply pouring hot coffee into a BPA mug. A group of cups were filled with regular coffee and a group of cups were filled with caffeine-free coffee. Now: if caffeine alone is able to draw out 20% more estrogenic BPA, just think what other sugars, fats, etc. can do!

Put simply, certain molecules including caffeine can "shuttle" estrogenic molecules out of plastics. So consider these plastic-stored beverages besides water "sources of drinkable estrogenics".

To close this section, let's shift to an estrogenic that people around the globe are consuming *intentionally*: EE2 (17α-ethinylestradiol).

Remember how the levels of EE2 were generally minimal in remote places like open oceans and restored wetlands? Unfortunately, drinking water is a different story. You've certainly drunk some EE2 at some point in your life and may even be drinking EE2 on a daily basis if you don't filter your drinking water.

Prior to looking at specific numbers, keep in mind that, because EE2 is a contraceptive hormone, it is specifically designed to stay in the body longer. It is *designed* to not become broken down or metabolized, meaning that EE2 is one *tough* little molecule. In fact, EE2 is probably the longest lasting estrogenic on the IRS 10 List. One study looked at 5 "endocrine disrupting chemicals" – chemicals that disrupt hormones and in this case all estrogenics. The researchers used native groundwater conditions and found that within 70 days there was no degradation of EE2.[34] Zero.

Looking deeper into scientific studies, I find a useful pattern emerges with EE2 and drinking water. This is something you can use to make an educated guess concerning the birth control hormone levels in the drinking water that concerns you and yours. EE2 concentrations in drinking water are generally most elevated where (1) fresh water is scarce and (2) where human population density is high.

In these cases, to put it bluntly, the toilet water is cycling back through the water table and EE2 is continuously re-injected via urine. Since our bodies are also not breaking down EE2, it passes right through...after contributing to predominantly 7 major health problems, of course; The 7 Deadly Things (Part 2).

Environmental scientists name this rapid recycling of water "recharging of reclaimed water" and they honestly acknowledge that potential for condensing the concentration of water pollutants such as EE2 is high.[34]

So, let's go back to China again. The population density certainly is high in China, so we'll launch EE2 drinking water explorations from there and illustrate the reliability of population density.

First, it's worth noting that China is an extreme example. Chinese women are extremely heavy birth control users. China maintained a draconian "one-child-only" policy from about 1970 to 2016 and currently have a "two-child-only" policy. In fact, according to the BBC, China's government has collected over 2 trillion yuan (over 300 billion US dollars) in fines for the "one-child-only" policy since its inception[35] and I can only imagine how much they collect on taxes of the birth control product sales themselves. Not to mention all the EE2 profits. Usage is substantial.

But let's begin by looking at a lower density Chinese region. Moving away from the crowded coastline of China, you find Yueyang. Yueyang is both a city and also a "prefecture-level city". A "prefecture-level city" is comparable, in some ways, to an American State. Yueyang, Yueyang, could be likened to New York [city], New York [state].

And for a size reference, the area of Yueyang is slightly larger than the state of Connecticut. In fact – continuing the comparison to

Connecticut – the population density of Yueyang is 950 people per square mile while Connecticut is 739. Again, similar.

Even in this region of China, EE2 levels are *far* above the "European Union [EU] Water Framework Directive" levels. The EU max allowable levels are 0.035 ng/L.[36] But the data here tells the complete story.

The lake *upstream* of Yueyang city – East Dongting Lake – has a "mean EE2 concentration" of 3.04 ng/L.[37] This, of course, is almost exactly 100 times the EU safety level, but it gets worse.

On the *downstream* side of Yueyang city – Honghu Lake – the "mean EE2 concentration" is 17.73 ng/L! That's essentially 500-times the EU safety limit of 0.035 ng/L!

What about a major coastline city like Beijing? Beijing has a population density of 3,400 people per square mile, which blows away Yueyang's 950 people per square mile. How's Beijing?

Well, I was able to find at least one impartial, non-government study. The study was published from sources outside China, specifically, in a Netherlands-based science journal called "*Chemosphere*" in the year 2005.

In the *Chemosphere* study, the researchers explained how they looked at water purified from the largest municipal plant in *all of Asia*. This water plant was located in Beijing.

Unfortunately, however, the scientists did not directly measure EE2 levels in the study. They instead used what is called an EROD assay ("enzyme 7-ethoxy-resorufin-O-deethylase assay") to test the treated water.[38] They likely used the EROD assay because EE2 levels were literally off the charts using direct measurements when the study was performed in 2005, but I don't know for sure.

Anyway, remember how the downstream Honghu Lake was 17.73 ng/L and 500-times the EU safety level? Well, *diluting* the Beijing *treated* water into the lab's *pure distilled water* – in other words, using 95% pure water and only 5% treated water – gave levels of EE2 *above* 100 ng/L. This number is hugely problematic for Beijing for sure. Lots of women *and* men, in other words, are "on heavy birth control" in that region.

Next, shifting closer to home – actually about 1-hour drive west of Boston, Massachusetts, where I happen to be writing this – you can find the beautiful Lake Quinsigamond. This lake is a hub for rowing teams, swimmers, and fisherman. In fact, Lake Quinsigamond appears too idyllic to be featured in a scientific EE2 study. However, the population density is very high in this area, so scientists thought it was worth an investigation. Specifically, Worcester is the nearby city and maintains a population density higher than Beijing at 4,678 people per square mile (Beijing = 3,400).

When researchers tested the Quinsigamond water EE2 levels, they found 11.1 ng/L.[39] This is over 300-times the EU safety level and, unfortunately, these same scientists did not test the nearby drinking water. We've already seen how effectively estrogenic compounds are generally removed from drinking water, though, so you might draw your own conclusions on that.

Anticlimactically, the Lake Quinsigamond researchers ended by stating that the "concentration [of EE2 that they found] may affect the reproduction of fish and other aquatic organisms in the lake due to its high estrogenic activity". Clearly, this is putting it mildly. I suggest that it *definitely* affects the reproduction of fish and other species based on the European restrictions but we can look into that further later. The fish reproduction and health is especially a concern because EE2 cannot possibly be the only estrogenic in Quinsigamond water.

For one final example, let's again stay within Massachusetts. Let's head down to Acushnet, Massachusetts, where the population density of 559 people per square mile is much less that Worcester. More precisely, this study was performed in the Acushnet River Estuary and again tested EE2 levels.[40] What was this study's conclusion? "Among three estrogenic compounds detected, EE2 has the highest concentration, up to 4.7 ng/L, at which EE2 may affect lobster and other fish abundance in the coastal seawater [where the river ends up] due to its high biological activity on fish feminization."

In summary, wherever the water is tested, the trend is clear: EE2 levels rise together with population density. And the levels are high. It is more of a city concern than a rural concern but it's important to recognize because the health of your family or extended family is on the line.

And, before moving to foods, I want to leave you with one final booster-shot of awareness regarding estrogenics in water.

EE2 "model predictions were compared to published measured concentrations" in a recent study. What that means is scientists compared mathematical *models* of EE2 in drinking water to actual water testing.

Models, they explained in the paper, are often used to determine water safety levels of EE2 *without using actual measuring* because it is easier and cheaper.

What did the study reveal? These scientists found that taking real, physical, measurements of EE2 "exceed those that would be expected from the model, despite very conservative model assumptions."[41]

This may help explain why government values are found so far below professional scientist's findings. The EPA, for example, with the Jersey-Shore Study, might be relying on models. This is why I prefer to see actual measurements and why you should too.

Eating Estrogenics

Serious estrogenic contamination "springs" from our waterways. From the water, estrogenics work up the food chain, into our seafood, veggies, cows, and, ultimately, into us. From nature's mussels into our dwindling muscles.

So let's talk about food.

To transition out of drinking water, it seems fitting to start with "seafood" both from the ocean and from freshwater. After that, we will move to "landfood" – especially beef and poultry.

Let's begin with nature's mussels. Mussels are "filter feeders". This means they eat plankton by siphoning water into one hole, filtering out and retaining the food – and the toxins – and shooting wastewater out a different hole.

Because of this lifelong filter-feeding behavior, scientists sometimes view mussels as environmental "chemical sensors". If chemicals are present, scientists find them in mussel meat. Like plankton, therefore, mussels are a first-rate model for investigating estrogenics.

Of course, with the high levels of estrogenics we've already seen across the board in our waterways and in open ocean zooplankton, it is a no-brainer hypothesis that high amounts of estrogenics are in mussel meats. Exhibit A: researchers retrieved and tested mussels. They measured levels of APEs in mussels from the St. Lawrence River above New York state. Not surprisingly, they found high concentrations of APEs.[42]

Importantly, the authors of the St. Lawrence River study made it a point to mention that their mussel APE levels were below "acute toxicity" levels. In other words, if you ate these mussels, you would be unlikely to have an immediate health emergency.

Long-term toxicity, however, is harder to gauge and is unpredictable. Long-term toxicity is frequently ignored, frankly, especially in human studies. We rarely do thorough long-term studies on humans. This is why randomized clinical control trials of tooth flossing find that flossing is useless, for instance.[43] Modern research time scales are too short to "pick out" slow changes. We are often left to assume *brief* time-scale studies give us all the necessary information to make vital medical decisions.

But let's go back to the mussel-bound researchers.

In this same study, the scientists did admit that the APE values they discovered "could be sufficient to introduce estrogenic effects and that their effects may be additive". In other words, they acknowledge the possibility of problems but can't say for sure. Notice the carefully qualified words like "could" and "may". Nobody has thoroughly tested longer-range problems from eating APE infested meats at varying APE levels.

And, since those researchers included this phrase "additive" effects, you should note that, too. Let's say a mussel is exposed to 5 of the IRS 10 List estrogenics while filter feeding. The exposed mussel will dutifully store away those toxicants in its tissues. Even at small amounts, any single IRS List estrogenic substance will cause health problems of *The 7 Deadly Things* variety so let's take sex-change in a mussel as an example. When a mussel is exposed to 5 estrogenics at one time – even only small amounts of each one – that same mussel now has no hope of reproduction, most likely, because the total estrogenic burden has now reached a tipping point. The minor effects add up, resulting in major changes. At that point, "overharvest" will probably be blamed for the ensuing mussel population crash and ever stricter harvest restrictions will be put in place.

Anyway, let's move into a rapid succession of some other studies isolating additional individual estrogenics.

First, high levels of *phthalates* were found in mussels from the Bay of Biscay.[44] Disturbingly, these mussels were specifically from the Urdaibai Estuary in the Bay of Biscay, which had been designated a "Biosphere *Reserve*" since 1984. Not so "reserved" after all, it would seem.

High levels of EE2 were found in mussels in Venice, Italy.[45]

High levels of BPA were found in mussels in the Kacza River in Poland.[46]

High levels of atrazine were found in mussels in many areas across the United States.

In fact, the atrazine levels were so bad, the Natural Resources Defense Council actually sued the EPA for failing to protect endangered mussel species.[47] 'Merica.

Studies of IRS estrogenics in mussels – in fact – are so common that researchers have shifted focus. Nowadays, they generally are not looking to see "if" mussels have estrogenic toxins. Today, the top publications listed on "estrogenics in mussels" all have to do with the *effect* of estrogenics on mussels. These include effects like "intersex" changes,[48] decreases in essential fatty acids, changes in glucose metabolism, and reductions in overall mussel reproduction.[49] Mussels have such simple anatomy but estrogenics *still* motivate a large number of health problems. It's definitely an omen of things to come.

But maybe you aren't a mussel eater. How about walleye "muscles"? Those are tasty.

Growing up in Minnesota, walleye was my Dad's favorite fish so we pursued them like stalkers. I even remember fishing long into the night with long glowing tube lights surrounding the inner edge of our boat. Little moths would hammer those lights as it got darker and the fishing would intensify! It was worth the wait because the bigger walleye would bite as the night would wax or wane – one of those – and then we would crash in the truck bed for a few hours and drag along home.

The trips clearly made a positive impression because I still make nighttime walleye pilgrimages every summer in Minnesota to these same "secret spots" and I still enjoy eating walleye. Most people do.

Strangely, however, complaints were recently made that walleye in the Wisconsin River were not so tasty. Reports said the walleye had a "sulfury" flavor taint. Scientists sprung to action and netted out a bunch of walleye. Can you guess what they found? The walleye meat was congested with estrogenic APEs![50]

The researchers in this walleye study speculated that the especially high levels of APEs were coming from an upstream paper mill.

Snooping into this, I discovered that not only are APEs used in paints, adhesives, inks, washing agents, pesticides, textiles, detergents, and leathers, but APEs are also added to pulp at paper mills.[51]

Once I learned this factoid, I realized that cheap brown restroom paper towels smell like alkylphenols (APEs). Try it. Smell a clean but damp paper towel, especially the cheap brown colored ones. You will then know what APE-waste smells like. Add that to your wine-tasting vocabulary arsenal.

Basically, we have never developed an ability to smell or taste *most* estrogenics – they are simply too unnatural. Mankind has never needed this tasting and smelling detection ability. But the good news for your health is that APEs give off a slight odor at dangerously high levels and they taste bad at such levels. Things like processed foods or fragrances in soaps are able to disguise this odor but whole foods like walleye will be unpalatable with APE contamination.

Moving along, another presumably "pristine" place – the beautiful alpine Lake Thun in Switzerland – was also investigated by scientists due to some ugly rumors.

The whitefish in Lake Thun, it seems, were found to exhibit "gonad deformations". In this case, the whitefish tasted fine but the reproductive organs looked strange. More APEs, presumably? Once again, scientists with nets were called in to investigate. This time they found high levels of *EE2* in the whitefish muscle.[52]

Looking at Lake Thun on a map, you would *never* expect to find estrogenics in it. The lake is surrounded by beautiful snowcapped Swiss mountains. Yet, looks can deceive. A river that flows into Lake Thun comes all the way from Bern about 30 miles away. This river was apparently transporting the EE2 into Lake Thun. To this day, in other words, Lake Thun feels the Bern.

Atrazine is probably the most unsettling estrogenic when it comes to fish. This is because farms and fields border the vast majority of our nation's lakes and rivers. The annual 80 million pounds of atrazine in America that takes a year or more to degrade? Yah, our seafood is swimming in that. And when it's in the water, atrazine ends up in the meat.[53]

Let's move to alligators. They are a good segue between seafood and landfood.

When I was attending college in Florida, it was a common thing to try eating some tasty alligator nuggets. I admit to doing it, my college buddies all did it, and even my Mom ate some, one time.

Of course, restaurant gator tastes like chicken because it is farm-raised and raised on corn pellets – like everything else – but that's another story. The real stuff looks grey and tastes like mushy fish. Don't ask.

Anyway, drug testing the urine of 50 *wild* alligators – yes, scientists actually did this and I somehow "missed the boat" and wasn't involved – revealed that high levels of *phthalates* were present in Florida-Everglade-gator pee.[54] Busted! Alligators on estrogenic dope.

Unlike the fish and mussels, however, these researchers did not mention anything about "gonad deformations," which would be difficult to determine with alligators. But if phthalates are in the urine on a regular basis, they are going to be in the meat although this study did not run these important tests.

Now, let's further take this topic out of the "gutter" and move entirely to dry land.

We haven't heard much about soy lately. What about phytoestrogens from soy?

Well, first of all, soy phytoestrogens end up in breastmilk, causing concern because they expose tiny infants.[55]

Similarly, in one recent Canadian study, not only were phthalates found in the breastmilk of over 50% of women, but maternal-baby transfer was explicitly shown.[56]

These, and other studies like these, are strong indicators that if a mother is exposed to an estrogenic, the baby will be exposed via breastmilk.

To explore this idea further, let's inspect animal milk. Especially since many adults today drink animal milk on a daily basis.

Milk purchased from an ordinary grocery store in Wisconsin was tested and found to contain APEs at high levels. Specifically, in standard cow milk, the APEs were around 17,000 ng/L. Goat milk from the same store was even higher at about 88,000 ng/L.[57] That is astoundingly high but the news gets worse.

Other plastic chemicals need to be considered. Phthalates have been found at "high levels" in all sorts of dairy products[58] and parabens, too.[59]

Where are the estrogenic APEs, phthalates, and parabens coming from? Predominantly, they leach in from the plastic milk containers, although processing milk and processed animal diets contribute to these high estrogenic loads.

"Clearly", there is something to be said for steel buckets, glass milk bottles, and your humble, small-time, "Polyface" farmers among us. Good milk is good...but increasingly hard to find.

What about atrazine? At this point in the book, you probably *assume* that herbicides like atrazine have a heavy presence in your dairy and beef...and, once again, you are correct.[60] Heck, the USDA even talks about pouring boiling hot water on your beef to extract some of the atrazine![61] Weird, eh? With atrazine levels at 739,000 ng/L in blood extracted from live, Holstein, cows,[62] how could you *not* want to extract some!?

ZEA, that "vegan" estrogenic mold toxin from the fungus family, is another factor to consider in food. Most people simply overlook ZEA because the topic is cows, not grains. Even scientists overlook ZEA in most cases. Yet this mycoestrogen is a "beefy" concern.

I have personal experience with cows and molds. Growing up in Minnesota, I raised a few cows. My family lived out in the country and owned enough grassland for me to fence, so fence I did.

Then, one cool spring day, I drove off to a cattle auction with a borrowed cattle trailer and some cash and "bought me some cow babies".

I'm glad I did because it turned out to be fun. From the experience of raising those cows, what I can definitely say with authority is that cows are not picky eaters. In fact, in the winter when I threw them their hay bales, my cattle preferred old moldy bales over the fresher ones I brought them. Strange creatures. Maybe it's analogous to a good, aged cheese?

Such places – the moldy hay or moldy grains – are where ZEA finally gets to "shine". Really, while many people forget about ZEA from the IRS 10 List beyond foods with grains, ZEA is as common as cows. And other animals eating grains.

Obviously, scientific studies confirm that ZEA is contaminating animal feeds.[63] It's even scientifically documented as "present" in moldy hay bales as well,[64] in case you had doubts about my limited personal experience. In fact, there are so many research papers published on ZEA relating to cattle that there is even a complete *review* written on the subject.[65] And for anybody who may not know, a "review" is basically a science paper that summarizes numerous experimental reports on a frequently studied subject. [66,67]

Naturally, when cows eat ZEA, this leads to meat and milk issues but let's look at some numbers. ZEA has been measured in milk up to 2,500 ng/L after feeding cows about 550 mg (milligrams) of ZEA per day for 21 days.[68] Among other health problems we will begin discussing in a couple pages, this ZEA exposure even *reduces milk production* in the cows.[69] In fact, *reduced milk production* – rather than human health – is one of the major reasons ZEA is so thoroughly studied in cows. Lots of money "goes down the tube" if dairy production diminishes.

This makes me wonder if estrogenics also cause lactation issues in humans. Not only is the recipient of the milk impacted by estrogenics such as ZEA, in other words, but the mother clearly is, at least in the case of cows. A thorough human study has not yet been done on this, unfortunately.

Like other estrogenics, ZEA also ends up in the beef – your burgers and steaks – according to this study.[70] So if your cow is eating it, you're eating it as well. This is a good argument for healthy, free-range, grass-fed cows, obviously.

That same study of ZEA in burgers also found ZEA in pork.

Heck, this mold-derived estrogenic has even been found in tests of buffalo burger at levels around 1ng of ZEA per gram of meat.[71] The conclusion is that it's nearly impossible to avoid ZEA if the grains are moldy!

Feedlot slaughter pens or other forms of mass-production animal farming are clearly the wrong answer. Animal- and crop-rotations win once again. They just can't be monopolized in the same way from a financial perspective so implementing these farms is an uphill battle.

To finish, let's mention chickens and polar bears.

Atrazine in chickens is, once again, a no-brainer hypothesis. Modern poultry farms use a corn-dominant diet and atrazine is used on corn more than any other herbicide. In fact, as far back as 1976, scientists were already finding "residues of atrazine in chicken tissues".[72] In the 70's, only *a fraction* of atrazine was being used compared to levels today.

Phthalates, too, are a concern in today's chicken meat because the meat is often wrapped in plastic rather than wax-paper. More specifically, according to one scientific investigation, chicken meats contained 0.08 milligrams of phthalate per kilogram (mg/kg) in *uncooked* meat, 13.1 mg/kg *after frying*, and 16.9 mg/kg *after packaging.*[73] And...that escalated quickly.

The scientists conducting the study concluded that the fried and packaged chicken meat far exceeded the European Union tolerable daily intake level (1.85mg, for a 50kg individual).

All of these studies support a very simple conclusion: that sordid treatment of animals leads to harmful animal and human health impacts. Furthermore, processing the food amplifies the problems.

Unfortunately, this type of animal harm and food handling is not rare.

Even eggs from mistreated chickens are not untouched by estrogenics.

For example, one study proved that estrogenics are ending up in eggs at disturbingly high levels.[74] This study became a whistleblowing event because the researchers discovered black market steroid use in many chickens.

What the scientists revealed was that estrogenics were being used illegally to create unnaturally chunky farm animals for greater profits.

They discovered that estrogenics were being directly used on the chickens, in this case, to make them fatter. When the estrogenics ended up in the chicken's eggs at astonishingly high levels, it tipped off the authorities. Law enforcement got involved, the whistleblowing authors reminded us, only on the *limited farms* that are being investigated. The true scope of the problem is really unknown.

As I have already alluded, we will talk about fattening effects of estrogenics in the next chapter. Using them to make farm animals fatter, though, is clearly unhealthy for everyone involved and unethical.

Hearing these things may even cause you to throw your hands up and ask: is nothing in the food aisles these days *good*?

The unfortunate state of our plastic-wrapped, dye-injected, herbicide-peppered, birth-control-tainted water and food is, indeed, almost overwhelming. And then we are "informed" that the *meats* or *fats* are the health problem?! Meats and fats that humans have been eating since the so-called dawn of time?! Who are we kidding?

The last chapter hopefully will restore some of your faith in food and humanity – at least give you some decent ideas – but I can't perform miracles. It's a mess. In the meantime, *The Ideal Foods Principle* you should follow is this:

2.

> **The Ideal Foods Principle:** *Try to find, use, and eat whole, unprocessed foods, from genuinely organic and naturally grown sources, preferably not stored in plastics, and raised in a healthy environment.*

Simple? Yes. A major challenge? Absolutely. But at least you understand what is going on, what to do, and what is best, regarding your foods. You can at least *minimize* the damage if you decide it's best for you and yours.

Let's end *Part 1* with one final "case study". I promised to include polar bears so here it is.

First, I know you don't eat polar bears – the livers have enough Vitamin A to actually kill you, in case you ever visit the Arctic Archipelago – but I think polar bears can memorably demonstrate the *global* nature of the problem we have created via estrogenics. Polar bear estrogenic tests reveal the far-reaching environmental impact we are having and the urgency to act.

The case study began by looking at estrogenic parabens, originating from things like plastics and cosmetic "fragrances". Specific paraben levels were tested in remote coastal animals, ranging from sea otters, pygmy sperm whales, various dolphin, and, yes, a total of 10 polar bears.[22]

Researchers began by measuring paraben levels in each mammal's liver. Here is the resulting graphic of the *average* liver paraben levels among test groups within each species, with units of nanograms (ng):

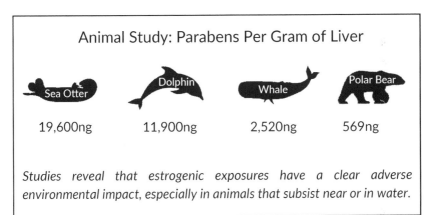

Animal Study: Parabens Per Gram of Liver

Sea Otter	Dolphin	Whale	Polar Bear
19,600ng	11,900ng	2,520ng	569ng

Studies reveal that estrogenic exposures have a clear adverse environmental impact, especially in animals that subsist near or in water.

As you can see, the levels are outrageously high. This clearly indicates that our estrogenic waste is circulating the globe, not only polluting us but polluting everything around us.

These researchers also measured the paraben levels in sea otter *brains* – presumably, because the brain is a protected or "preserved" area of the body due to the so-called "blood-brain *barrier*". The scientists found an average of *12,900ng* of paraben in Washington Coast, USA, sea otter brains. That. Is. High.

Finally, the scientists included some data that might further tempt you to blubber. If not, recognizing the pun probably will.

Rough-toothed dolphin *blubber* showed an average paraben level of 1,140ng. These are the open ocean animals.

This brings up an important question that we will finally pursue. What is the deal with estrogenics and fat?

Let's dig in. If you are standing, you might want to find a seat. A recent, 2015 study, for instance, found parabens in *human* fat cells to be at 17,400ng/g.[75]

PART

2

RISING DISEASE

CHAPTER 5

Depressing Obesity

Estrogenics in the Fat Stores

THE DIFFERENCE BETWEEN "GIRLFRIEND" AND "girl friend" is that little space in between we call the "friend zone".

Another story Allison enjoys telling friends is about her first experience co-riding my motorcycle. That's where the little "friend zone" space nearly became an uncrossable chasm between us.

This story took place in my later years at Ave Maria University. It starred a beautiful 850cc motorcycle that a friend of mine gave me. Let's begin the tale by introducing this matchmaking main character and circle back to the "friend zone" and the "laws" of attraction.

The 850 was a big, loud, and generous bike. It had lots of chrome, lots of power, and lots of space for an extra rider. It also sported dual tail pipes and sissy bar frames on the back end. The sissy bars served as a passenger backrest but also doubled as a luggage rack.

This motorcycle entered the scene just as another spring semester was winding down. For me, it was love at first sight.

It all began because I would frequently pop off to the beach to fish for sharks in the evenings, especially as I finished my final exams. On these trips, I would usually be joined by a mixed bag of friends. Sometimes Dave would come, sometimes as many as 10 people would join – 10 was the max capacity for the Fishing Club supplies at that time – and always Allison.

Allison loved coming on those sharking safaris because she loved fishing and appreciated the adventure. She also adored the ocean at night.

Before a typical fishing trip, all interested parties would meet up in the main parking lot and pile into a communal University van. From there, we would simply drive to the beach and fish.

As spring matured, a friend of mine was packing up to leave college for the summer. Most people on campus were leaving but I was staying. So was Allison.

As my buddy left town, he remembered how much I enjoyed going to the beach and how I appreciated his 850cc motorcycle. He also knew I had a 3-piece G. Loomis fishing rod that could be strapped to his motorcycle's sissy bar frame.

With all this in mind and just before leaving, he generously gave me his bike keys. He also passed along the deed. Obviously, I felt like a little boy. In a balloon store. With a sharp pin. Florida roads were perfect for open air riding and, at that time, I didn't even have a car. Freeeedom!

Soon thereafter, on one fine spring evening, Allison and I both escaped out the lab front door simultaneously. We had both been working long hours on tiresome lab experiments and it felt good to be done.

"After you," I said as I chivalrously held the door.

"I want that motorcycle ride you promised earlier," Allison announced.

"*That's right!*" I remembered. "*I had made that promise.*"

It was nearly sunset and both the sky and weather were peachy.

"Ok. Sounds good".

I drove my bike around the loop and pulled up near Allison.

"Chup, chup, chup" the 850 popped as it idled down. I tossed in a few good "revs" to keep the engine firing in 1st gear, but mostly to sound cool, and Allison walked over.

She hopped on the bike and threw her arms around my waist tighter than a boa constrictor.

I'm not proud to admit this but I responded by bristling and peeling her hands off. Over the noise of the bike, I requested Allison hold the sissy bars.

Allison, unfazed by such sharp demands, complied. We still had an asymptotic relationship at that time and I was shaky on the bike with another body on it – and other such lame excuses – so Allison graciously enjoyed the ride to the beach clutching cold, dead sissy bars.

More and more fishing bike trips soon followed. Allison became a regular on that bike and the hands would eventually find their way back without equal and opposite reactions.

In fact, our first official "date" was soon set for that summer's Independence Day. And, ironically, that particular 4th of July experience would only give her yet another reason to seek further Independence...from me.

Atoms and molecules, in a similar fashion to my early relationship with Allison, can be attracted to one another or they can repel one another. This is simple physics but, like my bike trips with Allison, this relationship can be slightly more complicated, too.

To simplify discussions about the electrical charges of atoms, most teachers explain attract-repel principles by holding up magnets and talking about "+" or "–" signs. This is good. It is, however, only a partial understanding. What sometimes is overlooked are the properties of oil versus water.

Oils, fats, and most hormones, usually float on water. Estrogenics, too. This repellent property is called "hydrophobic", which literally means "fear of water". In other words, estrogenics are technically "afraid" of water and they don't mix with it.

This fear of water isn't because estrogenics have a positive or negative charge. In fact, it's quite the opposite.

Oils, fats, and most hormones have absolutely *no electrical charge* or they have very little charge. Water, meanwhile, has a strong electrical charge with those magnetic positive and negative ends.

Conversely, scientists sometimes say that estrogenics are "lipophilic", meaning they "love fat", rather than saying "hydrophobic". You'll often see both words and each way of looking at this is correct. Fats, oils, and estrogenic substances mix. They have an innate attraction.

Now let's get pragmatic.

In practical terms, this means estrogenics in soap prefer your skin over water. It also means that estrogenics prefer to hide out inside fat cells when they are inside our bodies. Some find the muscles like we saw with beef, but most estrogenic substances find more permanent lodging in fat. We'll revisit this idea in a minute but it's significant.

Now, remember how much I "love" shopping? Well, a few days ago from the time of writing this, I was shopping for bar soap. I probably spent 15 minutes looking at soap ingredients. When I finally found a "clean" bar of soap I noticed that it had Red No. 40 in it! Soap with artificial red dye? Why would anybody ruin a good soap like that?

Now, it is usually obvious to people that *drinking* estrogenic red dye is a health hazard – it's illegal in Europe, remember – but red dye in soap? Am I being too extreme? Soap is "cleansing" so this can't possibly be bad. We wash it off, yes?

Well, estrogenic soap *is* bad. It's a wet and slippery Trojan horse.

In fact, along with soaps, don't forget about laundry detergent and dryer sheets as potential vehicles for skin estrogenics. The estrogenics, like APEs, phthalates, or parabens, for instance, are "afraid of water" so they hide out in clothing even during a wash cycle. In fact, you can usually smell the fragrances that are mixed with the estrogenics. Sniff testing is key. And your skin – in constant contact with clothing – can give you a slight but steady "dose" of estrogenics all day, every day. Like this scientific paper says: "[Phthalates are] a solvent and *vehicle* for fragrance and cosmetic ingredients and subsequent skin contact."[1] I like this descriptive term they use: "vehicle". I just imagine phthalates "driving" right into my skin, taking the highway toward Man Boobs.

It all begins with a common "talent" of skin: skin's ability to absorb things. Of course, your skin doesn't just absorb anything. It does a fairly scrupulous job of keeping out water, large items like proteins, and most other *electrically charged* molecules.

But *fat*... your skin is a sucker for fat! "Fat-like" substances, too, like hormones and estrogenics. These readily travel through your skin.

Keep in mind here that estrogenic molecules "look" and "act" like hormones. They are small in size and hydrophobic. Indeed, hormone-skin-absorption is why medical doctors sometimes give you hormone creams for "external use only". The creams work. Hydrocortisone is one popular example that comes to mind, but there are dozens of hydrophobic-based "topical" medications on today's drug market. They fool our skin's defenses and blast right through.

"Parabens, which can be dermally absorbed," affirms another scientific journal regarding another estrogenic substance, "are present in many cosmetic products, including antiperspirants."[2] This means parabens go through your skin, same as other estrogenics. And many people are rubbing them on their armpits. Daily.

This makes it clear why parabens are being found in crowded swimming pools at levels "concerning for children."[3] Yes: you might responsibly be taking a shower before you jump into that public pool, but chances are, Mr. I.P. Freely swimming nearby did not shower off. Mr. Freely's lotion, shampoo, and deodorant paraben particles are washing off into the pool. Next to him, his wife, Mrs. Ivanna Tinkle Freely, has heavy lipstick and many additional cosmetics that also are washing off into the pool. Too gross.

Parabens, it is said in another science paper, "are widely used in cosmetics, pharmaceuticals, personal care products and as food additives to inhibit microbial growth and extend product shelf life."[4] "Widely used," they say, not "occasionally used". To my dismay, beyond frustration in buying cosmetics, I sometimes accidentally buy corn tortillas that contain parabens. And I usually find out after I reach my home. Did I tell you I'm not much for shopping?

Unfortunately, you need to realize that parabens are not only found in "products". They are being found inside us.

"Fetal exposure to five parabens was investigated due to their endocrine-disrupting potential and possible impact on fetal development," explains authors of a research journal, rationalizing their study.[5]

"This study", they went on to note, "is the first to report the occurrence of parabens in human umbilical cord blood. Maternal exposure to parabens is widespread." Umbilical cords are basically the life blood from mother to fetus. How many u-cords contained parabens? Well, depending on the specific paraben of the five they looked at, 97.4% of the umbilical cords had one type, 94.75% had another type...and all five of the tested parabens were present in more than 40% of samples.

The parabens, the phthalates, the estrogenics, are blasting through skin.

Possibly the single biggest weakness in our skin's "defensive" ability, in fact, is blocking out *bad* oils and fats. This is why poison ivy is so nasty. The "poison" from poison ivy is an oil and doesn't readily wash out. The oil prefers the skin. And think about this: there hasn't been much historical need for our skin to block bad mercenaries, like poison ivy, because we were never commonly exposed. We generally avoid poison ivy after a single exposure. We learn from a single mistake.

But out trots the *artificial* estrogenics. In very recent history, we've managed to create fake hormones in science labs that go through our skin as quickly as most natural fats and oils. Yet these are unnatural and unhealthy. And here's the novel, ensuing problem: our body doesn't communicate to us – via a rash, or an astringent taste, or a negative smell – that this exposure is not cool. In other words, our skin, nor our tongue for that matter, has never adapted to rejecting these artificial estrogenics.

This raises another important question: does our skin really have *that much* fat? Yes, it does actually…in a sense.

Skin has some "fat". More importantly, however, keep in mind that every cell in your body is surrounded by a "lipid" bilayer. That means every cell in your body has a "fat coat" or a "fatty coating". This is how and why estrogenic molecules easily travel into your cells to be stored in your fat. Every cell is designed to allow such entry. Both conventional fat and your cell's "fat coats" allow estrogenics to travel right in.

Furthermore, when estrogenics travel our bloodstream, they journey to the land of fat. They go into conventional fat, like belly fat or butt fat; the stuff you generally think of as fat. It's the law of hydrophobic attraction.

Basically, once estrogenics find your fat deposits, they say "home sweet home". Why would they leave? You blood is like water, they are afraid of it! This raises the question how steroid hormones and estrogenics can even enter the blood at all. We'll discuss this in the next chapter and how it impacts your natural hormone levels but, for now, let's look at specific fat-storage examples, rapid-fire.

ZEA, the estrogenic stuff secreted by certain fungus family members, is stored in fat, according to researchers that conducted a ZEA study in birds.[6] In the study, they actually found that *healthy* birds are more resistant to ZEA basically because they are naturally very lean. Pigs, on the other hand – the same researchers note – are "highly sensitive" to ZEA. Pigs are fatty and so they store-away the estrogenic ZEA, which eventually comes back to haunt their piggy bodies.

A different study on estrogenic APEs find that APEs "accumulate in the body" and thereby act as "potential modulators of the allergic response."[7] Where do they "accumulate in the body"? The fat, naturally. Recognize, too, that the brain is basically the fattiest organ in the body – besides fat deposits, of course – so plenty is also stored in the brain. My new rallying cry for the brain is "remember the sea otter!"

BP [benzophenone] from sunscreen, is also called "bioaccumulative" in another article.[8] What does this mean? Essentially, this means BP "accumulates" in our fat. In fact, this particular scientific review article – in a journal called the *Environmental International Journal* – expresses general environmental concern due to this problematic BP bioaccumulation. The scientists note that despite the widespread use of BP, there is a lack of international testing for BP in water.

Next, there is this: a 2015 study of actual fat from human biopsies of 20 different people.[9] The investigators found 19 different substances that were either estrogenic or likely to be estrogenic, including BPA, some BPs, triclosan, and parabens in the human fat samples from all 20 people.

You seeing the overall pattern here? I don't think it's necessary to list every estrogenic substance imaginable and show how they "bioaccumulate" or are "cached" or "incorporate" into our fat. They do. Estrogenics act this way due to their "love of fat" – it's the way of nature.

Before moving on, though, I do want to add one final important consideration to the fat-storage story. It gets to this question of how long an estrogenic might remain in your fat. In other words, if estrogenics prefer fat, how long does your body store artificial estrogenics?

Unfortunately, there is no perfect study that has yet been done to answer this question. Today's "health gurus" incessantly talk about "toxin storage" – and it's an important point – but research on *length of time for toxin storage* is rare and sparse, especially with estrogenics.

I have found plenty of "references" about toxins being stored in fat on these same popular health guru's websites...and then find that they link back to their own websites or to some other dubious source. So, let's dive back into the original scientific studies.

First, to reiterate: *thorough* investigation of human fat storage – or brain storage, for that matter! – of estrogenics has not been done. I think it's not even on most scientist's radar, just yet. It clearly *should be* given the major health concerns literally "coming to the table" but the studies are "slim" to none.

But here's the "good" news: *drug* storage in fats also occurs. And drug storage in fat has been studied and is well-understood. I'm specifically referring to studies looking at *dangerous* drugs. But some recreational and pharmaceutical drugs have also been researched in the context of fat storage.

For understanding estrogenics, the drugs we are interested in are the hydrophobic drugs. Hydrophobic drugs parallel estrogenics because they have similar chemical properties. They act similar in terms of their fat-storing abilities. Water flushing might work for overdosing vitamin C, for example, but not for overdosing heroin, THC, or estrogenics. You generally need to use activated charcoal and a stomach pump ("gastric lavage" or "gastric decontamination") to medically remove overdosed hydrophobic drugs.

For a specific example, the appetite stimulant and hallucinogenic drug THC is hydrophobic. In other words, THC stores in fat similar to other hydrophobic substances. Let's check out the scientific research on THC.

The scientific discoveries begin with this excellent study called: *"Reintoxication: the release of fat-stored Δ^9-tetrahydrocannabinol [THC] into blood is enhanced by food deprivation"*.[10]

I think this is a truly great title because it basically suggests that if you stop eating for some time – you start fasting – you will burn fat. This will cause hydrophobic toxins like THC to release from your fat and re-enter your blood. Also, this study is a catch because it is 1 of only 6 papers with the word "reintoxication" in the title or abstract. Plus, it is simply a well-written paper.

The authors of this study start by explaining that THC "is a highly lipophilic drug that is rapidly absorbed and preferentially stored in the fat deposits of the body." Good. No surprises there. Lipophilic, remember, is that term that means "fat loving" – similar to our estrogenics on the IRS 10 List.

They go on: "THC is accumulated in rodent *gonadal fat* at significantly higher concentrations than in other organs such as the liver, brain, lungs and other fatty tissue."

Wait, what?

Not only is THC stored in fat, it prefers to reside in the fat surrounding the gonads – the testis or ovaries? Now, personally, I can't explain this but (1) it's bizarre and (2) it apparently happens. In essence, THC sounds like a "molecular Darwin" the way this story is unfolding. It sounds like natural *unselection* of fertile age groups. More to come in later chapters on this *unselection* regarding estrogenics.

The same researchers say that THC has been observed in human fat biopsies – not gonad fat but liposucked belly fat that was "generously" donated to research. In this case, the fat was taken one month after a final exposure to THC, one month after drug use. *And,* they add, THC is still found in "long-term cannabis users" – in urine samples – 77 days after total THC abstinence.

Obviously, 77 days is a long time. However, one thing this research study did not investigate was drug storage in fat over *even longer* periods of time.

Besides the funding issues, testing long-term fat storage of drugs is difficult research. There are increased numbers of variables. For instance, your diet or your estrogenic exposures could drastically change the final test results. Furthermore, crime-investigators talk about how certain drugs can actually "increase their concentration in blood post-mortem",[11] so waiting until people die might not be the best experiment.

Estrogenics are stored in fat – that much is clear – but how long they stay in the fat is still not *crystal* clear. I can tell you that it will depend on whether you are gaining or maintaining your fat or whether you are losing your fat.

When a person or animal is storing estrogenics in fat – like the pygmy sperm whales do via blubber, as we saw – the duration of those estrogenics may even simply be the duration of the fat itself.

So, this raises a new question: how old is your fat? How long does one fat cell persist in your body, on average? Well, one "hot" study using radiation-fingerprints from nuclear bomb exposures from the 1950s, found the average "age" that fat survives is just over 1.5 years. [12,13]

Of course, this all depends on where the fat is in your body and how healthy you are. Another similar study found fat cells as old as 10-years.[14] And *that* is some tenacious fat! Many people's fat might be older than their dog!

Estrogenics Are Causing Fat

The 7 Deadly Things
#1. Fat Gains

What I call the "Estrogenic Paradox" has two parts:

(1) That estrogenics are stored in fat and, also,
(2) Estrogenics stimulate fat growth.

We saw #1, so let's move on to #2.

As a spoiler, I can tell you that when you buy certain plastic-wrapped food items, you are getting a sort of "stimulus package". Fat stimulus. Also, when you drink EE2/atrazine/phthalate/paraben/BPA water – stimulus. Government approved, too. When you use most fragrance-containing deodorant? Stimulus. Boom.

Actually, cancer may even be related to this cell growing, fat boosting, characteristic of estrogenics, but we'll look into that later. Let's only focus on obesity for now.

In America – nay, in the entire developed world – researchers have recorded a steady growth in obesity rates for over 30 years. This has been carefully documented by the Centers for Disease Control (CDC). Entire books have even been written about this.

The shortest summary is this: in 1990, around 10% of Americans were obese. In the year 2000, it was around 20%. What about 2010? You guessed it: 30%. At this rate, by 2080, we will achieve 100% obesity!

Well, don't quote me on that – it doesn't *really* work that way. But the rise has been astronomical and will undoubtedly climb.

Can you guess what has also risen during those same years? Astronomically? Estrogenics in our everyday environments. Well, except in Europe. They banned a significant amount of estrogenics, as we saw before. Europeans simply have much higher standards regarding estrogenics. And Europe's obesity rates? You guessed it. They are almost exactly half of America's.[15]

Now, I realize that the rising use of estrogenics and the rising rates of obesity are not direct proof of anything. But I still find the parallel uncanny. In fact, as budding countries emerge into "modernity", obesity follows close behind. Farm chemical spraying? Obesity. Plastic convenience? Bam. Obesity.

Processed sugar, by the way, is Estrogenics' Wingman. It is usually blamed and usually dumped into countries as they "develop". An interesting article in *The Atlantic* reports in depth on this issue, in an article titled: "*Two-Thirds of Obese People Now Live in Developing Countries*". "Developing" in which direction, we start to wonder...

And, speaking of sugar, the scientific research on estrogenics and obesity seems to start with *insulin-resistance*. One such study published in the *Public Library of Science* (PLOS) begins like this: "There is an apparent overlap between areas in the USA where the herbicide, atrazine, is heavily used and obesity-prevalence maps of people with a BMI (Body Mass Index) over 30."[16] Ah! So I'm not the only one wondering about this.

Next, these researchers "treated" rats with "*low* concentrations of atrazine provided in drinking water". What did they find? Well, they inspected mitochondrial function and insulin resistance and they observed energy-producing mitochondrial functions were disrupted and the rats had developed various stages of diabetes. Serious health concerns, for sure.

An interesting side-note here come from Dr. Peter Attia. Dr. Attia is an insightful scientist known for his work on insulin-resistance ["prediabetes"] and how insulin-resistance potentially *causes* obesity – not the other way around, as is conventionally thought. In other words, people might *not* be "getting fat and *then* diabetic" but, rather, people might be "getting pre-diabetic and *therefore* getting fat". It's an important distinction.[i]

Of course, estrogenics don't stop at hindering insulin. Estrogenics spur on obesity outright.

For instance, one research study found that soy – our favorite allegedly "healthy" estrogenic – caused weight gains in rats, including increases in fat for pregnant rats and rat offspring.[17] Interestingly, in this same study, BPA did not cause "soy-big" weight gains (at least at the doses they used in this study or with the short durations of exposure that they employed).

Yet, does this mean BPA is innocent on the weight-gain front? Nope.

A different study in humans found "higher early childhood BPA was associated with excess child adiposity [fat stores]."[18] Heck, another study even discovered that BPA disrupts glucose (sugar) transport in the brain.[19] This is a serious issue considering that the brain's preferred energy source is glucose.[20]

Overall, the prevalence of both obesity and insulin issues have even spawned a new term in one research paper in the context of estrogenics: the term is "diabesity".[21]

A number of studies of other items on the IRS 10 List show similar findings. ZEA, the estrogenic from molds, has been used to *intentionally fatten* cattle.[22] There is no way that this is good... for us or the cows. And according to those same researchers, this practice has been banned by – who else – the European Union. It was outlawed on the basis that ZEA contributes to earlier puberty ages in children.

But even if it was legal, we shouldn't be doing it!

Unfortunately, "if it's legal, go for it!" is the motto of a surprising number of scientists. Morality is not our strong suit, too often.

I even personally know a scientist who teaches this motto – "if it's legal, go for it!" – in Ph.D. classes. Word-for-word. I know, because he was once my "teacher".

---

[i] Dr. Attia delivered an excellent TED talk on this subject that I recommend you check out sometime.

What about phthalates? Sure as water is wet, phthalates have also been connected to fat-gains. For instance, a study of obesity in children testing 7 different phthalates and some other "endocrine disrupting hormones" found that the phthalates were particularly associated with obesity.[23]

Studies of EE2 in promoting fat are slim but, of course, estrogenics fool women's bodies into thinking they are pregnant, so wider hips and storing some "baby fat" for emergency energy reserves is expected, scientifically.

In fact, one glance at Bayer® drug company's side-effects for Yaz® is telling. Yaz®, by the way, was a top selling oral contraceptive for many years running, including $781 million in US sales in 2009.[24] The drug sheet reveals this caution: "The risk of morbidity and mortality [when consuming Yaz®] increases significantly in the presence of other underlying risk factors such as hypertension, hyperlipidemias, obesity and diabetes".

And, in case you were wondering, the composition of Yaz® is EE2 and one other patented hormone imitator called "drospirenone". Virtually all oral contraceptive pills use EE2 and one other hormone. And all these EE2-containing pills include that same "obesity and diabetes" caution, I've checked the drug labels.

Realize that this is not saying "Yaz® causes obesity". But it undoubtedly contributes, in the context of what we are discovering about other estrogenics. Remember: long-term studies are rarely performed...especially on an issue like obesity, which isn't considered a "dangerous" side-effect for a drug. In fact, conventional scientists and doctors often consider it "your fault" if you have obesity, even if you are on fat promoting drugs.

In case you are wondering more precisely how estrogenics promote fat growth, it has been recently unearthed. Besides the insulin problems already mentioned, of course.

One group of scientists started by testing "tonalide" – a toxic "musk" found in many cosmetics and cigarettes, already known to promote fattening.[25] The scientists compared tonalide to four estrogenics: parabens, phthalates, APEs, and BPA. These scientists discovered that all of the 4 estrogenic substances were "obesogenic" – they caused fattening – through a protein called "PPARγ".

In other words, the 4 estrogenics *triggered fat growth* and the specific way they caused the fat growth was discovered. Meanwhile, tonalide also promoted fat growth but not through PPARγ. Tonalide caused fat growth some other way yet to be discovered.

Normally, I wouldn't introduce such technical terminology as "PPARγ proteins". In this case, however, many scientists today are calling PPARγ a "master switch for fat cell development and growth,"[26] so I feel compelled to specifically name something as powerful or controlling as a "Master Switch" for fat. And when I use the word "switch", you should think of a light-switch. Turn it on and you have fat growth. Estrogenics act this way: estrogenics flip the PPARγ-fat switch "on".

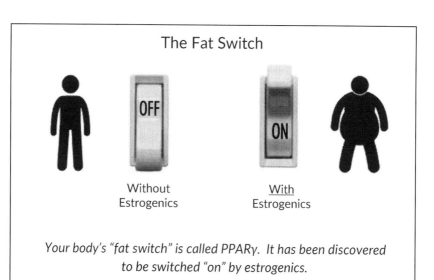

The Fat Switch

Without Estrogenics

With Estrogenics

Your body's "fat switch" is called PPARγ. It has been discovered to be switched "on" by estrogenics.

Depressing News Courtesy of Estrogenics

The 7 Deadly Things
#2. Depression

There is a strong connection between estrogenics and depression and, like the fat-gains, it's uncomfortable but something needs to be said.

First: literally thousands of studies have been done connecting obesity with depression. These studies indicate that obesity and depression are connected not simply because of a "body image" issue but rather they cause a chemical – and hormonal – imbalance.[27]

Because of this chemical connection and since we saw that estrogenics increase fat gains, it would be smart to investigate whether estrogenics also increase depression rates.

Unfortunately, not many direct studies have been done on estrogenics and depression. It's quite a challenge, scientifically.

For one, this as an area of research where studies usually take many years. Again.

Furthermore, animal models of depression aren't great. For example, how can you *know* if a mouse is depressed? And even if you think you can, how can you know your depressed mouse is relevant to some form of human depression?

Human depression studies are also cramped by rampant dishonesty. For obvious reasons, people with depression are not enthusiastically candid about their illness. Fat biopsies are easy to obtain but honest answers about depression are not.

Then there are the dozens of medical sub-categories associated with "depression" – a surprisingly broad term – adding another layer of complication (e.g. seasonal affective disorder [SAD], persistent depressive disorder, psychotic depression, postpartum depression, etc.).

Anyway, it would be poor logic to say "estrogenics can cause obesity; obesity can cause depression; therefore, estrogenics can cause depression". We need better evidence. And it exists.

Let's start with suicide numbers. What if I showed you a major study that discovered women who take oral contraception have a higher incidence of suicide? That would be telling, right? Well then, here you have it. Let's check out this study from the British Journal of Medicine – the *BMJ* – with over 45,000 women.[28]

First, I need to admit that I really admire the *BMJ*. This journal has never been afraid to "stick it to the man". The *BMJ* is one of the top-ranked medical journals – among the upper 5% internationally – and yet the *BMJ* still publishes research findings that you would never find in an American medical journal. Political toe-smashing, it seems, is a more prominent concern for American journals. For instance, *BMJ* articles take issue with certain vaccines (e.g. this article[29]). Good luck getting those sorts of studies past government-funded American research and peer-review committees...good data or not!

Anyway, the suicide study in the *BMJ* looked at the medical records of over 45,000 women and over half of these women were oral contraception users. The researchers compared the users and non-users and went back almost 40 years. They found that women that took oral contraception had a significantly higher incidence of "violent deaths", including suicides, compared to women that never took oral contraception.

I realize, of course, that this, again, is not direct "proof" of cause and effect. In fact, this further illustrates exactly why the depression issue can be so challenging. Even this simple discovery in the *BMJ* could be interpreted a number of ways.

For example, you can say that maybe *one type* of oral contraception causes depression but not all types. The study did not distinguish drug brands. Or you could say that maybe *those* oral contraception users have higher suicide rates because they came from disadvantaged households more often – I'm not sure they did, but it's an option. There are lots of other theoretical options. You might say that maybe *those* oral contraception users – they were from Great Britain – have genetics that are more prone to depression when exposed to artificial hormones from oral contraception. Other countries could potentially have opposite results. Or you might say that maybe *those* oral contraception users from 40 years ago had hormones that were poor quality – they used horse-hormones, back in the day, taken from horse blood – and maybe the older aged women skewed the numbers.

Lots of maybes. Lots of options. And these are valid points, not corybantic arguments. At least nobody can say that 45,000 people is too low a number. Suicides were up and numbers were huge. That's the reality.

Let's quickly investigate one more correlation and then close with more direct studies.

Every year, India has been making international headlines. The rates of suicide in India have skyrocketed and continue rising. But it's not actually widespread suicide. This suicide is specifically found within the farming profession. The suicide rates for the general population of India are fairly typical. But for farmers, suicide rates are now over 15,000 per year. This is "far above those of the general population [of India]" according to researchers.[30]

The suicides, of course, coincide almost exactly with skyrocketing crop chemical-spraying. This is partly due to the recent introduction of chemical-resistant plants in India, which allow farmers to more generously apply said chemicals.

Strangely, however, most scientific journal articles speculate that the recent suicide surge among farmers is likely due to "socioeconomic factors".[30,31] One scientific study even suggests mandatory reductions in alcohol consumption for farmers![32] Of course, these authors are probably just spit-balling. Who knows? Reducing booze could actually make the problem worse. I at least doubt that "nectar of merriment" is creating a suicide problem, in any case. I didn't see a lot of depressed people at the Guinness factory when I was in Ireland.

Meanwhile, not one single scientific author that I could find suggested decreasing estrogenic exposures for farmers in India. Of course, you can't compete in the "chemical race" if the "Joneses are doing it". Many scientists – once again – are resistant to suggesting decreases in things that are viewed as "productive tech enhancements". Using artificial chemicals to solve problems rather than natural methods is considered "technological", in other words.

And, indeed, the Joneses are certainly "doing it". Amidst much high-fiving in top-floor executive suites, presumably.

Let's not kid ourselves here. Farmers everywhere are being pressured to continue increasing the use of chemicals on our foods. Some of the pressure is coming from Syngenta®, for example, a top producer of atrazine weed-killer. Syngenta® sponsored an "Atrazine Benefits Team" of researchers who released a set of five papers in 2011 reporting huge economic benefits from atrazine use in agriculture.[33] And spraying chemicals is indeed more cost-effective than paying for manual labor to hand-pick weeds. But what is the *true* "cost"?

The long-term solution, it seems to me, is to eliminate estrogenics in conjunction with utilizing the best technology in farming machinery and engineering. The difficulty? The financial cuts. Dumping estrogenics – not literally but legally – will require public and government support. Yet, we've subsidized our way into huge-scale farms and simultaneously dug ourselves into an "Omnivore's Dilemma". Let's face it: throwing more money at the problem will probably just make the problem worse.

Here is where India's government stands. The "Ministry of Health and Family Welfare" drafted a 776-page "Food Safety Standards Regulations" report. It was sent out from Delhi, India in August of 2011 and sets the standards for the Indian government's "tolerance limits" for herbicides and chemicals. For atrazine, they include a tolerance limit of "nil". Most other chemicals had actual numbers but atrazine was "nil". Yeeaaah... that can't be good.

My question is: do they really believe no safety level should be set for atrazine or is there simply a giant corporation behind the scenes peddling influence? Government "service"?

Ironically, a scientific study of atrazine levels in Delhi's own ground water – where that government report was promulgated – found that nearly every sample was above the World Health Organization's (WHO's) allowable limits.[34] That's the result of a nil limit.

In fact, atrazine in Delhi water was even above the more liberal United States EPA allowable limits. The *average* atrazine level researchers found among the 20 samples they tested was 3,400 ng/L. Keep in mind that the American EPA allows 3,000 ng/L and the EU approves 0 ng/L. Further, the highest atrazine level they found in one sample was 17,300 ng/L! This is bad, especially because Delhi is presumably quite a distance from direct exposures: the active farms that are spraying and using heavy atrazine quantities.

Scientists working in Mumbai, India, had this to say: "Though herbicide use in India is insignificant compared to other countries in the world, the total intake of pesticide containing chlorine by an Indian is the highest [...]. Atrazine is a chlorinated herbicide [...] and it is *probably the most commonly used herbicide in the world.*"[35]

But is atrazine *causing* the suicides among the farmers? I don't honestly know. Among artificial estrogenics – or among my IRS 10 List items, all of which bind the estrogen receptor – atrazine is one that has not been directly studied in relation to depression.

In fact, around 2003, "hormone replacement therapy" – the attempt to replace declining hormone levels as people age – uncovered an "estrogen influence on the female brain" for menopausal women.[36] This therapy, however, used natural – not artificial – estrogen. And the study with natural estrogen found it "*improved* the mood and menopausal female well-being, but it does not act on clinically depressed women". In other words, researchers have tested natural estrogen for use in mood-improvement with an eye toward assisting depressed individuals. Again: natural estrogen. Something in the brain is clearly disrupted or displaced by artificial estrogenics.

Because of this positive finding with natural estrogen, a few researchers have looked to soy for use *against* depression. They found absolutely nothing in the postmenopausal women they studied.[37] This is telling because a lot of money is poured into soy. And, in my experience and research, I can tell you that anything that *might* be spun in a positive light, *will* be spun in a positive light, regarding soy.

So, by now, you're probably still wanting some additional, more direct, proof. Check out phthalates. Phthalates have been "associated with adult depression,"[38] plain and simple. Phthalate levels in people's pee have been compared with people diagnosed with depression. And a follow-up study found phthalates correlated with depression in elderly populations as well.[39]

BPA, too, has been linked to depression. Frequently.

First of all, as I mentioned in Chapter 2, both estrogenic Red No. 3 and BPA are connected to ADHD and hyperactivity. ADHD is defined by the National Institute of Mental Health as "a brain disorder marked by an ongoing pattern of inattention and/or hyperactivity-impulsivity that interferes with functioning or development." The key word for me here is "brain", as in "it alters your brain".

Fast forward to a study of thousands of people exposed to high BPA, like many of us in recent years. "Analyses indicated," the research authors concluded, "that *prenatal exposure* to maternal BPA concentrations were related to higher levels of anxiety, depression, aggression and hyperactivity in children."[40] These disorders all trace back to issues in the brain.

This explains a *lot*. A lot about me, for instance. I have certain ADHD tendencies. And even while lead paint government approval was fading fast, BPA was common when I was growing up.

Researchers have even uncovered a so-called "biomarker" for depression that BPA activates,[41] indicating precisely how estrogenics may function to increase depression, scientifically.

How about EE2 in contraceptives? Well, one study encapsulates the mood in this area of research. The scientists report: "Oral hormonal contraception [containing EE2] may induce *serious mood disturbances* and should be administered with care, particularly in patients with affective disorders." The title of that study is *"Rapid relapse in depression following initialization of oral contraception with ethinyl estradiol [EE2]."*[42] Rapid relapse in depression sounds weird but also ominous.

To wrap up this topic of estrogenics and depression, I want to extend my reach beyond the IRS 10 List. I want to include an estrogenic that is called diethylstilbestrol, or DES, for short. I only bring it up because (A) DES is estrogenic and (B) DES has been studied in the context of depression.

At one time, DES was commonly found in meat because it was used in animal feeds to "improve feed conversion" – a euphemism meaning it "caused weight gains".[43] DES is now banned but it wasn't always. The trusty FDA once allowed DES to be prescribed as a drug. This is a powerful story you will see later. The story will actually close out the book.

For now, the relevant DES study, however, was based on people who used antidepressants. The study concluded that "the neurophysiologic [brain] effects of *in utero* exposure to DES could lead to an increased risk of depression in adult life."[44]

At this point, if over 45,000 women, farmers in India, phthalates, BPA, EE2, and DES haven't convinced you that estrogenics are likely underlying many, many cases of depression, I'm not sure what will.

Let's move along to some of the most immense and best established health problems with estrogenics.

CHAPTER 6

Estrogenic
Sexual Assault

Low T

BACK IN THE LAND OF saw palmetto and palm, a hot spring evaporated into a hot summer and my first date with Allison drew near.

Dave and I, around that time, had solved the mystery of how to catch sharks and, through the Fishing Club, we began helping novice or even first-time fishers catch their first sharks. Allison caught her first shark that spring, for example, along with many other Ave Maria University students and staff.

One day, however, my ambitions were re-directed away from sharks. I learned about a prize-fighting fish called "tarpon". Instantly, I knew I wanted to battle and catch one. Bagging a tarpon suddenly seemed a far greater accomplishment than catching a shark and that opiate became my new mark.

Like testosterone, which we will introduce in this chapter, tarpon are generally thought to be synonymous with the words "muscle" or "power". Also like testosterone, tarpon are much more interesting and intricate than it would seem at first glance.

Tarpon fish, you should know, have a strange mystique about them. Within fishing communities, tarpon are spoken of in a hushed reverence with a touch of admiration and awe. They are probably even the object of worship in some ramshackle fisherman's hut somewhere. Undoubtedly, in fact, Dan Brown is writing a novel at this very moment about tarpon worship and how Christianity is actually less about Jesus, in its origins, and more about the tarpon fish.

Like a muscle-bound Mr. Olympia contestant, tarpon veneration begins with their size. These fish are massive. They grow up to about 300 pounds. But size is just the beginning.

Tarpon are the color of untarnished precious metal. This gives fishermen the illusion that they are pillaging the seas for gleaming treasure. They even seek tarpon at a spot marked "X" on their GPS treasure maps.

Furthermore, I happened to believe that tarpon, of all the fish in the world, jump the most and jump the highest when they are hooked. While they are being reeled in, desperate tarpon have even been storied to leap straight over boats, from one side to another. I believe those tales.

Of course, leaping only occurs when tarpon actually get hooked, which adds to the mystique. Hooking them is rare. Hooking tarpon is a major challenge for 3 reasons: (1) they have lengthy lifespans and become educated over the years by hordes of sun-burned fisherman out to catch and release them, (2) they have *jumbo* eyes, keen to notice your fishing line, and (3) tarpon have rock-hard jaws which are suitable both for a tasty snack of stone crab or for liberating your unworthy fish hook. It's like trying to set a hook into a granite tombstone.

Truly: witnessing a tarpon shaking its head when it is hooked, rattling its gill plates, and spitting a hook is an experience that leaves even the most lionhearted among us dazed and weak in the knees.

So, too, does a first date.

Amidst all the shark fishing fun, my first date was rapidly approaching. And, as I worked in the lab or went fishing, my mind continually circled back to this thought.

When the 4th of July finally arrived, my evening with Allison commenced as planned. It began with us biking to the beach together on the infamous 850. The particular beach I chose, "Lowdermilk" it was called, was one of our favorite shark fishing beaches but this time and for the first time, we brought no fishing gear.

From Lowdermilk beach, we appraised a sunset and then a firework show. The fireworks went long into the night and we talked about our summers, our science, and our friends. The event was colorful and romantic but mostly unscandalous. The motorcycle ride home is where things took "a turn".

To this day, I maintain that the stoplights were largely at fault. In Naples, Florida, the stoplights go to sleep as early as the snow-bird denizens. Starting around 9 or 10 P.M. if I remember – certainly by 2 A.M. when Allison and I appeared on the scene – the stoplights on major roads in Naples would go green for the remainder of the night while the crossing side-streets would stay red. In other words, the Naples nighttime stoplights didn't blink yellow after hours but actually remained fixed on red or green.

As you pulled your car up to one of these after-hours side-street red-lights, a sensor would detect your presence and the light would promptly flip to green. All good. If you had a motorcycle, however, the light switch simply would not change. The stoplight would remain red until you either ran out of gas or suffocated on poisonous carbon monoxide fumes.

As a late-night motorcycle nightcrawler, therefore, I had become a habitual red-light runner prior to that 4th of July. And then I finally got busted. On my first date. By one of those rare cantankerous cops who felt he needed to teach me a lesson for "endangering the girlfriend". Or was it "girl   friend" now? I wasn't sure. Anyway, it's funny how the collage of red, white, and blue represent freedom until they're all flashing behind you in humid stinkler air at 2 AM.

"Please remove your helmet, sir, and give me your driver's license."

Meanwhile, to continue my streak of bad luck, I never managed to catch a tarpon that summer. In fact, I never even caught a tarpon before graduating Ave Maria University.... I hooked a few and came fairly close – even once reeling a small tarpon almost within reach in the dead of night on Key West – but I never closed the deal. Alas, I graduated Ave Maria University empty handed.

Well, not entirely empty handed.

Just before graduation, my science mentor, Dr. Peliska, handed me a letter. It was postmarked from Boston. The official stationary inside communicated a need for scientific skills in a premier Alzheimer's research lab. I pursued this favorable lead and ended up being whisked away to Boston for a great job immediately after I graduated Ave Maria.

Allison, meanwhile, stayed on to finish her final year of college. And rather than remaining in Florida, she embarked on a semester abroad in Austria in the coming fall. She ended up 5,000 miles away.

Our fishing and dating, it seemed at the time, would soon only be a distant memory. Far distant because Allison and I had literally moved on. Or had we?

Whenever scientists thoroughly research estrogen (and artificial estrogen!), testosterone seems to be irrelevant but ends up on the scene playing a vital role. It seems unlikely that these two hormones are deeply interconnected, yet they are. This association is what this chapter is all about.

First, it begins with brain changes. Estrogen and testosterone both play important roles in the brain cells. As the mind shifts from pursuing sharks to pursuing tarpon, for example, brain cells physically rearrange to some degree. Moving from Florida to Boston also conducts hormonal brain changes. In fact, many diverse behaviors, maybe even *all* behaviors, are connected to estrogen and testosterone brain cell rearrangements relating to estrogen and testosterone interplay.[1]

Scientists call this capacity of the brain to rearrange "neuroplasticity" or "neurobehavioral plasticity". And brain researchers have learned that neuroplastic changes occur, at least in part, because brain cells have *both* testosterone receptors and estrogen receptors. In other words, these very different, almost *opposing* receptors, can be found in the *same* brain cells.[2]

To better introduce this strange estrogen and testosterone relationship, let's start from the foundation and build up.

In our bodies, there are four main types of hormones:

(1) *Eicosanoid Hormones* – derived from fatty acids
(2) *Protein Hormones* – derived from amino acid chains
(3) *Amine Hormones* – derived from single amino acids
(4) **Steroid Hormones** – derived from cholesterol

As we saw earlier, the defining feature here is that all these hormones are created in one cell, organ, or gland, and they act on a different cell, organ, or gland. Like radio signals. It doesn't matter if you're talking about eicosanoid hormones, protein hormones, amine hormones, or steroid hormones, they are created "here" and delivered "there".

Now, I only included all four categories to give you some context. Our sole focus will be the steroid hormones and you can ignore the rest.

Also: the 3 estrogen hormones created by your body – namely, E1 [estrone], E2 [estradiol, not to be confused with EE2, which is synthetic], and E3 [estriol] – are steroids, just like testosterone (T) is a steroid.

You don't need to remember any names or abbreviations for estrogens, either, but just recognize that estrogen can come in slightly different forms. Keep in mind, too, that testosterone and estrogen are both steroids because they are both built from cholesterol in your body.

Ahh – yes – and I cannot go forward without mentioning my good friend cholesterol. I did my 300-page Ph.D. dissertation about fats and cholesterol ([3] in case you want to join the club of about 5 people whom have actually read the dissertation). Cholesterol is a misunderstood and underrated building-block for your body's steroid hormones and this highlights one – of many – important and healthy roles of cholesterol in your body. We will revisit the important topic of cholesterol in an upcoming *Chagrin & Tonic Series* book about good fats but let's get back to steroids.

The average person who hears the word "steroids" is more likely to think of Arnold Schwarzenegger than cholesterol or especially estrogen. Estrogen is a legitimate steroid but we usually think of the big "T"; we think of testosterone.

Amazingly, research into facial skull bones indicates that human testosterone levels have been *steadily declining for thousands of years*.[4] Researchers call this phenomenon "craniofacial feminization" meaning lower testosterone levels lead to a more "feminine" facial skull bone shape. This means, essentially, a rounder and less-bony face.

But even while human testosterone has been diminishing for thousands of years, testosterone has seen an *especially* dramatic dropout in recent history. A truly massive drop. All about the time estrogenics have been rising, "coincidentally".

In the 1940's, for instance, when scientists were actually able to measure testosterone for the first time in history, the average middle-aged males were approximately *double* the levels we are at today.[5] That's a rapid fallout with massive health and strength consequences!

Unfortunately, I have not been able to find women's testosterone levels from around the 1940's – it is probable that women's testosterone levels in the 1940's were completely ignored – but I have a hunch those levels, too, were *far* higher back then. Unfortunately, even scientists today have barely investigated trends in women's testosterone levels.

But, on the topic of women's testosterone, I did come across one science conference convened at Princeton back in 2001. The theme was "Androgen Deficiency in Women".[6] Androgens, by the way, include testosterone.

While it was noted at the Princeton conference that "currently available assays [to measure testosterone in women] are found to be lacking in sensitivity and reliability at the lower ranges", women were still shown to have diminishing testosterone levels in recent years. Below healthy levels on the average.

Even so: as a woman, why would you care if your testosterone is low? Isn't testosterone a "dude thing"?

Well, that same Princeton conference on women included this nice summary: "[Testosterone] affects sexual desire, bone density, muscle mass and strength, adipose [fat] tissue distribution, mood, energy, and psychological well-being." Enough said, unless you are one of those women who isn't concerned with your sexual desire, bone density, muscle mass and strength, adipose tissue distribution, mood, energy, and psychological well-being, of course.

Anyway, middle-aged men are currently around 400ng/dL and middle-aged women these days are around 20ng/dL.[7] These are "total" serum testosterone numbers, for those who know what that means, and these numbers came from a massive multi-ethnic study of almost 7,000 people. In other words, these numbers represent a reliable "average" for testosterone levels.

Now, I must legally advise you to consult your doctor in your own potentially unique case, but I personally believe healthy middle-aged individuals should *generally* be doubling these testosterone numbers: that would be a target number of 800ng/dL for men (total testosterone) and 40ng/dL for women (total as well). In fact, middle-aged women should probably triple 20 – aiming for 60ng/dL – using professional bloodwork monitoring and, ideally, natural methods to bring up testosterone, which is outside the scope of this book. My idealized testosterone levels are still within medical chart recommended ranges, so this isn't too extreme. My recommended numbers are just on the high end.

And why should you aim on the "high" end of the range?

Well, first of all, most people feel more alive at the high end of the scale. Plus, we are just so abysmally low compared to our ancestors that I believe it's unhealthy. These are the same ancestors who were physically much healthier in many ways than we are today, as Paleo researchers will tell you (stronger bones, teeth, etc.).

Also, around age 40, our natural testosterone levels plummet. Actually, women's testosterone levels nose-dive earlier than men's, usually around age 30. So, let me ask you: do you want the steroid levels of an elderly person? The whole diminished "sexual desire, bone density, muscle mass and strength, adipose tissue distribution, mood, energy, and psychological well-being" shebang? Or do you want *optimal* levels?

Additionally, there are the assortment of medical journal papers with titles like this one: "*The impact of testosterone imbalance on **depression** and women's health*".[8]

Now, we just finished discussing how estrogenics can provoke depression in Chapter 5 – further proof that estrogenics can directly impact our brains – so let's mix in testosterone imbalance and supersize that argument. In other words, along with high environmental estrogenics, low T *in women* further explains at least some of the modern explosion in depression rates.[9]

One final preemptive prophecy on this topic: medical doctors generally will inform you that you are "satisfactory" when you have your testosterone checked. You will probably fall within a certain range on the lab test and they simply go with those lab test results. No sense risking a hard-earned medical license thinking outside the box. No sense wasting time and money explaining the principle of health *optimization*.

Well, I have news. Like our vitamin D numbers, our current testosterone-range numbers are based on micronutrient-starved, under-exercised, indoor-dwelling, poorly-postured Americans. And the numerical *ranges* are laughably huge – like 250 to 1,000. That's like me recommending that you go for a daily jog between 0.2 to 26.2 miles, every day. "Somewhere in there is good. Have fun."

Plus, the testosterone numbers are bottom-heavy. In other words, testosterone level 'recommended ranges' vary from "*severely* low" on the low end, to "eh...probably a bit high" on the high end. Sticking with my jogging analogy, that would be equivalent to a doctor's recommendation to "walk one block in length every day" at the low end. This recommendation is not health-optimal, if we're being honest.

Of course, to be fair to the people drafting these hormone ranges and the doctors using them, T levels vary throughout the day and also differ from week to week. The levels depend on how much cholesterol we are eating, what time of day we are eating, how much we are sleeping, how we are acting – a whole host of things.

So, when should you have your T measured? Well, besides the annoying answer "as soon as possible", definitely check your testosterone in the morning. Every time. Also, be sure you don't eat before having your blood drawn or at least eat the *exact* same thing you ate last time you had your T checked. Stuff like that. In essence, be consistent when you have follow-up tests.

Finally, to compound all the testosterone "range" problems, the medical lab testing corporations don't even agree on numbers. For an example, here is a chart I compiled based on actual lab testing companies. The particular chart only highlights "middle-age" people to keep it simple:

	LabCorp	AnyLab TestNow	Quest Diagnostics
Recommended Free T Levels (for MALES)	7.2 – 224	35 – 155	46 – 224
Recommended Free T Levels (for FEMALES)	0.0 – 2.2	0.1 – 6.4	0.2 – 5.0
Recommended Total T Levels (for MALES)	348 – 1197	250 – 1100	250 – 1100
Recommended Total T Levels (for FEMALES)	8 – 48	2 – 45	2 – 45

All "Free T" units are pg/mL and "Total T" units are ng/dL

You can see that the "recommended range" numbers vary widely between different companies.

Believe it or not, during the process of writing this book, I had to update these numbers. One of the companies recently increased their upper-range testosterone values. The word is finally starting to get out that we are appallingly low on testosterone and the upper end of the testosterone range is much healthier, for males or females.

Hopefully, this thinking will gain momentum. "Steroids" are often seen as the lowest form of sin, despite their critical importance in our health, but let's moooove on and talk about cows.

"Testrogenics": Where Testosterone and Estrogen Meet

The 7 Deadly Things
#3. Hormonal Disruption

Some *fascinating* dairy cow research – I can't believe I just said that – was recently "spilled" regarding testosterone. The study showed measurements of *cow estrogen* "Of Milk and Men" and how that might impact your T levels.

Unfortunately, as fascinating as the study was, the scientists only measured natural *cow estrogens* and not artificial *estrogenics*. This, of course, is a true shortcoming. "Industrial" cows, as you have seen, eat and drink numerous artificial estrogenics from the IRS 10 List (Chapters 2 and 4). To make matters worse, major processing plants further introduce the milk to plastics.

Of course, despite these shortcomings, this particular dairy study was still informative.

Apparently – according to the study – "modern genetically improved dairy cows continue to *lactate throughout almost the entire pregnancy.*"[10] This is not normal. In other words, we have created super-cows in the dairy industry, through selective breeding. The result is unnatural milk production endurance throughout pregnancy.

The researchers went on to explain that milk collection during cow pregnancy introduces a variety of human health problems. The problems arise because (1) pregnant-cow milk has exorbitantly high levels of cow estrogen and (2) farmers continue to collect this pregnancy hormone-ridden milk and mix it with all the other milk, and, not surprisingly then, (3) the researchers find high levels of cow estrogen in grocery store purchased whole milk.

Here's the key: the researchers also found high levels of cow estrogens in the urine of *all* the boys and men they tested after drinking whole milk. These boys and men were tested after they underwent a milk-fast. But the problem went beyond males simply urinating out cow estrogens.

One of the major findings of this study was summarized by this frank statement: "testosterone significantly decreased in men". And the significant decrease occurred within 1 hour after drinking milk. One hour! This was standard grocery store milk!

In the study's conclusion, the researchers maintained that the significant testosterone reduction was due to high levels of cow estrogen in the milk. Unfortunately, the study lacked long-term measurements and only tested changes within hours, not days or weeks. Long-term information would still be valuable to investigate, especially because many people actually drink milk every few hours (I used to be one of those people...).

Now – again – this was "natural" estrogen. It was from cows. Well, not entirely "natural" – it came from pregnant cows that, unnaturally, continue to be milked during late pregnancy – but the estrogen was not "Made-in-China" synthetic.

So why is male testosterone dropping from exposure to estrogens? Let's find out.

Testosterone, in our bodies, *mainly* originates from testicles in men and ovaries in women.[i] The ovaries are obvious "targets" of estrogen –

---

[i] The adrenal glands can also secrete testosterone.

and artificial estrogen – but testicles are actually estrogenic targets, too. In other words, testicles are impacted by estrogen.

For an example, here is a quote from a recent research article about estrogen receptors in testicular tissue: "Estrogens act through specific receptors and regulate testes development and spermatogenesis."[11]

What the researchers here are essentially saying is that estrogen is a "player" in the testes. Estrogen can have an impact on how testes function, how much sperm is created, and how testes *develop*. That, in fact, is one of the ways males are "feminized" by estrogenics but we'll investigate feminization of males shortly.

First, what you need to realize is that there is a key blood circulation estrogen and testosterone transaction at play here. What does this mean, you ask?

Well, cholesterol-derived steroids – the definition of *steroid* hormones, remember, is that they derive from cholesterol – need to be circulated through our bodies. How can they circulate? More specifically, how do estrogen and testosterone travel around your body?

Surprisingly, this is not a trivial question. Think about it for a second: testosterone and estrogen are like cholesterol. They "fear" water. They are "hydro · phobic". And if you add testosterone or estrogen to a glass of water – or blood, by the way – the hormones will float. This would be like adding butter or oil to a glass of water. Testosterone or estrogen and blood simply won't mix well.

So how do these important hormones travel around your bloodstream if they can't mix properly with your "water-based" blood?

SHBG (sex hormone-binding globulin), that's how. Both estrogen and testosterone bind to SHBG, which is a huge sugary protein. SHBG is literally, "sugary", as in "it has sugars all over it" (the scientific term is "glycoprotein"). Proteins and sugars go into water just fine and, therefore, so do testosterone and estrogen...as long as they are snuggling into a SHBG protein, the limo service of the steroid classes.

Here is where it gets interesting. Of the total testosterone and estrogen in your blood, about 98% is bound to SHBG, riding the limo. That leaves 2% or so "free". This is where the term "free testosterone" is derived. Free testosterone is the stuff not bound to SHBG in your blood. Therefore, free testosterone is the most useable, accessible, stuff.

Your muscles need some testosterone? "Free T" is where it's at. Your brain? Free T to the rescue. Accordingly, not only do you want optimal testosterone ranges of T overall, but your "free testosterone" numbers are especially important.

Estrogenics, importantly, can *also* ride the SHBG limo around your bloodstream.

This gives rise to another important scientific consideration: how much artificial estrogen in your blood is "free" and how much is "bound" to SHBG? Even substances that some scientists consider "weakly estrogenic" can have unexpectedly large impacts on our health and bodies when they are "free" in high percentages.[12] They are more *free* to do damage in your body, a detail most scientists today aren't even considering.

Additionally, a larger problem arises because our exposures to estrogenics directly alter our levels of testosterone.

According to medical research: "Conventional oral contraception causes a *decline* in androgens [i.e. testosterone] because of *higher levels of SHBG*"[8]. In other words, oral contraception, which is just one example from the IRS 10 List – *decreases* your *useable* testosterone levels *and* your *overall* testosterone levels! Or, put another way, if you are exposing yourself to estrogenics, you are likely bringing both your bound T and your free T down!

This further sheds light on why sperm counts in healthy men have correspondingly dropped by more than 50% in the past 50 years. This observation has been confirmed in various ways by a number of studies. Especially poor quality semen has been found in *younger men*, too.[13] Generation Plastic could be our new name. Or Estrogeneration. And we'll blow open the fertility floodgates soon, in *Part 3*.

Furthermore, recognizing that estrogenics lower free testosterone explains why moo-juice lowered male testosterone, in case you wondered earlier.

Finally, there is also good evidence that estrogen and testosterone each protect DNA from shortening with age.[14] The lowering of free testosterone, therefore, elucidates how artificial estrogenics may speed up the aging process, as you'll remember we saw specific examples of this accelerated aging in Chapter 2 with both BPA and parabens. It will also shed light on other things you are about to discover.

Hormonal Side-Effects of Our Estrogenic Exposures

Now, it's time to talk about a hot topic phenomenon scientists refer to as "feminization of males". This issue is related to our heavy estrogenic exposures and our testosterone declines and is a serious concern.

As exclusive as "feminization of males" sounds, women are not sidelined here. Estrogen – remember – acts both on the testes and on the ovaries.

What that means is the sexual issues arising from estrogenic exposures are first and foremost "hormonal" rather than merely "male" or "female". The sex problems emerge because they mess with everyone's hormone levels. And estrogenics seem to have unique but, nevertheless, equally problematic hormonal effects on both men and women. To illustrate this, let's begin with young girls and puberty.

Ominously, the onset of puberty in our society has been shifting. On average, puberty today is coming-on far earlier than ever before in documented history[15] and, by far, this is more extreme in girls than boys.[16]

Puberty that arrives years before normal is unusually and unnaturally stressful for a girl. It is a major psychological adjustment, for instance, when older boys or men start pursuing younger and younger girls. Early puberty is also a stressor for parents.

Next, there are the concomitant health problems arising from early puberty in girls. Like a thing called "hyper*andro*genism", which essentially is an excess of *male* hormone in a *female's* body. "Andro-" is simply the Greek word for male. This surplus of male hormones in girls due to early-onset puberty is a well-documented side-effect.

Hyperandrogenism brings up a related side point. Artificial estrogens interact in various ways with the estrogen receptor. Scientists have terms for these interactions, like "agonist" and "partial agonist" and "antagonist", but what you must know is that these interactions can be complicated. Not only are the direct estrogen receptor disruptions variable in unhealthy ways, estrogenics can even interact in more than one way with our testosterone regulating abilities. To add even more complexity, other hormones can be impacted by estrogenics, too.[17,18]

We could go through many other health issues stemming from early puberty but what I want to know is: why the sudden shift in puberty age in the first place?

Well, here is a quote from a medical journal, attempting to explain this phenomenon:

> **Estrogenic pollutants** must be taken into consideration [for early-onset puberty] since environmental and epidemiological studies have shown that humans and some animal species are **adversely affected** by environmental chemical substances that interfere with the endocrine [hormone] system and are known as endocrine disrupters. Environmental pollutants acting as endocrine disrupters include estrogens and **estrogen-like products that are universally present in the form of hormones used in stockbreeding, chemicals employed in industry and agriculture, and substances naturally contained in plants and cereals.**[15]

So, today, ladies and gentleman, boys and girls, we are all being swamped by estrogenic "body pollution" from our surrounding environments. This leads to run-on sentences like the one above being published in professional science journals, expressing concern over "estrogenic pollutants". The title of that paper, by the way, is "*Premature thelarche and environmental pollutants*". "Premature thelarche" is the premature onset of female breast development.

It has also been discovered that estrogenics, like parabens for example, act directly on the pituitary gland.[19] The pituitary gland is considered a "master regulator" of many hormones in children and adults.

Undoubtedly due therefore, at least in large part, to high levels of artificial estrogens in our environment, early onset of puberty has recently become extremely common.

In fact, early puberty has become so common that medical doctors are considering changing the "normal" age-range of puberty for both boys and girls.[20] Changing the age range! Believe it or not, testosterone has already undergone this re-adjustment (remember: we have sub optimal levels of testosterone). Similarly, "normal" vitamin D recommendations ranges have undergone re-adjustments (hint: we have sub optimal levels of vitamin D). So, precedents have been set for changing "normal" recommendations based on our culture's "average people"; people who sit in offices/classrooms indoors most days. Hurray for average!

And before we further incriminate sexual-assaulting estrogenics, you might be wondering: why the heck would any right-minded lab or doctor promote modifying the puberty age-range? Why on earth would someone want to adjust the puberty age-range younger?

Well, moving the puberty age-range younger makes a host of increasingly common issues ("early onset puberty [disorder]" or "premature thelarche" or "premature adrenarche" etc.) immediately disappear. Voilà, our society is "healthy" again.

If the age range was changed, for example, it would no longer be considered legally or medically "abnormal" or "pathologic" when girls entered puberty at age 7 – despite the obvious fact that this *should* be considered abnormal. Young children are simply not prepared to start having children.

So, kids are clearly entering puberty earlier than ever. Are the estrogenics really to blame, I mean *really*?

Absolutely. In fact, a single scientific review paper[21] incriminates BPA, phthalates, atrazine, and ZEA mycoestrogen in "precocious puberty" – "precocious" being another way of saying "early-onset" for puberty. And there are many studies about APEs (alkylphenols) affecting onset of puberty (e.g.[22]) and soy (e.g.[23]), etc. In fact, every single IRS 10 List estrogenic is able to alter puberty in some way when thoroughly investigated scientifically.

Now let's move our discussion a few years down the line. Let's look at college enrollment and then shift focus entirely to males to finish this chapter.

In 1950, about 70% of undergraduate students were male.[24] By 1970, this number was around 60%. Next, by 1980, undergraduates were equally men and women. By 2006, undergraduates were very nearly 40% male and 60% female.

Noticing the trend?

While I was doing my Ph.D. at Boston University, in fact, there were more than 60% women present: 3,691 more women than men were enrolled at BU.[25] That number of women, by the way, is more people than the entire study body of Ave Maria University while I attended!

Meanwhile, the US Department of Education estimates that this gender gap will continue increasing slightly every year.[25] What is going on?

Well, first, I realize this is complicated.

But I also think to merely say "it's complicated" is a cop-out. Women have become more active and visible in society, certainly, but it goes beyond that as we see a notable *imbalance* today opposite from merely a few years ago.

A contributing factor here, I believe, is that many boys and men around us – not every single boy or man, but many – have become more apathetic and indifferent in recent years. Many of us can attest to this from personal experience and if you disagree, that's fine. But even enrollment in boys' sports including basketball, football, baseball, and soccer are all on the decline in America.[26]

Frankly, apathy is not a historical "norm" for males. Regarding this specific topic overall, I recommend that you check out Dr. Leonard Sax's books titled *Boys Adrift* and *Girls on Edge*. Dr. Sax presents detailed analyses of many chemical and environmental "motivation" issues, including examinations into the shrinking "nucleus accumbens" portion of the male brain. Further, a contributing factor to overall male apathy, Dr. Sax argues, is the artificial estrogens. Don't forget the sea otter study we looked at in Chapter 4: where 12,900 nanograms of paraben were found in the average sea otter *brain*.

To put it frankly, we males today are being "feminized" via estrogenics, especially in developed countries.[27] Brains, bodies, everything. And, yes, I grimaced and raised my own hand here. Estrogenic pollution is hard to avoid. Furthermore, I personally never attempted estrogenic avoidance for many years of my life.

This term "feminization of males", you should know, is not at all my homemade term. Scientists everywhere are using this phrase, sounding the alarm. In fact, the term has become common in scientific studies so let's dig deeper.

The hormonal disruptions from estrogenics seem to have a unique anti-motivating factor in males compared to females. This goes beyond the sex-drive issues we'll discuss shortly. Again, I'm talking here about a *physical* neurological [brain] change.

In the scientific research, it begins with my all-time favorite protein: brain-derived neurotrophic factor (BDNF). When I studied Alzheimer's disease, I learned that researchers often call BDNF "Miracle-Gro® for the brain". You need to see this to believe it but when brain cells growing in dishes are dosed with BDNF, these cells sprout new growths – *stalks, branches, everything* – like an exploding or fast growing tree. Exercise releases a massive dose of BDNF, by the way – especially in children – but that's a different story for a different day.

In a study of estrogenic impacts on young male rats, BDNF was discovered to "act in a concerted, network-like manner to affect [*motivational*] behavior". [28] What was BDNF "networked" with? Steroid receptors. And the study specifically illustrated how the male steroid receptors and therefore the so-called "homeostasis" of *behavioral motivation* was impacted by estrogenics. This was all connected to BDNF!

In another study about "*motivation* and cognition in male rats", researchers found "*estrogenic* functions may play a more *prominent role in young male behavior and development* than has been previously assumed."[29] Seeing the possible connection to college enrollment? It could be unrelated but it could also be a major contributing factor. The science research suggests the latter.

Let's move into the dating scene.

First, I want to reiterate that "feminization of males" is not my own, home-brewed, sensationalizing term. This is a term used by literally thousands of hot-off-the-press scientific articles.

"Fish are adequate sentinels for feminization effects," judges one scientific journal article, published in 2015,[30] reminding us of those sexually deformed whitefish we looked at in Chapter 4 near Bern, Switzerland.

Why are fish "sentinels" – like measuring devices or sensors – for male feminization? In essence, fish basically "breathe" the estrogenics in their environment as we observed throughout *Part 1*.

Painted turtles have a similar male feminization crisis. Recently, these turtles have been discovered to have unusual hormonal alterations, gonad dysfunctions, behavior changes, and developmental problems...at least when they were exposed to BPA.[31] And, like the fish study above, this finding was unshelled in 2015.

Here are a few more hot new examples of scientific studies that affirm the reality and problem of male feminization.

One scientific group begins by saying that it is an "urgent affair [...] to restrict the use of nonylphenol ethoxylates [APEs]" because they harm the reproductive systems of male fish, amphibians, and mammals.[32] This, by the way, was written in a Chinese journal, commemorating the fact that China has banned many APEs even while America has not, as we saw in Chapter 2.

"Demasculinization and feminization of male gonads by atrazine: consistent effects across vertebrate classes,"[33] reads another journal title. This study included humans and human male gonad impacts, making it more clear why Europe has an entire ban against atrazine.

The synonym used in the atrazine study for male feminization – namely, "demasculinization" – is also seen in an "Assessment of phthalates/phthalate alternatives in children's toys,"[34] which was the title of an article published in one of the Nature journals and, again, written in 2015. The impact to children is especially dramatic because lower artificial hormone "doses" have larger impacts.

And how, exactly, is male feminization occurring? Simple: it's hormones.

Steroid hormones have thousands of effects each time they are unleased into our bloodstreams. These effects, to review, are long-term effects rather unlike our lightning-fast nerve signals. These estrogenic effects strongly impact many elements of male development and behavior potentially *for life*. It's called "harm" by scientists for a reason.

We'll dig deeper into the actual time span of these long-term and reproductive impacts in *Part 3*.

"Phthalates," says another scientific journal called the Science of the Total Environment, "have been shown to possess estrogenic activity and display anti-androgenic [testosterone-lowering] effects."[27] This ties into the beginning of the chapter because lowering testosterone is a form of feminization. And remember the moo-juice study? Now I'm adding phthalates from plastic.

To finish, let's look at one final highly specific way this male feminization occurs.

Regarding testosterone, scientists are finding that male testosterone receptors are being diminished by estrogenics. This study[35] is one example specifically looking at APEs.

To understand what this means, recall the radio analogy. This was where a signal – the hormone – was sent from one location and picked up by another location. The signal is picked up by the radio or receptor. Testosterone receptors pick up testosterone "signals".

Therefore, lower levels of the testosterone receptor, due to estrogenics, means that even if you have *perfect* levels of testosterone, your body would not be able to "pick it up" or use the proper amount. This doubles-down on our modern low T problem and apparently also alters sex drive.

To add insult to injury here, certain estrogenics and possibly all estrogenics even *block* testosterone from binding the receptor. Here is a study showing this exact effect from sunscreen 4-MBC.[36] That, I must say, is a good way to conclude the *ménage à trois* of estrogenic impacts: they decrease your testosterone, give rise to less testosterone receptors, and block testosterone binding to its necessary receptor in your body.

CHAPTER 7

Super-Cancer-Fragilistic-Extra-Allergy-Doses

It Begins with Your Immune System

DURING ALLISON'S "ENDLESS SEMESTER" TRAVELING the world and studying in Austria, I was creating a new life for myself in Boston...alone.

Things were good but my life was definitely missing something... somebody.

I began saving money and bought an engagement ring for Allison. I also hatched a meticulous wedding proposal plot that was so meticulous it had to be scrapped at the last minute.

The plan began with me buying an evening flight from Boston to Fort Myers after Allison was back in Florida for her final semester. Simple. The plan included some phone calls to college friends and I scheduled the flight, most unsuspiciously, for two days *before* Valentine's Day – Thursday, February 12th. Allison had no idea I was coming. Or was I?

My "perfectly timed" evening flight was delayed and then it was delayed some more.

"It's already late in the day," I worried, *"will the flight even go through?"* This was a problem of epic proportions based on the state of my nerves.

From the airport, I called Allison's roommate Christa. She was "in" on everything. Christa arranged to keep Allison awake.

I found out later that Christa's strategy for inducing insomnia was to watch what turned-out to be a bizarre movie. Ironically, it was called "Brideshead Revisited". Allison and Christa started watching with the popcorn, drinks, and furry blankets.

As the bottom of the popcorn dish began to see more and more lamplight, a fresh problem arose. Allison didn't like the movie. She didn't want to finish. Christa, therefore, had to pretend like some really important plot twist was just around the corner. I don't think she'd ever even seen the movie herself but Christa heroically persisted in encouraging Allison to "just keep watching".

Meanwhile, my flight finally arrived around midnight. The 12th had transitioned to the 13th. Friday the 13th.

Behind the scenes, the hero of this story was my friend Mike. He was the unsung hero because he lent me his brand new shiny-red crotch-rocket bike so I could hopefully rev up some good memories with Allison. In case you wonder, there was no backrest and no sissy bars on the back of Mike's bike.

So, thanks to Mike, not moments after the 2-hour and 14-minute movie ended, Allison heard a chainsaw pulling into her driveway. She had already become suspicious at this point – due to Christa's movie watching insistences – and Allison was elated that her suspicions were confirmed in the best way.

Allison pulled on a long-sleeve shirt – it was February and a wintery 63 degrees – and we said *adios* to Christa, and we drove on Mike's Red Bull through the romantic nighttime stinkler air.

My surprise destination was our favorite shark-infested fishing and fireworking beach, Lowdermilk. I proposed and she said "yes".

A Ph.D. scientist friend of mine in Boston – Chris – had suggested I attach the engagement ring to a fishing line and have Allison reel it in. Yet as much as this was a genius idea, my proposal was more one-knee normal. In the ocean, sharp-toothed predator fish are attracted to shiny things and, just this once, I wasn't looking to attract a fish.

Now, for those of you who think I'm exaggerating for the sake of the story about the centrality of shark fishing in the selection of our favorite beach, you need to know what we did the next day.

After parading Allison's ring-finger around campus on Friday, we geared-up and left for the land of the 10,000 Islands and Pat O'Donnell's shark nets. As the leader of the Fishing Club, I had become a regular on biologist Pat O'Donnell's shark-tagging expeditions, so I had pulled-some monofilament strings and arranged for an engagement-day-night trip.

The trip would go like this: O'Donnell would leave at sunset, dinghy boat attached to his houseboat. He would weave through the maze of mangrove islands and sharp oyster bars. When O'Donnell determined that we had arrived at a shark hotspot, we would use the smaller boat to string out a series of long nets. Next, we would all simply wait on the houseboat until we either saw the net floats bobbing – using a flashlight to check every so often – or wait until we heard violent splashing noises.

Upon pulling up a net containing a captured shark, we would put it in a pool of water in the houseboat and do sciencey things. After that, we would release the shark and go catch more.

For our engagement trip, we caught several sharks – most notably a bonnethead shark from the hammerhead genus – and, overall, Allison and I had the best of times lounging on the upper deck of the houseboat, watching shooting stars.

Also, we would see tarpon roll on the surface in the spotlights that night – they were too smart to swim into a net – which drove me to wonder: will I ever catch my first tarpon? Based full-time in Boston, it seemed more insurmountable a goal than ever but some old wounds never truly heal. Those shifty silver monsters!

One thing many people do not know is that scientists find the immune system to be extremely shifty and elusive. Immunologists find research far more challenging than you might expect due to experimental disruptions unique to the immune system. Specifically, when immunologists try to study immune cells, they agitate them, dismember them, and make them behave abnormally. Immune cells resist, attack, and react, like sharks. It's how they function. It's a mess.

All 3 Nobel laureates I've eaten lunch with have told me the same thing. I asked them individually one of my favorite questions: "What are the newest frontiers, or areas we know very little about, in science today?" They listed off a couple different new frontiers but they *all* included the immune system answering my question. The immune system is a future frontier in science because it is more mystifying and less understood than the average person realizes.

Furthermore, like some strange betrothal, the immune system and cancer are inseparable. We will talk about cancer soon but the more we discover and learn about immune system dysfunction, the more we discover and learn about the involvement of cancer. This adds to the challenge of curing cancer...

The 7 Deadly Things
#4. Immune Dysfunction

Let's start with lymph.

As much as we hear about blood circulating our bodies, it is easy to forget we have this clear and colorless "lymph" stuff that circulates as well. Lymph includes our immune system cells. It doesn't have that ostentatious blood-red color but it's there. Lymph runs all throughout your body just like your blood and just as important.

Regrettably, scientists have traced estrogenic destruction back to immune cells, those cells circulating in our lymph. Researchers, for example, find that estrogenics interact directly on "lymphoid target cells".[1] Exactly how and why estrogenics behave this way remains a mystery but estrogenics certainly interact, collide, and conflict with immune cells.

To try to understand what's going on with artificial estrogens and our immune system, let's start with one specific example: lupus.

Lupus is a strange-sounding, chronic, autoimmune disease that occurs when our own bodies – our immune systems – eat us. Yes, eat. The immune cells are like little Pac-Man characters that go around devouring things.

In lupus, the eating may include things like your own organs or joints. So-called lupus "flare ups" can be horrific. Remember: normally, immune cells would be chewing-up invading bacteria and virus – not you – so the "chewing" process is otherwise natural and normally healthy.

Estrogenics are involved because they have been shown to cause lupus flares.[2]

Indeed: pregnancy is especially associated with lupus attacks because, according to researchers, "estrogenic hormones possess both immunostimulating and immunosuppressive properties."[2]

Wait. That statement is clear as mud. Immune *stimulation* and *suppression* at the same time? It sounds like drinking coffee that also contains sleep meds to make you drowsy. But that's how it goes. We don't make the rules, we discover them – a fundamental principle of both philosophy and science.

Researchers also find that estrogenic immune system stimulation/suppression frequently occurs in a bad way, as in "those estrogenics are *stimulating* immune cells to eat joints", or, conversely, "those estrogenics are *suppressing* immune cells to allow infections or cancer cells to grow". We'll look further at this yin-yang, shortly.

Meanwhile, studies have also shown that testosterone-blocking drugs "activate" lupus. In fact, testosterone-blockers kill mice that have lupus.[3] Apparently, immune system "self-attack" is too much for immune-compromised grey squeakers. I'm not sure how they get mice with lupus in the first place but there it is. This also smacks at that critical interplay between testosterone and estrogenics we discovered in the previous chapter.

Furthermore, as any woman who has been pregnant will confirm, there are a series of "ups and downs" of the immune system during pregnancy (and beyond) due to hormonal changes.

"Pregnancy, a period of high estrogen levels," begins one research paper, "affects the maternal *immune system* to permit fetal development, negatively modulating cell-mediated immunity."[4] That's good. You won't want your immune system to attack your unborn baby.

Artificial estrogenics, on the other hand, are not good. They scam this process, confusing our poor immune cells. This helps explain the "chemical abortions" we noted earlier, which occur with high doses of estrogenics. Disrupting both hormones and the immune system via estrogenics can be a life or death equation, in other words.

This seems like a good time to revisit DES (diethylstilbestrol). In a previous chapter, we brought up this once-common estrogenic substance. We also saw how DES can cause weight-gains and increased risk for depression. And, to reiterate: DES may not be so common in our foods today but it is certainly estrogenic. Therefore, by representing all other estrogenics, DES contributes to our understanding of *immune system* dysfunctions.

Researchers studying DES do not hesitate to label it "immunotoxic"[5] – or "toxic to our immune systems". This is strong language for nerdy scientists and professional academic journals, believe me.

Other studies of DES add the disturbing news that *developing immune systems* – infant's and children's immune systems – are at greater risk than immune systems of the adult for immunotoxicity following DES exposure.[6] In other words, your children's immune systems are likely to have greater negative impacts from estrogenic exposures and more lasting issues, too. This helps explain the ever-rising allergy rates – allergies and sensitivities of all forms – we've been experiencing in America in recent years.

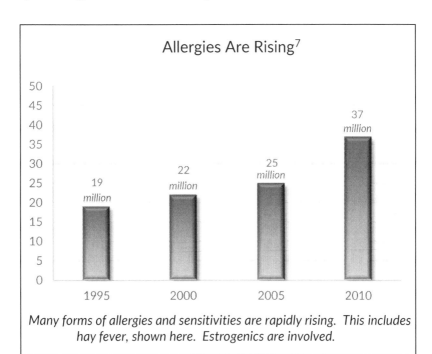

Allergies Are Rising[7]

Many forms of allergies and sensitivities are rapidly rising. This includes hay fever, shown here. Estrogenics are involved.

Soy, too, has been studied in regards to the human immune system. Soy has even been investigated regarding *children's* immune systems. Researchers in a 2003 edition of the *Journal of Pediatrics and Child Health* comment about soy consumption in infancy and childhood, saying: "There is an increasing number of recent reports that suggest adverse effects with respect to [...] immune function and thyroid disease."[8] The title of that paper was *"Soy, infant formula, and phytoestrogens"*. Once again, I have to ask: why would anyone add soy to infant formula?

ZEA (zearalenone), from fungus and things like moldy grains, is another "immunotoxic" substance. "*Zearalenone, an estrogenic mycotoxin, is an immunotoxic compound*" is the bluntly written title of yet another science research report.[4] And when scientists are crafting *titles* of papers like that, you can be certain that "immunotoxicity" is well-established.

Despite all this, there is some good news. Regarding ZEA and immunotoxicity, one fascinating study found that one species of probiotic bacteria *neutralized* the estrogenic ZEA.[9] Fascinatingly, the researchers found this probiotic bacterium in "Tunisian artisanal butter".

This shows, once again, that healthy gut bacteria can actually protect you. They protect against soy and flax, they protect your immune system against mold estrogen. And the probiotic species matters! In other words, higher quality gut bacteria equal less adverse estrogenic impacts.

Phthalates and BPA too, are, not surprisingly, called "immunotoxic" in a number of studies (a 2015 scientific *review* can be found here[10]).

Atrazine – also immunotoxic, at least in mice and rats. Researchers in one study, for example, discuss significant suppression of immunity in fighting infections due to atrazine exposures.[11] And greater "suppressions" have been found in male rats compared to females, strangely.[12]

Even EE2 from oral contraception, is now considered "immunotoxic" in fish[13] – but of course, fish are an exception because they are "constantly exposed" to EE2 unlike us...hmm.

Let's briefly look at two final estrogenics.

Remember how red food coloring dye is estrogenic? Well, after reminding us that in the past 50 years, synthetic dye use in foods has increased by over 500%, researchers authoring this paper[14] say that these dyes are "able to act in *stealth mode* to circumvent and disrupt the immune system". And, yes, a professional science journal author just sounded like a video game junkie. Wow.

To close, a scientific review of APEs (alkylphenols) and "immune system modulation" starts with this sentence: "The prevalence of allergic diseases has increased in recent decades. [APE's...] tend to **accumulate in the human body** and may be associated with the adverse effects of allergic diseases. Recently, new evidence has supported the importance of alkylphenols in the *in vitro* allergic response."[15] Evidence that APEs are guilty of "Disturbing the Immune System Peace" is accumulating even as APEs are accumulating in our bodies.

This brings up an interesting side point. The commonly touted "dose makes the poison" phrase is not always true, especially within the context of the immune system. As we saw earlier and are seeing again here, estrogenics can accumulate or build-up within our bodies. Are we still wondering why allergic diseases are on the rise?

Curdling Your Blood (Clots)

The 7 Deadly Things
#5. Blood Clotting

Let's briefly overview the blood clotting issues arising from estrogenics before moving into cancer.

As you clearly know by now, estrogenics are in the "mega-money" corporate category. And while I find myself tempted, here, to think only of birth control – which is specifically sold *because* it is an artificial estrogen – the money trail extends to plastics, fragrances, food products, artificial colorings, and chemical crop sprays.

In Chapter 3 – mainly to illustrate these influences of money – I held an awareness-boosting workshop on various aspects of scientific conflicts-of-interest (COI) and hidden agendas. Also in Chapter 3, we reviewed a study that indicated phytoestrogen has "potential" for heart disease "risk *reduction*".[16] In fact, the authors made the bold and controversial claim for "potential risk reduction" within the very title of their paper. How can estrogenics be involved in blood clotting if they *reduce* heart disease?

First, you may remember that the scientists qualified their assertion later in the publication, in the middle of the paper, where most people will never see it. They qualified their statement about heart protection long after readers probably already concluded that they should load up their pantries with more soy products to protect their tickers.

Despite that carefully-worded opinion about heart disease risk *reduction*, I can tell you that most scientific studies uphold the opposite view. Estrogenics *increase* blood clots, heart attacks, strokes, and various other embolisms. These issues are so common and so *collective* among estrogenics that blood clotting, therefore, made *The 7 Deadly Things* list. There is definitely a common thread here.

For instance, together with breast cancer – an eye-opening topic which we will discuss shortly – blot clots are generally the most common side-effect from birth control.

In fact, a medical condition exists called "thrombophilia", which can be provoked in people by estrogen-therapy.[17] This issue, thrombophilia, means the patient has an increased tendency to form blood clots.

The clots that doctors find with estrogen therapy are wide-ranging and bad blood clots, too. The clots may show up in people's brains – as you would find in a stroke – or arise around people's hearts – as you find in a heart attack – or elsewhere. Thrombophilia. Even as far back as 1984, medical doctors were considering oral contraception a prominent "suspect" when patients emerged with thrombophilia.[18]

Non-thrombophilia clotting issues have been noted regarding oral contraception containing estrogenic EE2 as well. Specifically, I'm referring to conditions with outlandish names like "thrombotic thrombocytopenic purpura" [19] – which means blood clots that are found in tiny blood vessels.

And we're just getting started with the strange names. Using clinical trial research from the oral contraception drug Yaz®, you can find that the "Physician Label" from the Yaz® contraception drug includes "thrombophlebitis" – vein inflammation – "arterial thromboembolisms" – artery clots – and more. These are all listed as "Adverse Reactions" to taking the Yaz® drug and are reactions that oral contraception users are frequently not specifically told. An analogous chart was shown near the end of Chapter 3 for Alesse®.

From that chart, the Yaz® Adverse Reactions list also includes "pulmonary embolisms" – where the arteries in the lung become blocked by a blood clot – and "myocardial infarctions" – a medical way of saying "heart attacks" – and even "cerebral hemorrhages" – an emergency condition arising from bleeding inside the brain. Oh, and Yaz® includes "cerebral thrombosis" as an Adverse Reaction – a related problem regarding blood clots found within the brain.

Now it might seem like I'm picking on Yaz® specifically. And I am. But you should also be aware that the other EE2 oral contraception drugs include nearly identical "blood clot" warnings. This includes Alesse®, Loestrin®, Ortho-Cyclen®, Kariva®, Cyclessa®, Ortho-Novum®, and many others. You can see for yourself if you're really that interested. I posted the actual "Physician Labels" for these drugs on my website.[20]

This is all very serious. In fact, women's use of contraception has even led to questions and issues regarding blood donations[21] but let's move on to other estrogenics.

Now, considering the connection between estrogenics and weight gains as well as the connection between EE2 contraceptives and various blood clotting issues, you would think hundreds or maybe thousands of studies would be done on IRS 10 List estrogenics to investigate clotting or thrombosis. This is low-hanging scientific fruit.

Surprisingly, however, the fruit has not been picked. Nothing that I could find has even been done on big-time estrogenics like ZEA, APEs, or even atrazine regarding blood clotting problems.

You will further find the lack of research in this area appalling once you hear this: an observation in 2007 was made by several medical doctors from 3 different countries – Belgium, Australia, and the USA. These professional doctors found that IV (intravenous) insertions into *children* were resulting in deep vein thromboses.[22] Blood clots. In kids. What did the IV injection material have in common? The tubing was made with phthalates. The doctors saw this as a "major concern" jeopardizing the health of all children.

How many follow up studies were done? Just one. From Germany and also in 2007. It's called "Particle release from infusion equipment: etiology of acute venous thromboses".

The finding from that study was not good news. But just *one* study? How many people have an IV put into their arm at one time or other? And, undoubtedly, the problem is compounded when those same kids get blood that is full of birth control estrogenic, or they are on various forms of birth control, on top of the plastic tubing estrogenics.

One final study I want you to be aware of is called "phytoestrogens as a *risk factor* for cerebral sinus thrombosis."[23] It centers around soy isoflavones and brain blot clots that arise from "alternative medicine treatments" using soy isoflavones.

Just please say "no" if your alternative doc tells you to go on soy as a treatment for anything. "No" is the correct response. "No". Let's shift focus to cancer.

Estrogenics and Cancer

The cosmos of cancer is messy.

Yes: incredible advances have been made in cancer research, especially in the area of antibodies and personalized treatment approaches. Surgeries, too.

In fact, I always find myself telling people with cancer about antibodies against various forms of cancer. Some of these antibodies are amazing.

But there is also misplaced energy, misplaced money, and misplaced sensationalism within cancer research.

For example, each year for the past 5 years, the US government has spent around 5 billion dollars funding "cancer research". I surround this phrase with quotes because universities skim over half of this grant money for "overhead". So, if I was awarded a 1-million-dollar grant at a University, my lab might see about half-a-mill for actual research and salary payments. But that's only the beginning.

When so much money is at stake, both for universities and scientists, there are many billions of reasons why everything around us seems to somehow increase our odds of getting cancer. The money can't be extracted without a justifiable "need" – written in the form of a grant to a disinterested committee, as we discussed earlier. So "needs" are found. Everywhere.

This all sounds harsh but it is the way the current system operates. And make no mistake: today's scientists must go to great lengths to "justify" their work and "market" their findings. They need to emphasize the importance of their work or they get sent home.

Furthermore, the system promotes playing-it-safe and doing the same, tired, experiments everybody else is doing. Hedging bets and then sensationalizing the mundane findings is, unfortunately, the secure career path in science today. And, that, my friend, is one of the reasons why I am personally not out on that academic "ball field", playing hard and wearing my team's cap, cleats, and tight pants. It's too bad, too, because I do look amazing in tight pants.

Next, there is the double-dipping. As I indicated above, a lot of government "research money" – cancer or otherwise – is actually detouring the research and ending up in university bank accounts. Strangely, much of the government research money also goes back to the government in some form or other.

For instance, the average cost to bring a drug to market is supposedly over \$2.5 billion.[24] This is inflated for commercial reasons according to Marcia Angell,[25] but still: costs are exorbitant. And I have friends in biotech who have informed me that they literally have filled *entire* semi-trucks with paperwork for a single FDA "New Drug Application". Today of course, the drug companies crash computer servers rather than waste truckloads of paper but it's still a dinosaur system. Everybody is trying to avoid getting sued in every direction while truly creative research is stagnating.

But at least non-profit cancer research in America is a well-oiled machine, right? All those armies of people walking-for-the-cure?

Well, as the current President of a medical non-profit, it irritates me to no end that dozens of "cancer research" charities are literally spending less than 5% of their budgets on actual cancer research. Most of their money goes to the executives for salary or funding "solicitation campaigns" rather than funding cancer research.

To ensure that you are not – ironically – tempted to think I am sensationalizing the state of non-profit cancer research, allow me to indulge in some examples.

The "Cancer Fund of America" raised a total of \$86.8 million via solicitors over 10 years and paid their solicitors \$75.4 million. They ended up giving exactly 1.0% to actual cancer research.[26] Oops.

Same story with the "Breast Cancer Relief Foundation": 2.2% of the $63.9 million they raised went to actual cancer research. Your local annual "walk for cancer awareness" could probably be named the annual "walk to fund more solicitation and raise executive salaries". Not good. At least they have incredible mission statements, so there's that. And they are politically correct (PC) to support...

To go one step deeper, here is a listing, from this CNN article reference[26] of a few non-profits that made over 1 million dollars and paid less than 5% of that to cancer research: the "Children's Cancer Recovery Foundation", 0.7%; the "Children's Cancer Fund of America", 4.6%; "Project Cure", 0.0%; the "Woman to Woman Breast Cancer Foundation", 0.3%; the "National Cancer Coalition", 1.3%; and, finally, the "Hope Cancer Fund", 0.5%.

Did you notice the 0.0%? It's cringeworthy. Of course, many other non-science or non-cancer non-profits do this same thing and this is one of many reasons you might consider preferentially supporting *local* work. When things are local, you can support people you know personally. This is where reputation matters more than government approval, which is a good thing. This is also why "the best government is the smallest possible form of government" – aka, "subsidiarity" – can be seen as the smartest solution to such problems.

Ok. So, the cancer field is a mess, rife with waste and exaggeration. You get it. How do you find the reliable research? How do you find what really causes cancer?

Well, as always, you start by looking at the big-picture. You look for multiple research studies that verify the same thing using different experiments and different approaches. Estrogenics are perfect for this type of verification because there are so many estrogenics and the estrogenics often act in a similar way. Think of the collective nature of *The 7 Deadly Things*.

Next, you have to assess the quality of each study. This is where professional background and reliable references are imperative. I cannot stress good references enough. I read online articles all the time that are completely devoid of references. Furthermore, at ridiculously high doses, nearly anything can cause cancer, so doses especially matter in cancer studies.

Is the research done in animals or humans or cells growing in dishes? Is there potential for spin? These factors are important to consider.

Finally, understanding the biology and the disease matters. The better you comprehend the disease and the context, the more you can judge the implications. Hopefully, and as always, I can save you the time and energy by highlighting the most important "estrogenics + cancer" research.

The 7 Deadly Things
#6. Cancer

So, like we did for hormones and receptors, let's review what cancer is, briefly. Then we'll look at estrogenic impact.

All types of cancers – lung cancer, breast cancer, etc. – arise because DNA (or epiDNA but let's not go there yet) ends up with a critical mutation. We're not talking about just any mutation, we're talking about something "critical". To give rise to cancer, the mutation must be on a DNA gene involved in cell growth, cell multiplication, or cell spreading (scientists call these actions "proliferations, propagations, and metastases").

And it generally isn't just one mutation. A study of 12 tumor types found that an average of 2-6 mutations in "critical" genes gave rise to those tumors. That's 2-6 mutations in genes involved in cell growth, multiplication, and spreading.[27]

In your body, many of your more "exposed" cells – like your skin cells, blood vessel cells, or intestine cells – acquire mutations all the time.

We all have over 3 *billion* base pairs of DNA, so it still generally takes a long time to "hit" one of our important genes involved in cell growth, proliferation, and propagation. Even exposed cells take a long time to acquire such mutations. In fact, colon cancer requires – on average – over 11,000 mutations in the DNA before a random "hit" is made in a gene involved in cell growth, multiplication, and spreading that leads to cancer.[28]

The key word here is "random". In other words, 11,000 random mutations give rise to mutations in "critical" DNA areas purely by chance.

So, the deeper point I'm making is that cancer is a numbers game. You "increase your odds" for cancer by eating and drinking estrogenics. Like a "devil's lottery" where lottery tickets are DNA mutations.

And after you get those mutations, the messed-up cells, the cancerous cells, still need to survive. You may remember how I placed emphasis at the beginning of the chapter on the relationship between the immune system and cancer? Well, if your immune system detects a strange cancer, it can beneficially chew it up or eat that cell and rid your body of it. This is why over a quarter *million* studies have been done on "immune system + cancer". It's a hotbed of research.

Because of this relationship between our innate immunity and cancer, chemicals that cause immune system damage might be predicted to also cause cancer.

Let's look at the scientific proof revealing that estrogenics are involved.

First, estrogen works by binding an estrogen receptor inside your cells. This is step one. It is just like connecting two puzzle pieces. Then these two connected puzzle pieces – estrogen plus receptor – bind directly to DNA. Binding DNA is step two.

Knowing this information – as a scientist – leads me to basically *expect* that estrogen cause tumors when somebody tampers with estrogen levels. Even beyond the immune system red flags. The estrogen, or estrogenics, act *directly* on DNA when estrogen is bound to a receptor, directly on the site where cancer originates. This has the potential to lead to all sorts of DNA problems.

Sure enough, multiple estrogen "replacement therapy" studies – attempting to benefit older women – have been halted prematurely. Why stop an expensive study early? Because the rate of breast cancers in the estrogen-treated women started to rise too high.[29] Many forms of breast cancer have long been known to link to estrogens and estrogen receptors.

I mentioned rising rates of breast cancer in this book's *Introduction* but I want to add to that. The global increase in breast cancer between

1980 to 2010 was 256%. The Philippines saw the biggest rise in those same years. Rates increased 589% in the Phillipines.[30]

As you might guess, you find similar risks with oral contraception and cancer. First, however, I want to go over the *positive* benefits of oral contraception. I frequently hear about these oral contraception "benefits" and they involve cancer.

The benefit involves decreasing your risk for ovarian cancer.

On the one hand, companies selling contraception want everyone to be aware that oral contraception *decreases* risk for ovarian cancer. I find this intriguing. This is one of very few positive aspects of EE2 – the active ingredient in birth control – so let's check it out.

Unfortunately, this "decreased risk for ovarian cancer" is truly minimal. In a 2013 study (meta-analysis) of 6,476 research papers, oral contraception use correlated to approximately a 0.5% lifetime reduction in ovarian cancer incidence with *no observed reductions in mortality*.[31] Half a percent reduction. Now that's pretty tiny – let's be honest. Especially with no changes in the death rates.

Yet people in my profession talk about this contraception "benefit" like it will guarantee women will never get ovarian cancer if they are frequent EE2 pill poppers.

From what I've heard from women, this "decreased risk of cancer" takes center stage for many medical doctors, as they prescribe these drugs. They are sure to talk about this benefit.

This is because the companies – behind the scenes – make sure doctors regularly hear about this "decreased risk". It's at the front of their minds. And there's nothing illegal about advertising true health benefits. Of course, companies selling birth control also hope word doesn't get out how tiny the benefit truly is. Or how massive the adverse effects list is.

Meanwhile, the *serious* adverse effects are generally underplayed. If you doubt this, ask someone who has been prescribed oral contraception – what "adverse effects" were you informed about? Were you given a full printed list? As I noted before, the "Physician Labels" are linked to my own website[20] so you can see the side-effect list for yourself. The list is long. Ultimately, putting this list in the shadows for lay people by using long-names and 100's of pages of unimportant information stems from corporate interest and influence. I'm not blaming the medical docs, here

– although the best ones are telling people about oral contraception problems and they're aware that benefits are truly minimal – but I would like to see improvements in simplicity and lay-person accessibility.

Furthermore, regarding the published "benefit" analysis ("no reduction in mortality") from the 6,476 papers, I found it comical that there was a reproving letter written to the editor by some medical docs. Presumably, they were involved in marketing oral contraception in some way but who knows. This letter to the editor reads: "we believe that further studies still are required [before it can be said that oral contraception does not reduce ovarian cancer mortality]".[32] More studies beyond 6,476? Seriously people?

Let's get into estrogenic risks regarding cancer by the numbers. Oral contraceptives increase risk for breast cancer [33], various liver tumors,[34,35] and cervical cancer[36] but what are the numbers here?

For brevity, let's take breast cancer and the increased risk there. Unlike the tiny positive benefits we saw regarding ovarian cancer, we find legitimate increased risk numbers for breast cancer. The numbers aren't huge but they are more than 0.5%. Read the oral contraceptive pill Alesse® (EE2 + levonorgestrel) manufacture's label:

> The risk of having breast cancer diagnosed may be **slightly increased** among current and recent users of combination oral contraceptives. **However**, this excess risk **appears to decrease over time after** combination oral contraceptive **discontinuation and by 10 years after cessation** the increased risk disappears. Some studies report an increased risk with duration of use while other studies do not and no consistent relationships have been found with dose or type of steroid. Some studies have reported a small increase in risk for women who first use combination oral contraceptives at a younger age. **Most studies** show a similar **pattern of risk** with combination oral contraceptive use regardless of a woman's reproductive history or her family breast cancer history.

Actually, not too bad. And all the other EE2 containing contraceptive drugs have nearly the exact same caution – basically verbatim. Breast cancer risk is "slightly increased" and no numbers are offered.

Sleuthing into this, I am relieved to say that it appears they are being honest. One scientific study I found looked at the medical charts of over 100,000 women and found up to about 3% increased risk of breast cancer among oral contraception users.[33] Not huge numbers but more than 0.5 in 100.

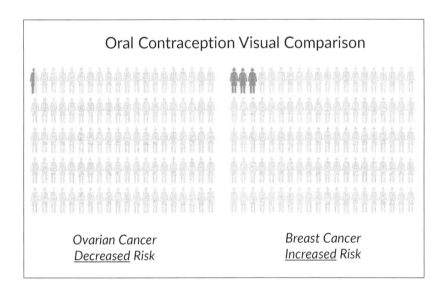

Oral Contraception Visual Comparison

Ovarian Cancer
Decreased Risk

Breast Cancer
Increased Risk

Importantly, the increased cancer risks can widely vary depending on other factors like race (genetic background), or diet, or health, or how many other estrogenics you are consuming. Keep in mind, most people are exposed to plenty of other IRS 10 estrogenics. Factors like these can confuse emerging studies. And, overall, breast cancer rates are rising meteorically alongside EE2 increases, which is disturbing.

Something that also needs to be said is that teenagers taking oral contraception and EE2 are especially vulnerable to breast cancer risks and hormone imbalances. Unnatural hormone alterations in teens is always a different discussion. Just like teen athletes taking steroids.

One additional thing all the drug companies say – undoubtedly, they need to state this by law – is that "oral contraceptive should not be used in women with a known or suspected carcinoma of the breast or personal history of breast cancer" (again, this was taken directly from Alessa's® drug sheet). Risky stuff, considering *anyone* might have undiagnosed early stage breast cancer. Cancer begins at the level of a single cell.

Let's move on to other estrogenics, starting with grains. Most people eat grains.

Comparing two regions in Africa – one with grain that had consistently higher levels of estrogenic ZEA from fungus and one with lower ZEA – researchers found that people had "considerably higher" levels of esophageal cancer from the group eating higher ZEA amounts.[37] A study of Chinese people observed basically the exact same problem. Esophageal cancer was up in heavily-exposed Chinese ZEA groups.[38]

In a different study about ZEA from another African country, Tunisia, researchers also found a potential role for ZEA in humans developing breast cancer.[39]

An added issue for grains is that they also contain atrazine. Think about it: most times, atrazine and ZEA provide a double-estrogenic ambush. Add EE2 in there and we're really upping our cancer risks.

Uncharacteristically, on the topic of cancer, however, atrazine appears "innocent". It may cause reproductive problems, feminization, hernias, and brain development problems, but probably not cancers.

From what I read, most studies are in agreement with this statement from the *Journal of Environmental Science and Health*: "[Atrazine's] potential impact on humans appears to be primarily on reproduction and development and is not related to carcinogenesis."[40] That's good.

One cautionary reminder, though, is that atrazine *is* a mega money-maker. Recall: Syngenta® is one of the world's largest crop-chemical producers, if not the largest, and they have scientists on staff like Dr. Charles Breckenridge publishing positive papers eulogizing atrazine.

I especially feel a spasm of concern when I read a statement like this in a professional science journal: "Atrazine is *possibly* carcinogenic although discrepant results have been reported."[41] Discrepant results? Researchers here found that atrazine promotes prostate cancer cell proliferation. Meanwhile, studies in humans regarding atrazine are difficult because basically *everyone* is exposed so, yes, discrepant results are bound to exist.

Continuing to follow the money down the IRS 10 List, what about soy?

Well, like atrazine, soy appears to have a dualistic role in breast cancer. A few scientific reviews, however, suggest that soy *decreases* breast cancer and prostate cancer.[42,43] Then again, a 2016 study published in a journal called *Nutrition and Cancer* says: "several recent reports challenged the health benefits of soy isoflavones and associated them with *breast cancer promotion*."[44] You find these conflicts a lot when money is involved in science. Such a mess.

Let's take a break from "food" for a minute and talk sunscreen and cancer. We'll revisit the topic of "consumables" soon with Red No. 40 and plastics.

Personally, I have a strong dependency on sunscreen. I literally *need* it for long fishing trips. Yet I cringe when parents are lathering up their kids or themselves just to go outside to take out the trash.

BP (benzophenone) from sunscreen is featured in a number of cancer studies. BP has been shown to promote ovarian cancer,[45] prostate cancer (the researchers in this study also included estrogenic triclosan and found it, too, promoted prostate cancer),[46] breast cancer,[47] and just general cancer metastasis (spreading).[47,48]

That's an ironically large number of cancers we increase to try to prevent skin cancer. And this is just from the BP in the sunscreen. We haven't considered the fragrance or the 4-MBC also present in the same products.

Stress from the sun actually brings up another critically important point.

Remember how cells need mutations in "critical" DNA genes in order to become cancerous? How mutations need to occur in genes involved in cell growth, proliferation, and propagation? Well, frequently, when cells – like, say, your skin cells – accumulate a lot of mutations and are "stressed out", those cells simply die. And, P.S., this is a good thing.

For instance, let's say some of your skin cells are blasted by a bit of sunshine and they die. Not too many but some. This is good. The reason this is a *good* is because if those same cells lived too long, they would be more likely to become cancerous. Yes – a reasonable amount of sunshine is good. Who would have thought?

This is *also* why the newest research – from 2015 – is finding that "antioxidants" actually *promote* cancer.[49] You've been told the opposite. I know. However, even as far back as the mid 90's, scientists were starting to see that antioxidants can promote cancer. Wait. What?!

Yes. The 1994 antioxidant study was "perplexing" at the time. Researchers found that mega-doses of antioxidant beta carotene actually *increased* lung cancer in smokers by 18% and antioxidant vitamin A *increased* lung cancer in smokers by 28%.[50] Smokers, remember, are stressing out lung cells and, therefore, their lung cells are more frequently developing mutations and/or dying. This study was called the "Vitamin A, Beta Carotene Cancer *Prevention* Study Group". Oops, no prevention here.

Now think about this for a second: if you are putting cells that ought to be dying on "life-support" – i.e. antioxidants – and then those cells live and continue to accumulate more mutations, you are more likely to end up with cancer. Your antioxidant-treated cells are more likely to become cancerous from all those additional mutations. The extra mutations occur during their prolonged lifespan.

Cell death is normal and cells are constantly being replaced so don't get all emotional on me, here. In essence, too much sunscreen probably increases your odds of *getting* cancer by simply "overprotecting" your skin cells, during short exposures to sunlight. And then, to make matters much worse, the BP and 4-MBC (4-methylbenzylidene camphor) can directly cause cancers because they are estrogenic.

So back to 4-MBC, as promised.

Besides BP, the other sunscreen estrogenic from the IRS 10 list is 4-MBC. Research in 2005 found that "4-MBC accelerates cell proliferation in estrogen-dependent human breast cancer cells".[51] Cell proliferation, incidentally, occurs when cells are growing and dividing and increasing in population. In the context of cancer, that's bad.

These scientists also made the argument that I've been making throughout this book: 4-MBC is estrogenic and therefore it potentially stimulates any and all dysfunctions that other estrogenics may cause. It reminds me of a college graduation ceremony honorary degree award.

The ceremony statement goes something like: "By the authority vested in me, I admit you to the rank of Doctor of Laws, and grant to you *all the rights and privileges therein*." By simply being estrogenic, a substance is often granted all the "rights and privileges therein", *The 7 Deadly Things*. That is *The Estrogenic Effects Principle*:

3.

The Estrogenic Effects Principle: *If an item is estrogenic, it is likely to cause health problems that match other estrogenic items.*

So, let's again get back to the food. Remember how estrogenic Red No. 3 was partially banned in the US? Not in food but cosmetic products? Because of this bad press, most companies switched over from Red No. 3 to similarly estrogenic Red No. 40.

Unfortunately, even during the 1980's, researchers began to show "acceleration of tumors" from Red No. 40.[52] However, despite this fact, not many studies have been done on Red No. 40 in general or specifically with Red No. 40 and cancers. What I can tell you is that I'm not going to wait for the negative studies to come out to motivate me to stop drinking sports drinks with Red No. 40.

Unlike Red No. 40, thankfully, thorough research *has* been done on parabens, phthalates, and BPA. These are all definitely implicated in cancer formation. Over 100 studies for parabens, 500 for phthalates, and about 700 for BPA. And while a detailed analysis of +1,000 cancer studies would bore us all to tears – myself included – let's discuss the major types of cancer these 3 IRS 10 estrogenics play a role in and then close with APEs.

Parabens have been shown to clearly drive development of human breast cancer. Many studies verify this.[53,54] Since breast cancer is the dominant concern from most estrogenics, this is important. Paraben fits the overall pattern. Recent studies (2015) are further finding parabens in ovary tumors – present in the actual tumor itself[55] – which makes me wonder how many other tumor types will be found containing high levels of parabens in the near future.

And, even though I am starting to feel like I am a song on "repeat", phthalates are implicated in breast cancer,[56] but it doesn't stop there. Phthalates are also incriminated in leiomyomas – muscle tumors usually found in the uterus, intestines, or esophagus.[54] And the carcinogenic properties occur because phthalates "deregulate cell proliferation" or, to put this in plain English, phthalates cause cells to grow and divide out of control.[57]

BPA, too, increases breast cancers.

What is scary with BPA, however, is that cancer risk continues long after the BPA exposures. For example, in studies of fetuses exposed in the womb to BPA, offspring had an increased propensity to develop breast cancer *during adulthood*.[58]

But nobody is exposed to BPA, right? All our water bottles are full of phthalates but at least they are "BPA-Free", yes? Well, not exactly. And don't forget about this virtually identical BPS plastic.

In a 2004 study of over 2,500 children around the age of 6, urine samples were collected. From these samples, *93%* were positive for BPA.[59] In other words, as those children become adults, they are still more likely to develop breast cancer from that early BPA exposure.

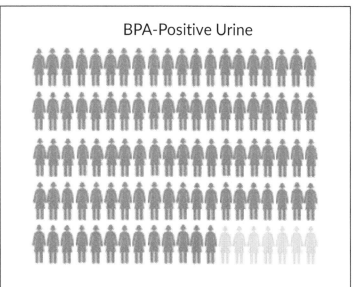

BPA-Positive Urine

BPA-positive urine was found in 93% of kids. Breast cancer risks from childhood BPA exposure <u>continue</u> into adulthood.

A final industrial ingredient we need to mention are the APEs (alkylphenols). Keep in mind the accumulation of APEs in our bodies powerfully impacts the immune system, an important system in our body for preventing cancer.

A number of studies find that APEs exert "estrogen-like" activity on breast cancer cells.[60] This is a serious issue for women.

A serious issue for men, too. Men are also at risk of developing breast cancer from estrogenics. Breast cancer prevalence is not high in men but it is rising.[61]

For men aged 15 to 45 years, the *leading* cause of cancer – from "industrialized" countries, anyway – is testicular cancer.[62] And estrogenics are also major contributors to this type of cancer. "APEs", says the same research study as cited above, "trigger testicular cancer cell proliferation *in vitro* and *in vivo*."[62]

Now, *in vitro* literally means outside the body – like experiments that test cells growing in dishes – and *in vivo* simply means "inside the body". So, basically, all forms of testing show APEs trigger testicular cancer.

The study I just referenced also discovered an even more alarming effect: APEs altered "germ cell" DNA – the DNA we pass on to our children. We see this with other estrogenics and cancer. Let's shift to the last section of this book to discuss that vital issue.

PART

3

TODAY AND TOMORROW

CHAPTER 8

"Passing On"
Cancer and Obesity

What the Heck is Epigenetics?

"WE ARE ALL GOING. IT'S God's way. His will be done, not ours."

These are the final deathbed words spoken by the 25th President of the United States, William McKinley. They were uttered just as McKinley died by the bullet of an assassin. Honorable words to leave behind.

What will your legacy be and how long will it endure? What actions in your life come to mind when you think of your legacy?

Based on McKinley's life's actions, his legacy was that of an outdoorsman, an honorable man, and an American president. He was famously idolized by gold prospectors of his day, in the early 1900's, because he championed the gold standard, for example, to protect against arbitrary currency manipulation and inflation. As gold prospectors tamed some of that rugged Alaskan tundra, therefore, they named the highest peak in America after McKinley. That's 20,000 feet of legacy.

Recently, however, things have changed. In the throes of a power-struggle for greater PC, an executive order officially changed the name of Mount McKinley. It must now legally be called "Denali". Ironically, McKinley was assassinated by an anarchist who actually believed in this sort of thing: executive operations and rapid eradication of historical institution. A different sort of legacy.

From Homer, through Moose Pass, back up to Anchorage, past Mount McKinley to Fairbanks, and back down the oil-pipeline to Valdez, Allison and I trekked and toured our way through a grand 14-day honeymoon in Alaska. There, we fished for halibut and salmon, hiked on baby blue glaciers, and feasted on reindeer sausage. We learned some history and spoke to many interesting characters – wolf trappers, arctic char fisherman, truckers from the town of Deadhorse – and we even visited a musk oxen farm.

Overall, we had a splendid honeymoon in the great outdoors of Alaska, but – as much as I would have liked – we certainly didn't rough it. Today, in fact, we joke that we went on a Best Western Tour of Alaska because we stayed at some Best Western nearly every night...the nicest hotel you can find in most of remote Alaska.

Following our trip to Alaska, Allison and I took a 180-degree turn back to Boston. I began my Ph.D. studies and went from iced mountains to iced coffee, clarion rivers to the Charles River, and from hiking to sitting. And, as much as I enjoyed science and lab sleuthing, the country-city contrast was a stone-cold sacrifice for me.

In Boston, I began to live and witness a glaring reality: people living in cities – myself included – were much less healthy in general. Inner city dwellers are more inflicted by infertility, more depressed, more.... well, insert any of The 7 Deadly Things here.

I believe urbanite health declines are unfoundedly due, in part, to greater estrogenic exposures compared to people living in rural America. I'm specifically referring, of course, to the rural America that isn't decimated by industrial chemical spraying and the like; an important clarification most researchers would overlook.

It's worth noting, for example, that around the time of this New England move, I developed allergies for the first time in my life. My testosterone also declined. In general, I fought desperately to find the health I had once had growing up in small town Minnesota. My own health seemed to be slowly collapsing like a car in the jaws of a trash compactor. And it would take a final trip to Florida to inspire yet another reawakening....and a tarpon fishing success story.

But what I've come to learn is that legacy goes beyond our words and actions. Today, our chemical exposures impact our future generations or lack thereof.

The problems we've looked at thus far arising from artificial estrogen exposures, aside from the III Reproductive System (IRS) 10 List Unique Features, have included:

- Fat cell growth and fat storage of estrogenics
- Depression
- Hormonal imbalances
- Immune system dysfunctions
- Various blood clotting complications
- Certain types of cancer

In essence, we have looked at 6 headliner issues. For the last of *The 7 Deadly Things*, let's talk reproductive infertility. This is the most ominous concern because it is truly the most lasting. Infertility is included in *Part 3* of this book because of its inherent connection to our legacy.

The infertility begins in first-generation exposures. You and I. These are significant depending on exposure durations and levels, as you'll see.

Second-generation infertility levels, however, are higher. And, as drastic as it sounds, third-generation infertility levels are even higher. At least according to the newest research. This generational infertility issue is called "*trans*generational" infertility, as I mentioned in Chapter 1. "*Trans*" means "across" in Latin. In essence, infertility is being passed across generations on to our children via epigenetic mechanisms.

Epigenetics! If you know what this term means, kudos. Epigenetic research will only grow and will undoubtedly become one of the largest fields in future science and personalized medicine – much larger than the DNA field. But many people haven't even heard the term, yet.

In fact, because of my forecast about the prominent future of epigenetics, I personally have considered starting an epigenetic sequencing company. The notion came to me when I contacted an existing company about having my "epi-genome" sequenced and they wanted $18,000. Just for me. Per our conversation, the company representative basically told me that their main customer is academic scientists. Government funds, in other words.

I think it would be incredible to have an epigenetic sequencing "product" that would cost under $100. This product would identify the epigenetic status of your most important "epi fingerprint": the epi-genes that are best understood in science today. Since epigenetic "marks" can change, too, it is more than a one-time customer service. You could track diet changes and other health concerns optimally.

Anyway, I've casually dropped the words "fingerprint", "marks", and "epi-genes". These will become more common terms in the future. What do they mean?

Put simply, epigenetics is the "study of marks that are made to your DNA". So, an "epi-gene" is like one, single, mark. It is one imprint on your DNA. Since this might still be confusing, here is an analogy I developed to help explain this.

In music, you have black dots – notes – written on lines called a staff. You might find just one string of notes indicating to a musician to play "Mary had a Little Lamb" or some other song. Don't overthink this now, just imagine a few black dots on a staff. One black dot, then another dot, then another dot. All dots representing letter notes and a simple song.

In this analogy, the simple song is your DNA. You can easily pass this simple sheet music to somebody else and – easy! – they can play or sing "Mary had a Little Lamb". They just need to follow the notes, like our bodies follow our DNA code and make proteins.

A more advanced musician would not just play one note at a time, however. They might play chords, or multiple notes played together that sound pleasing. Right? The main melody of "Mary had a Little Lamb" is still there – the DNA – but now additional "notes" are added on top of the main notes. That is epigenetics. "Epi" means "on top of" in Greek. It is all about marks that are installed "on top of" the main string of DNA code.

Alternatively, marks can be made to the "histone" – proteins wrapped around the DNA – but we'll keep it simple and think only about DNA.

These epigenetic DNA marks are simple molecule groups like methylations – similar to methane gas – or acetylations – similar to acetylene gas – and the list of chemical items that can make these marks could go on and on.

DNA Building Block

Epigenetic marks like this one can be passed to future generations.

Currently, we best understand methylations in epigenetic research. This is because methylations can be readily sequenced using robotics and computers. It might cost a crippling $18,000 but at least you can already sequence your entire epi-genome.

Obesity and Cancer Across Generations

Ok, so musical notes on top of the main melody notes are like epigenetics. The marks on top of DNA. And we all have epigenetic marks in totally unique sequences. That's why I like to think of these marks as "fingerprints". They are all unique. They harbor very powerful information in terms of your health.

But let's shift the discussion back to that new term in scientific research within the last few years. The term is "transgenerational", as in "transgenerational epigenetics". As I said, "trans" simply means "across", so we are literally just talking about epigenetics that are passed across generations. In other words, it's not merely your DNA that is passed along. Your marks on the DNA get bequeathed.

Now let's focus on how artificial estrogenics act to change our epigenetic "fingerprint" in a negative way. Let's investigate how a problematic "fingerprint" on our DNA can be passed along through generations. The science of transgenerational epigenetics is a brand-new concept, but the IRS 10 estrogenics are definitely involved.

First, some history and context. The discovery of inheritable epigenetic traits originates from scientific investigations into an unfortunate historical tragedy. This calamity is known as the "Dutch Famine" and sometimes the "Dutch Hunger Winter". It was a massive famine with more than 4 million people affected. Scientifically, the short duration of this famine was the key.

According to one science paper: "a commonly accepted date of [the Dutch Famine] onset is mid-October **1944**; its end was sudden, when the Allied armies liberated Holland [from Nazi Germany occupation] on May 7, **1945**."[1] Less than one year.

This same research paper, published in 1975, recorded birth weight declines around that time from babies born to famine exposed mothers. Birth weight declines from famine exposed babies were predictably lower – less food, less weight. No surprise there.

The shocker came many years later.

In 1996, it was discovered that birth weight declines had *continued* to occur. Weight declines were discovered in Dutch babies whose *grandmothers* had "suffered acute starvation in mid pregnancy" from the Dutch famine![2] This caused science to sit-up and listen. This same 1996 paper even included the speculation that the insulin-like *growth factor* genes might be involved, since these growth factors are major players in, well, growth.

Fast-forward 10 years later. Researchers, sure enough, found that babies *in the womb* during the Dutch Famine were associated with "lower methylation of the insulin-like growth factor 2 [...] 6 decades later."[3] In other words, the epigenetic "fingerprints" – marks on top of the DNA – were still being altered some 60 years later.

The 1996 article, impressively, was starting to look prophetic: insulin-like growth factor (#2) was at least one of the epigenetic marks altered by the Dutch Famine. Today, it's all just more precisely understood with less speculation.

These "inheritable" epigenetic changes lit a fire under many researchers. Transgenerational changes – epigenetic changes – were an incredible idea and spawned much interest. Scientists promptly found associations in humans between "ancestral food supply with longevity and with cardiovascular and diabetic mortality."[4] They even found that the inverse is true: so called "over-nutrition" can increase propensity toward obesity and metabolic disease in *future generations*.[5] Yes, you heard that correctly. Obesity can be passed on.

We've seen how estrogenics are involved in turning a "fat switch" on in humans but passing obesity on? Through estrogenic exposures?

Yes. A 2016 research paper from the Andrology Journal summarized their newest findings like this:

> We started by exploring how a synthetic estrogen could change development in experimental animals and humans and discovered that many chemicals in the environment are 'estrogenic', we have progressed to uncover unexpected biological activities embodied in various environmental compounds that can alter metabolism and contribute to obesity and diabetes among other outcomes. Some of these changes become part of the epigenome and persist throughout life and indeed into other generations.[6]

Other generations indeed.

Scientists that study animal models are the ones really accelerating these transgenerational discoveries. Most lab animals – grown as "models" of various human diseases – reproduce rapidly. Transgenerational epigenetics, therefore, has been giving rise to literally entire careers' worth of experimental projects for scientists, during our modern epigenetic research boom.

And speaking of animal models, another interesting epigenetic research study amazingly found that "*male* mice with pre-diabetes have abnormal sperm methylation, and *pass on* an increased risk of diabetes to the next *two generations*."[7,8]

This means males are not off the hook for health and reproductive contributions: even *male* diet and lifestyle can alter future generations!

Let's move on to cancer.

Like the newest research on obesity, it's quite remarkable that a disposition toward cancer can be passed down to offspring. This is disturbing. In fact, there are currently about 100 research papers on cancer and transgenerational epigenetics.

"[Our] results," reports one such cancer paper researching generations of mice, "support the hypothesis of an *epigenetic* and/or gene expression-based mechanism for *transgenerational carcinogenesis.*"[9]

They mention epigenetics as supportive but this study does not offer direct proof. Plus they also include other cancer transference options. How else might cancer be passed along to future generations?

Direct DNA damage. Red 40, for example, was found to directly damage DNA in certain experiments.[10] We can find similar evidence with other estrogenics, too. ZEA, for instance, causes "genotoxic activity" meaning ZEA causes a large array of different types of DNA mutations.[11]

But while DNA damage may or may not be inheritable, epigenetic evidence is stronger.

"The liganded *estrogen receptor*," says one key study, "is linked to long-range changes in higher-order chromatic organization and *epigenetic dysregulation in cancer.*"[12] In lay terms, this sentence is saying that estrogenics cause epigenetic changes that can lead to cancer.

In this particular study – surprise, surprise – the transmitted cancer was breast cancer. Breast cancer, as we've seen so many times, is one of the more common cancers collectively associated with the various IRS 10 List estrogenics.

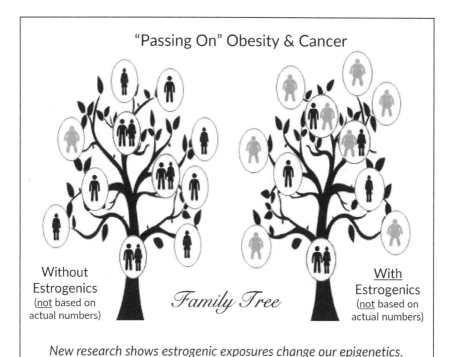

"Passing On" Obesity & Cancer

Without Estrogenics (not based on actual numbers)

Family Tree

With Estrogenics (not based on actual numbers)

New research shows estrogenic exposures change our epigenetics. This results in increased obesity *and* cancer passed to future generations.

Next, here is a quote from another paper that studied DES, the banned estrogenic substance:

> Interestingly, our data suggest that this **increased susceptibility for tumors** [from DES] is **passed on** from the maternal lineage *to subsequent generations* of male and female descendants; the mechanisms involved in these transgenerational events include genetic and **epigenetic** events.[13]

Might DES be causing direct DNA damage? Probably. But epigenetics are more clearly involved.

Finally, both BPA and phthalates have given similar results in cancer studies, revealing long-range inherited changes.[14] BPA and phthalates are causing us to essentially "give" cancer to our kids, or at least increase cancer likelihood in our offspring. Exact numbers and doses, especially in humans, are still being worked out. Just remember that minor doses of hormones can have major impacts.

CHAPTER 9

Defoliating
Your Family Tree

To Infertility and Beyond

IF WEST VIRGINIA IS ALMOST heaven then Montana is heaven outright.

By far the most "estrogenic-free" fish I have ever eaten were fresh-caught in the upper reaches of the Rocky Mountains. I caught those fish with my friend and future brother-in-law Victor, in his home state of Montana. Despite Vic's local knowledge, the fish didn't come easy.

The adventure began with us completing an ultra-marathon car ride. We had been fishing all throughout Wyoming and Montana so you would think we would have adapted to hard travels, but we were far from fresh. Plus, progress was slow. Long after we exited the highway, we found ourselves creeping down gravelly mountain roads in an inadequate rental car. The sun shone bright but phone and radio signals went dark.

The good news was that Victor knew the area and exuded confidence that we would have success. In fact, he was so confident in the fishing and I in him, we soon discovered that we hadn't remembered to pack any food.

After narrowly slithering by some cliffs, I parked the car on Victor's command. We looked at some grizzly bear sign, looked over our shoulders, and began hiking to this secret mountain lake.

Vic, at that time, had just taken over the Ave Maria Fishing Club Presidency. He was still in college but this trip took place during the first days of summer break so, more than usual, we were making a break for it and cramming everything in.

Soon after we began hiking, the terrain rapidly intensified. Woodland mountain slopes became jagged, loose-shale crags. It was "better than a good day in the office", we both agreed, but then we had to stop talking to bite our fishing pole handles with our front teeth. Both hands had been conscripted to climb the loose rocks.

Despite all hardships, we trundled on, bent on finding this secret lake and a fish called grayling. Sharp rocks, dislodged by our slipping feet, clattered down the mountainside for unnervingly long distances.

We trekked this way because arctic grayling are unique. These fish require icy-cold water and die if the water gets too warm. This means they either live closer to the geographic poles or they live at elevations closer to heaven. We had chosen to pursue them in heaven.

After a few hours of hiking, we finally began cresting a peak. The suspense revived our spirits, and then, even more, the sight of a beautiful lake. It was clean and clear to about 30 feet deep. To our dismay, however, there was still quite a bit of ice on the lake.

"Too bad", I announced through the thin mountain air, "this may not work".

"This will work fine," responded Vic, "watch".

What happened next was comical: Victor started casting out his line and landing his fishing lure on the smooth surface of the melting ice. He then bounced the lure across the ice until it fell with a little "plunk" into an open water hole, his target all along.

After the lure sunk in the hole, Vic would let out line. Next, he would jig the lure up and down. It was a technique worth imitating. The grayling were hungry and immediately bit.

I scrambled to prepare my rod.

Besides the unexpected ice, packing no food was a temporary cause of concern. The concern dissipated because we caught a mess of grayling, made a fire directly on the rocky shoreline, and cooked the fish on sharpened aspen sticks. It was an idyllic scene, pure and simple.

As a contrast, we had also fished in other streams throughout Montana earlier in the week. Victor knew the best places and we had caught fish. It was noble country but not as idyllic as the mountain top. In fact, one of the most successful trout streams we visited harbored a shameful "secret" to expert fishermen – the stream was heavily stocked by nearby fish hatcheries. In other words, we were basically just catching farm-raised fish.

This is ludicrous, if you think about it.

All across America, fish are being re-stocked into lakes and rivers via hatcheries. Professional fish breeders run full-time operations raising millions of fish in cramped tanks. They feed these fish corn pellets, similar to most of America's standard diet, and then these fish breeders truck the corn-fed fish to lakes and streams. And we wonder why our omega fats are imbalanced?

When you visit fish hatcheries, you can often actually buy a handful of fish-food pellets for a quarter and throw them to the fish. The pellets come out of old-fashioned vending machines that were originally designed for hard-candies and it's actually quite fun. I visit hatcheries all across the US – from Oregon to Minnesota to Connecticut – and I bring my kids. Seeing the great white sturgeon of Oregon is especially worthwhile, if you ever have the chance.

As we have seen in Chapter 4, our drinking water has high-levels of IRS 10 List estrogenics. It's worth remembering, however, that as bad as the drinking water is, the "raw" lake water is worse – it's heavily burdened with estrogenics.

Because of these estrogenic loads in our water, fish fertility has been jeopardized. Yet, rather than *solving* the problem, we *treat it*. In this case, we "treat" the issue by stockbreeding fish at high capacity and pumping them full of corn. Sounds familiar, yes? Treating problems rather than solving root causes?

What people don't often realize is that natural fish reproduction has declined to such an extent that most American lakes and rivers *need* an artificial "boost". Many lakes would be entirely *without* game-fish if there were no fish hatchery injections.

To make matters worse, the small-time fishermen are scapegoated – Pop and his daughter are blamed for "keeping too many fish", in attempts to explain fish population declines. Government officials prowl the boat launches wearing clean khakis and looking for low-life "criminals" that retain one extra fish above already meager limits. You have to enforce the law but, meanwhile, estrogenic atrazine is being sprayed just across the road. It is then leaching into the streams that feed into those same fish-depleted lakes.

The 7 Deadly Things
#7. Infertility

Let's close *The 7 Deadly Things* List by putting a magnifying glass on infertility. Specifically, I want to show you proof that infertility can be caused by estrogenics. Direct infertility, in men and women. After that, we'll investigate infertility that is being *passed along* to our kids.

For immediate, first-generation infertility impacts, let's start with a popular Montana renewable resource. Let's look at an important study that performed some experiments on the rainbow trout. I happen to love rainbows... with butter, so this study jumped out at me.

The title of this science paper says it all: "***Short-term** exposure to 17 alpha-ethynylestradiol [EE2] decreases the fertility of sexually maturing male rainbow trout*".[1]

Even at extremely low levels of EE2, researchers observed around a 50% reduction in the number of rainbow trout eggs reaching an early stage of embryonic development. A 50% reduction from "short-term" exposures!

How much EE2 was used? The dose tested in this study was 10 ng/L. So this study was done for a short-term *and* using a very low dose. It's worth remembering that 10 ng/L is a lower dose than Lake Quinsigamond, Massachusetts EE2 levels, a mere 1 hour drive West of Boston [Chapter 4].

Meanwhile, still *lesser* levels of estrogenic EE2, studied in a different research lab, have been found to cause a "complete population failure" in zebrafish.[2]

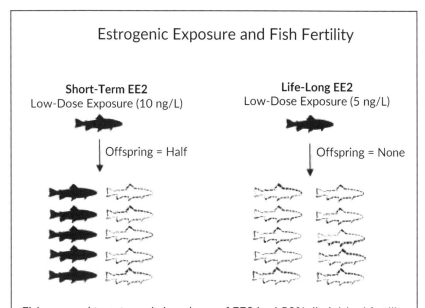

Estrogenic Exposure and Fish Fertility

Short-Term EE2
Low-Dose Exposure (10 ng/L)

Life-Long EE2
Low-Dose Exposure (5 ng/L)

Offspring = Half

Offspring = None

Fish exposed to extremely low doses of EE2 had 50% diminished fertility with short-term exposures and total infertility with life-long exposures.

In the zebrafish study, scientists used *only 5 ng/L of EE2* but exposed the fish for their entire lifespan. This lifetime exposure more accurately mimics what we see in lakes...well, excepting that 5 ng/L is conservatively *low* compared to many American lakes. Plus, these studies oversimplify. The reality is that numerous other estrogenics are *also* present in our lakes. It's not just EE2. Think of the atrazine in Texas, for instance. Or the parabens, the phthalates, the BPA...

Further bad news is that even goldfish – a relatively hardy fish – were discovered to be made infertile at a 5 ng/L life-long estrogenic exposure.[3]

At this point, it's worth mentioning again that fish reside full-time in estrogenic water. Frogs, too. In essence, exposures are frequently more cruel to water dwellers and, therefore, such research *might* be less relevant to humans. But the key word is "might". This is especially true because fish and frog *eggs* sit directly in the estrogenic water and raw eggs are hyper-sensitive to hormone imbalance. Does fish and frog science transfer to mammals?

In short, yes. Mammal fertility is massively impacted by artificial estrogens from the IRS 10 List. But let's not leave the jury out on this one. Let's dry off and have a closer look. Where does the research specifically discuss estrogenic infertility in mammal species?

Well, studies are ubiquitous.

First, it begins with two broad categories of infertility. One is direct sexual organ dysfunction due to estrogenics and the other is embryo or fetal dysfunction or death. Both cause infertility but both are different. The bad news is that you find *both types* of infertility with estrogenics.

For example, ZEA – the mold estrogenic - has been shown to cause total infertility in various animals. In one study, for example, ZEA was given to female swine at high doses.

Before looking at the conclusion of this study, it is worth noting that high chemical doses are often used in animal studies because (1) sometimes we are actually exposed to these exact high doses and (2) because it speeds up research studies. In other words, problems that might take 9 years to become manifest can *sometimes* be pinpointed within 9 months using higher toxin doses.

Anyway, in the female pigs, ZEA was given at doses ranging from 25,000 ng/L to 100,000 ng/L. Next, this laundry-list of problems resulted: "infertility [in some], constant estrus, pseudo pregnancy, diminished fertility [in others], reduced litter size, smaller offspring, malformation, juvenile hyper-estrogenism, and probably fetal resorption."[4]

"Juvenile hyper-estrogenism"?! What does that mean? From the etymology of this medical term, we can probably infer that it means "waaaayyy too much estrogen" in those little piggies, that's for sure.

And if you look closely at that list of problems, you find both types of infertility in the pigs. Sexual organ malformations and various direct fetal problems.

This is not an isolated finding. ZEA has been discovered, for example, to cause "chemical abortions" according to this human "exposure assessment" study.[5] The scientists were investigating ZEA contaminants in "rice, bread, puffed corn snacks, and wheat flour" and refer to ZEA as both a "potent estrogenic" and "primary toxin". This is all extremely strong language for a substance that most American's are consuming on a daily basis with our rice, bread, puffed corn snacks, and wheat flour.

On the subject of grains, atrazine, too, gave rise to abortions in mice babies[6] and so did the soap estrogenic triclosan, according to this study.[7] In fact, the triclosan study also determined triclosan is guilty of causing chemical abortions *in humans*. You read that right: not just mice, humans.

To get straight to it, estrogenics should simply be considered "reproductive toxicants". Scientists already use this new title regarding phthalates[8] and other estrogenics often are classified as "reproductive toxicants" as well. Yes – the same phthalates that are in our "BPA-Free" plastics, the same chemicals you are rubbing on via "fragrance" in your soaps, etc. The classification as "reproductive toxicant" is accurate and used by scientists because it includes both direct reproductive organ dysfunctions and the embryo health problems, or the two major categories of infertility.

Furthermore, these "toxicant" effects extend beyond pregnant females and babies in the womb. Estrogenics are even reproductive toxicants *in men*.

Soy has been shown to "lower semen quality,"[9] for instance. Also, APEs [alkylphenols] and BPs [benzophenones] are associated with overall *human* male infertility.[10]

EE2, too, has even been found to cause decreased sperm counts[11] but men aren't taking EE2 contraceptives, right? Of course we are, it's in the drinking water.

BPA? Yes, BPA has been discovered to "inhibit sperm motility."[12]

Shoot – even dog sperm quality has declined due to "pet food chemicals".[13] Moldy grains are undoubtedly partly to blame in the dog foods, along with atrazine content and even some artificial red food coloring, if your dog is "lucky" and has food that "looks like" salmon.

To sum it up, fertility is clearly at risk where estrogenic burdens are high or where estrogenic burdens are sustained. My fertility is at risk and so is your fertility. So is your children's fertility.

Because of the immensity of this problem, in fact, some scientists are even suggesting we start being safe rather than sorry. Or before rare animal species are all extinct. Like the polar bear problems we looked at earlier.

One scientific review says, in essence, that (1) various fish, rodents, and mammals have *decreased fertility* due to estrogenic exposures, (2) *humans are similar* in terms of reproductive systems and comparable embryonic formation-stages [compared to these "model-animals"] and, therefore, (3) *humans should be concerned* about estrogenic infertility *even where direct research has not yet been performed.*[14] Based on the actual research and parallels between animal studies and human studies in the field of estrogenics, I agree with this more cautious approach. Estrogenic = bad and we should start admitting it openly.

Also, keep in mind that human infertility is particularly difficult to study. The time frame and questions of ethics come to mind, for instance. Some issues are hard to prove and, all too frequently, attempts are not even being made. Clearly, it would be unethical to dose people with estrogenics in order to find a dose that results in total sterility. And many estrogenic damages take years or even generations to sink in, as you will see shortly. This reflects findings we looked at earlier regarding immune system reprogramming. Estrogenics often lead to long-term or festering damages. I recommend you err on the safe side.

Estrogenics to Extinction

While the newest obesity and newest cancer research in humans is beginning to show transgenerational impacts from artificial estrogens, decreased fertility across generations is still a brand-new concept. At least in humans.

In fact, for the reasons I just mentioned, I doubt first-rate long-range fertility studies will be performed in humans in the near future because (1) the timeline of a perfect study in humans may be 100s of years and (2) people signing on for fertility studies are already excreting high levels of estrogenics.

In other words, beyond issues of duration, our current estrogenic exposures skew the end results. We have eliminated a "pure" control group for comparisons. Another way to think about this is to ask: how many remote Alaskan natives can we afford to recruit? The study we discussed before is not a commonplace research model.

But here's the good news: animal models have proven parallel to human research throughout the estrogenic field. This includes rats and mice but even fish and frogs. In other words, when you see "feminization of males" in the fish you also see it in mice exposed to estrogenics and then you also see this issue in exposed humans. Or when you find certain tumors in rats exposed to BPA, you find those same types of tumors in BPA-exposed people.

And *animal studies* of transgenerational infertility are starting to pile up.

Leading the pack, a 2015 study is the most straight-forward as well as the most alarming in the area of transgenerational infertility.[15] Once again, it involves fish.

This was a study wherein numbers of fertilized medaka fish [Japanese rice fish] eggs were exposed to either BPA or EE2 within 2 different test groups. BPA and EE2 exposures are an extremely common occurrence found "in nature" these days, so they were looking at generational impacts. This study was unique, however, because these fertilized eggs were *only exposed for 7 days*, which is an aberrantly short duration compared to our "current" native lake, river, and ocean fish exposures.

In fact, in this experiment, the BPA or EE2 water was replaced with highly-filtered pure water just after *7 days* of BPA and EE2 "treatment" and so the fish lived in extremely pure water most of their lives.

Next, the researchers simply waited and counted fish. After 3 fishy generations, the scientists found a strong and alarming pattern: in subsequent generations, the fish fertility "tanked".

Yet the findings were even more astonishing than diminished fertility. We've seen diminished fertility already. No. Even without additional exposures – just 7 days of estrogenics in that 1st generation – the 3rd generation fertility was *worse* than the 2nd generation. Fertility continued to plummet!

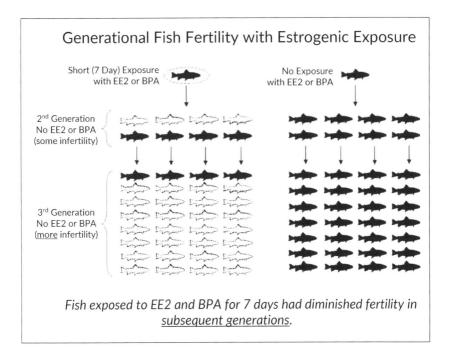

Generational Fish Fertility with Estrogenic Exposure

Short (7 Day) Exposure with EE2 or BPA

No Exposure with EE2 or BPA

2nd Generation No EE2 or BPA (some infertility)

3rd Generation No EE2 or BPA (more infertility)

Fish exposed to EE2 and BPA for 7 days had diminished fertility in subsequent generations.

This is an alarming discovery, the finding that infertility can be *amplified* in future generations merely from a single BPA or EE2 exposure. This occurs due to epigenetic changes and gives rise to *The Estrogenic Epigenetic Principle*:

4.

> **The Estrogenic Epigenetic Principle**: *Estrogenic changes can be passed along to future generations via epigenetics and such inheritance can inflate these health problems.*

In this case, the researchers stopped the study at the 3rd generation but the problem could have extended further. The 3rd generation deadline was probably because of pressure to publish such shocking findings. Publish or perish. But hopefully future studies will continue to extend the timelines. This, of course, will be difficult if all the research animals become extinct as the population crashes, but the studies need to be done so we know.

It is worth adding that the scientists from the medaka fish study *concluded* that "**epigenetic reprogramming** events in germ cells [cells that give rise to egg or sperm] are believed to be **complementary to the mouse**". This conclusion further supports the point that parallel ties exist between animal species and humans in these types of estrogenic and fertility studies.

What about BPA and EE2 *doses* in that medaka fish study? "The dose makes the poison", right? Dose must have been outrageously high to have such a strong effect as to extend across generations!

Actually, yes, BPA was high. The dose of BPA used for that 7-day exposure was 100,000 ng/L. Extremely high.

EE2, however, was not highly dosed at all. EE2 was added at only 50 ng/L. *Fifty.* And 50 gave an almost identical outcome as 100,000 ng/L of BPA. This truly illustrates how EE2 is designed to stay in the body longer; designed to have more potency at lower doses. It is powerful stuff.

This fish study should teach us several lessons. The obvious lesson is to avoid estrogenics if you ever plan to have kids. Even if IRS estrogenics didn't harm you, your grandchildren are likely to be profoundly impacted. That's *The Estrogenic Epigenetic Principle*.

Secondly, EE2 from birth control acted the same as BPA overall. Other estrogenics could have also been added and probably would have behaved similarly, which illustrates and substantiates an earlier *Principle* in this book: *The Estrogenic Effects Principle*. That *Principle*, to reiterate, states: "If an item is estrogenic, it is likely to cause health problems that match other estrogenic items".

Finally, one exposure giving rise to 3rd gen infertility is severely destructive. This is a truly legitimate health crisis.

And, as you might expect me to say by now, other research studies have similar findings. A study looking at generations of fathead minnows, for example, concluded that "population dynamics" were "disrupted" from EE2 exposures. Specifically, 2nd generation fertility was reduced 51-97%.[16] And there are quite a few other similar EE2 and BPA studies – to the point that it gets a bit redundant and repetitive.

Let's close the book with what we can do to avoid these issues but before moving on, I want to better illustrate *The Estrogenic Effects*

Principle in combination with *The Estrogenic Epigenetic Principle.* For this, we move outside the IRS 10 List just briefly.

First, zebrafish awash in an artificial estrogen called benzo-a-pyrene (BaP) gave rise to "multigenerational effects" and "developmental deformities".[17] This indicates the effect is estrogenic and common to other estrogenic items.

Next, "Agent Orange" – the war chemical tetrachlorodibenzo-p-dioxin, which also interferes with the estrogen receptor[18] – was found to reduce fertilization success and egg release *in future generations.*[19] Cruel stuff.

Finally, we've mentioned diethylstilbestrol (DES) previously. What I appreciate – and hate – about DES is that human studies have been done. In fact, in a 2016 study, doctors uncovered "transgenerational transmission of defects in male genital tracts" of *children exposed in utero to DES.*[20]

Since these are human children, this raises the question: why were human children exposed to estrogenic DES for a scientific study? Well, because – and pay attention here, this is the unsettling part – DES was *prescribed* as a human drug right up to the day we put a man on the moon:

> Diethylstilbestrol (**DES**) is a potent estrogen mimic that was predominantly **used** from the 1940s to the 1970s by **pregnant women** in hopes of preventing miscarriage. Decades later, DES is known to **enhance breast cancer risk** in exposed women and cause a variety of **birth-related adverse outcomes in their daughters** such as **spontaneous abortion, second trimester pregnancy loss, preterm delivery, stillbirth, and neonatal death**. Additionally, **children** exposed to DES **in utero** suffer from **sub/infertility** and **cancer of reproductive tissues**.[21]

DES, you see, was a patented drug until the patent expired. And it wasn't just "used by pregnant women", as these scientists suggest, but rather it was *prescribed* by licensed medical doctors. It was prescribed just like birth control is prescribed today – the only estrogenic on the IRS 10 list that is *professionally prescribed.*

Now, as you may expect, the epigenetic fertility-dysfunction list could go on. But I want to close this chapter with a title of a recent phthalate discovery that sums it all up succinctly: *"Plastics derived endocrine disruptors induce epigenetic transgenerational inheritance of obesity, reproductive disease and sperm epimutations."*[22] Welcome to the Estrogeneration.

CHAPTER 10

What You Can Do

Sauna Like It Hot

YOU HAVE NOW DISCOVERED THE 10 estrogenics we are all being exposed to on a daily basis and *The 7 Deadly Things* arising from these estrogenic exposures: fat-gains, depression, hormonal imbalances, immune system dysfunctions, blood clotting issues, certain types of cancer, and, finally, infertility that deflowers future generations. You know where they are and what they do.

Now it's time to discuss what to do. You need a strategy for how to expertly avoid these estrogenic items. That's the most important thing. That also makes this the most important chapter.

But before presenting avoidance strategies, I find that two major hurdles present themselves whenever people decide to dodge estrogenics. Both are motivation destroyers, good-will hunters.

First, estrogenics seem to be so pervasive that the average person is tempted to give up. This is understandable so I've created customized *Gold, Silver,* and *Bronze Level Estrogenic Avoidance Plans* with simple and specific guides. I want you to clearly see this path to better health and how it can be attained. It's not easy but it's also not hopeless.

Secondly, avoiding estrogenics doesn't have the health and diet razzmatazz of the so-called "miracle cure". That's the hard truth and one that deflates the "quick fix" crowd.

Often, estrogenic avoidance does not lead to immediate satisfaction or changes, although you might be pleasantly surprised. I'm not promising you will lose 10 pounds *in 10 days*, for example; however, I'm also not ruling that out.

Let's be real. Estrogenics don't usually cause abrupt bloating or pain that makes you double-over. We know this and it's all well and good.

The problem is that immediate health problems are motivating health problems. If our bodies were to react dramatically against estrogenic exposures, our own bodies, our future generations, and even our wildlife populations would be better off.

Estrogenics, you see, are *somewhat* natural. Essentially, estrogenics – substances that closely resemble estrogen – usually aren't going to "shock" your body. They fool your body but they usually don't shock it.

Instead, estrogenics creep. They are like a lukewarm pot of water slowly heating up. People eating, drinking, and swimming in estrogenics are like frogs soaking in this pot. The heat rises. Changes take place but they happen slowly. The problems don't register. It doesn't help that a few officials are standing by reassuring everybody that the frogs will be fine. Suddenly, it's not fine. The water boils...

In essence, estrogenics seem fine. "Everyone is doing it," we are told. This is almost true. But – and this is a big but – as we continue to eat and drink estrogenic creepers, these little "health-parodies", we make ourselves and our future generations more infertile. We gain a few extra pounds every year for the next 20. We slowly develop allergies. Or maybe, just maybe, our cells slowly build up mutations and become cancerous. We certainly increase the odds for cancer, after all, as we continue to accept our increased exposure to Ill Reproductive System (IRS) 10 estrogenics. This is the *modus operandi* of *The 7 Deadly Things*. They are slow, deliberate, and vile.

As always, don't just take my word for it. The World Health Organization [WHO] is even raising a skull and crossbones flag here by classifying certain EE2 oral contraception drugs as "Group 1 Carcinogens in Humans".[1] These festering health issues are not the *Princess and the Frog* fairy tale that we desire.

So I have a few important and simple "pre-game" recommendations for you. These are the positive suggestions I have for you to jump-start your health as you begin eliminating estrogenics from your life.

First, you can improve your omega-3 to omega-6 fatty acid ratio. New research has discovered that phthalates make people physically weaker – most likely due to hormonal imbalances – but they stumbled across a new finding: better omega-3 to omega-6 ratios *improved the estrogenic strength loss.*[2] Athletes, more than most, hear about this study and say "where do I sign-up?"

You can easily improve your omega-3 to omega-6 ratio by increasing your omega-3 intake. Specifically, you increase your omega-3 intake by taking fish oil or krill oil pills, eating more seafood, and eating more grass-fed animal products. Improving this ratio also means that you fastidiously avoid corn oil, safflower oil, grape seed oil, cottonseed oil, sunflower oil, and margarine, specifically. I'm already assuming you also avoid soy and soybean oil, but you might find it valuable to know that "vegetable oil" is frequently another way of saying soybean oil (30% of the time) or it is simply soybean oil mixed with other oils (80%).[3,4] So avoid "vegetable oil" too.

Since even our best efforts will probably leave us with trace amounts of estrogenics, improving your omega-3 numbers is good "health insurance". It is preventive insurance. Especially since omega-3 fatty acids have so many other health benefits. Don't forget the kids, here, and their fish or krill oil!

Next, learn about "Natural Family Planning" (NFP) for postponing pregnancy. It is also called the "Fertility Awareness Method" (FAM) and is more than 99% effective.[5] A class or a book like *Natural Family Planning: The Complete Approach* (Kippley) might also help get you started. There is even an NFP app called "Natural Cycles" which is also side-effect-free.[5]

One final suggestion is to eliminate estrogenics *already* stored in your body. Specifically, target your preexisting fat. We all have fat, even if our BMI (Body Mass Index) is low. And estrogenics are not only stored in fat – up to 10 years, remember – but they can also cause fat. We need to break that vicious cycle quickly.

How? Consider eliminating stubborn estrogenics stored in fat cells using heat. You need to halt your estrogenic exposure, yes. But if you want to rid yourself of estrogenics you've been carrying in your fat for years, heat is a one-step starter plan for you.

Specifically, sit in a hot sauna for at least a few sessions. Depending on your health state, probably start with 10 minutes and work your way up slightly and slowly. Do some research regarding your specific situation and always consult your doctor. Don't start doing sauna sessions if you are pregnant, for example.

Why saunas? Saunas are great. They are even being used by medical researchers to treat mold-toxin exposures.[6] And even if scientist weren't doing this, an important principle is at play that makes the technique "most likely to succeed".

The principle is this: heat speeds up molecules. Any molecules. In your body, especially on that huge organ we call "skin", increases in molecular motion enhance the elimination of waste or toxic molecules. Toxins like estrogenics. Your body is constantly undergoing this waste/toxin removal process and heat simply speeds it up.

Think of water. Water molecules literally jump out of a heated pot, turning to steam in the air. Water also jumps off your skin as you sweat, carrying some of the heat with it, to cool your body.

In a similar fashion, estrogenics stored in fat will move out of those fat cells at a more rapid pace when they are heated. This allows your body to rapidly eliminate them. You pee them out, sweat them out, even breath them out. Since estrogenics lingering in your fat are so excessively unhealthy, sooner is better. Rapid is good.

The clearance of estrogenics by heat also helps explain the supposedly "strange connection between saunas and longevity", discovered recently by scientists.[7] As you draw out these unnatural chemicals, you get healthier. Why does conventional medicine find that so "strange"?

Two final tips.

First, as you speed up your estrogenic detox using a sauna, drink lots of water before you get "baked". Next, continue to drink plenty of water during your sauna session. Not excessive amounts but plenty. You want urine and sweat to freely flow.

Secondly, you should consider a fast. Don't eat food for a period of time. Ideally just before your sauna sessions. How long? Usually a period that is slightly challenging for you is best.

Not eating food will put your body into fat-burn mode. This will shock your body and change your physiology. I wouldn't be recommending this challenging strategy unless it really worked. It does. It increases something called "autophagy" – cellular eating – and helps your body "turnover" fat cells [exchange the old fat for improved cells] and clear ever more stored estrogenic substance.

In case you have a choice, infrared saunas are better than normal saunas. Infrared heats your body more from the inside.

Avoidance Plans

Now let's get specific about estrogenic *avoidance* and introduce the *Gold, Silver, and Bronze Level Estrogenic Avoidance Plans*.

To drill home the gravity of our current situation just once more, I want you to read this block quote from a Taiwanese medical journal. This particular excerpt features phthalates and really calls a spade a spade. It includes most or all of *The 7 Deadly Things*. Also, I am including it because it is highly motivating. Here's the quote:

> Studies have suggested associations between **phthalate exposure** and **shorter gestational age, shorter anogenital distance, shorter penis, incomplete testicular descent, sex hormone alteration, precocious puberty, pubertal gynecomastia, premature thelarche** [breast development]**, rhinitis, eczema, asthma, low birth weight, attention deficit hyperactivity disorder, low intelligence quotient, thyroid hormone alteration, and hypospadias** in infants and children. **Furthermore,** many studies have suggested associations between phthalate exposure and **increased sperm DNA damage, decreased proportion of sperm with normal morphology, decreased sperm concentration, decreased sperm morphology, sex hormone alteration, decreased pulmonary function, endometriosis, uterine leiomyomas, breast cancer, obesity, hyperprolactinemia, and thyroid hormone alteration** in adults. **Finally,** the number of phthalate-related scientific publications from Taiwan has increased greatly over the past 5 years, which may reflect the health effects from

the **illegal addition of phthalate plasticizer to clouding agent in foodstuff over the past two decades.**[8]

Now that's a grave list. Grave in a very literal way. What can you do?

First, find things that say "Estrogenic-Free" or "Free of All Estrogenics" or things that obviously do not contain any IRS 10 items. If you have a choice between glass or plastic, for instance, choose glass. Glass food storage containers, for example, are always free of estrogenics. Preferentially select those sorts of items.

To help consumers, I support and endorse the use of "Estrogenic-Free" approval stamps. Companies that produce or package relevant items, especially personal care items (shampoo, lotion, toothpaste, etc.), should considering using "Estrogenic-Free" stamps on product labels. "Estrogenic-Free" is simpler than saying "Paraben-Free", "Phthalate-Free", "BPA-Free", etc. In other words, simply saying "Estrogenic-Free" is better than listing each individual estrogenic item on warning labels. It encompasses all those nasty things.

Companies have not yet begun to add "Estrogenic-Free" assurances to labels but I won't rest until they do. You'll see them everywhere before too long if we team up on this. This book is only the first step.

In the meantime, money talks. Support companies like The Honest Company®, which lists ingredients for personal care products and is conscientious about avoiding the IRS Top 10 items, well, excepting lavender. Check them out as one example among many. As always, I receive nothing for saying this and that's how I like to keep it.

Additionally, my good friends at *Timberlocked* are another premier example. They make kids toys, among other things, and work hard and smart to avoid estrogenics.

Besides simplicity, another reason we need the "Estrogenic-Free" label is that current consumers are unknowingly making huge mistakes. For example, people are buying "BPA-Free" items that either contain BPS – which is equally bad for your health – or they contain phthalates, which are worse for your health than BPA. But people are trusting that "BPA-Free" must equate to something good.

In a recent chat with a famous biohacker, for example, I was asking why some of his key liquid supplement products came in plastic bottles (vs glass). His immediate response was that "there is no BPA in the plastic". He also added that using plastic lowers the amount of fuel required, making plastic the better *environmental* choice.

Yet – as much as I appreciate this person's health work – the environmental argument needs to be reexamined. It's a common one. Scientists publishing in environmental research journals have this to say: "While cheap petroleum fuels from which most plastics are derived was *once justified* to introduce them in place of traditional materials like glass and metals, this plea cannot hold any more since the cost of non-renewable fossil fuels increased several fold during the last 3 decades."[9] Use glass, just recycle. More importantly avoid plastics, "BPA-Free" or not.

Next, beyond "Estrogenic-Free" labeling and increasing education and awareness, corporations, government, and scientists need to start working to collaborate to ensure things are free of estrogenics. The goal of this joint effort should be to improve our current estrogenic mess. If nothing else, oceanic organisms cannot wait. Rapid die-offs are already underway, as we saw, along with transgenerational infertility.

To move things along and enhance our society's health, the government especially needs to become more active. As I said before, the smallest form of government is the best but this has become a *massive* problem. This health crisis demands federal-level support with a focus on health, not corporate interests.

Based on the current status of our laws (Chapter 2), the USA is dragging along behind many countries, especially in the health interests of our infants and children. Behind Russia and China in certain cases and far behind Europe in many cases. Americans need to start *leading* the way in eliminating artificial estrogen substances and promoting optimal health. That's what preventative health is all about. We shouldn't be making complicated scientific or legal excuses. We should start improving laws. Immediately.

For legal considerations, as a general rule, substances that impact our estrogen receptor, i.e. things that are estrogenic, should be considered "hazardous to health" until all *The 7 Deadly Things* are thoroughly researched. Even then, regulators should remain skeptical and cautious. Studies with heavy spin and bias should be assumed, anticipated, and exposed.

Furthermore, artificial chemicals should be considered dangerous until proven safe, not safe until proven dangerous. We have transformed the lead paint culture so I know we can transform the newly hatching Estrogeneration.

Of course, the government cannot *merely* ban certain estrogenics. When bans are imposed, unethical companies simply shift to other ingredients or substances that are comparably bad for health. Or they use substances that are worse for health. And they outcompete ethical companies in the process.

We must demand transparency. We live in a digital age. Companies know what they put into products so everyone else should too. Access to ingredient lists should at least be accessible with 1-click. Regarding estrogenics, simple and cheap transparency keeps companies honest and still allows small companies to succeed.

Next scientists should get involved. Scientists should begin flagging corporate bias within studies and funding, for instance. And they should be rewarded for this, not blacklisted. We need to stop mincing words on certain items like soy or birth control and start seeing the bigger health crisis here. We should not be standing idly by and watching science journal editors with high moral standards voluntarily stepping down from the worsening climate of spin. Those are the editors we need.

For scientists and physicians, it should go without saying that promoting estrogenic products under the ruse of "science" needs to stop. As I illustrated in Chapter 3, it's worse than most non-scientists realize. Items like soy or oral contraception come to mind, where scientists and doctors strongly headline minor favorable aspects while underplaying massive negative health impacts. This is a calamity that leaves a calamitous legacy.

And why are medical facilities still using plastic IV bags and other plastic items? Healthcare needs to care and I understand that things haven't been made clear but they are now. Time to act.

Blood donation centers also need to step it up. Mandatory screening questions should be in place regarding oral contraception use. Tiny

Timmy's blood transfusion should not contain EE2. Nor should Tiny Theresa be taking EE2 pills. Period.

Finally, for scientific researchers, we need totally anonymous grant awards and paper review systems. Seriously already. Anonymity will help distance scientists from politics and politicking.

Ok. Let's shift and move into those *Estrogenic Avoidance Plans*. For printing purposes, these can be found on my website.[10]

GOLD LEVEL PLAN

You want to follow the *Gold Level Plan* because you are an Olympian, a professional athlete, part of the military special forces, or some other high-performance individual.

Or you want to adhere to the *Gold Level Plan* because you find one or more of *The 7 Deadly Things* runs deeply in your family. This especially includes major health problems like obesity, infertility, or depression. Or your allergies are simply just too much.

You may also be pregnant or have children. You want to protect their highly sensitive hormonal states by maintaining the *Gold Level Plan*. You are smart and motivated and more protective than the average person.

Your *Plan* is to:

✓ Avoid ingredients that include *"benz-"* or *"phen-"*
✓ Eliminate dietary grains, including all corn products
✓ Eliminate dietary peanuts, cheap coffee, and cheap chocolate
✓ Eliminate liquid dairy products unless grass-fed and in glass
✓ Eliminate butter unless grass-fed
✓ Eliminate all dietary liquids stored in plastics, especially oils
✓ Eliminate fragrances in all personal care products
✓ Eliminate fragrances in laundry detergent and dryer sheets
✓ Travel and sleep with a pillow case washed without fragrance
✓ Eliminate processed foods
✓ Eliminate plastic shower curtains

✓ Eliminate vinyl flooring/tiling, wallpaper, and plastic countertops
✓ Avoid standard industrial bathroom hand-soaps
✓ Avoid cannabis
✓ Avoid candles except beeswax
✓ Avoid plastics in your environment, including plastic toys
✓ Eliminate carpets or use "Green-Label Plus" certified carpets
✓ Avoid foods canned in metal
✓ Only eat *wild* seafood from pristine waters
✓ Only eat *grass-fed* organic meats, preferably in wax paper
✓ Only eat *grass-fed* organic animal fats, with no plastic contacts
✓ Only eat *free-range* chicken eggs
✓ Use charcoal-filtered water for all drinking and cooking
✓ Use charcoal-filtered water for showering
✓ Use all glass and/or stainless steel coffee makers
✓ Use "Estrogenic-Free" cleaning products
✓ Use "Estrogenic-Free" kid's toys, especially chewable items
✓ Use "Estrogenic-Free" zinc sunscreen
✓ Avoid moldy environments
✓ Eliminate soy and soy byproducts
✓ Eliminate flax
✓ Eliminate lavender products
✓ Eliminate oral contraception
✓ Eliminate plastic cups, sippies, or plastic-lined mugs
✓ Eliminate artificial red food dyes, including finger paints
✓ Eliminate microwaving food in plastics

SILVER LEVEL PLAN

You want to follow the *Silver Level Plan* because you are careful and mindful about your health but not intense or obsessed. You recognize the destructive impacts of *The 7 Deadly Things* and want to avoid these issues but you don't want an "Extreme Home and Food Makeover".

Although you are not a professional athlete, you still need to function at a high level. You greatly value and prioritize your health and the health of future generations. You might cheat on the corn and buy organic corn products but you are determined to strictly follow the *Silver Level Plan* for at least one month before any minor cheating. You are practical and expect to see some tangible health benefits from your efforts. Your improved health will spur you into deeper and longer health commitments.

Your *Plan* is to:
- ✓ Avoid ingredients that include "*benz-*" or "*phen-*"
- ✓ Eliminate dietary grains, including all corn products
- ✓ Eliminate cheap coffee and cheap chocolate
- ✓ Eliminate liquid dairy products unless grass-fed and in glass
- ✓ Eliminate butter unless grass-fed
- ✓ Eliminate oils stored in plastics
- ✓ Eliminate fragrances in all personal care products
- ✓ Eliminate fragrances in laundry detergent and dryer sheets
- ✓ Use "Fragrance-Free" washed pillow cases for extended travels
- ✓ Eliminate highly processed foods
- ✓ Eliminate vinyl countertops
- ✓ Avoid standard industrial bathroom hand-soaps
- ✓ Avoid cannabis
- ✓ Avoid foods in metal
- ✓ Only eat *wild* seafood
- ✓ Only eat *grass-fed* organic animal fats, with no plastic contacts
- ✓ Use charcoal-filtered water for all drinking and cooking
- ✓ Use all glass and/or stainless steel coffee makers
- ✓ Use "Estrogenic-Free" cleaning products
- ✓ Use "Estrogenic-Free" kid's toys, especially chewable items
- ✓ Use "Estrogenic-Free" zinc sunscreen
- ✓ Avoid moldy environments
- ✓ Eliminate soy and soy byproducts
- ✓ Eliminate flax
- ✓ Eliminate lavender products
- ✓ Eliminate oral contraception
- ✓ Eliminate plastic cups, sippies, or plastic-lined mugs

✓ Eliminate artificial red food dyes, including finger paints
✓ Eliminate microwaving food in plastics

BRONZE LEVEL PLAN

You decide to follow the *Bronze Level Plan* because you are honest and find the *Silver Level Plan* and *Gold Level Plan* too difficult. You love grains, dairy, and corn. You correctly expect that the *Bronze Level Plan* has the biggest payoff for the least effort. While you certainly don't hate yourself, you also like to treat yourself. You are also more skeptical than most people, despite all the strong science research. You are open to improving your health but do not have high expectations either way.

Your *Plan* is to:

✓ Avoid ingredients that include *"benz-"* or *"phen-"*
✓ Diminish dietary grains
✓ Diminish liquid dairy products unless grass-fed and in glass
✓ Eliminate oils stored in plastics
✓ Eliminate fragrances in all personal care products
✓ Eliminate fragrances in laundry detergent and dryer sheets
✓ Eliminate highly processed foods
✓ Avoid cannabis smoke
✓ Only eat *organic* corn products
✓ Use charcoal-filtered water for all drinking water
✓ Use all glass and/or stainless steel coffee makers
✓ Use "Estrogenic-Free" kid's chewable items
✓ Use "Estrogenic-Free" zinc sunscreen
✓ Avoid moldy environments
✓ Eliminate soy and soy byproducts
✓ Eliminate flax
✓ Eliminate lavender products
✓ Eliminate oral contraception
✓ Eliminate plastic sippies

✓ Eliminate artificial red food dyes, including finger paints
✓ Eliminate microwaving food in plastics

Plastic Numbers

Let's briefly run through the plastic numbers for the benefit of you and your health. Then we'll explore other estrogenic avoidance principles in more detail.

If you must manufacture or use plastic for something, the general rule I recommend is to choose recyclable plastic #2, 4, or 5.

Plastic #1 is polyethylene terephthalate (PETE) and phthalate is in the name, so it needs no explanation. Similarly, plastic #7 is BPA or BPS, so this plastic number is self-explanatory.

Plastic #3 is polyvinyl chloride (PVC). This plastic contains phthalates in nearly every case[11] and even has other stand-alone toxicity issues,[12] so it's no good.

Next, plastic #6, polystyrene (PS), is actually not estrogenic.[13] That's a good start. Yet #6 also has stand-alone human toxicity and environmental problems[14] so it should be carefully avoided. This includes Styrofoam plates with hot foods and especially Styrofoam cups.

Again: these are last resorts rather than recommendations but let's briefly inspect plastic #2, 4, and 5 since these are better.

Plastic #2 is high density polyethylene (HDPE). This plastic resulted in only about 15% of unheated and unshaken samples leaching estrogenics into salt-water[15] so it's less of a health gamble. Furthermore, plastic #4 is low density polyethylene (LDPE), which means it is less dense and more susceptible to leaching estrogenic materials than #2, but still "less bad" than 1, 3, 6, and 7.

Finally, plastic #5 is probably best. Again, phthalates are often added[16] so I'm withholding applause for plastic #5, but there you have it.

Last Resort Plastic Numbers Guide

Avoid plastics in liquids and foods. Avoid excessive plastics in your environment. When you must use them, go with numbers 2, 4, or 5.

Other Avoidance Principles

General principles are great because they can further guide you within your unique circumstances. They can provide a better framework for recognizing potential estrogenic sources. Let's establish some anti-estrogenic principles and include a bit more detail.

First, improve your gut bacteria. Earlier, in Chapter 2, we saw how gut bacteria help protect us against flax phytoestrogens. We also examined, in Chapter 7, how good bacteria from butter can destroy some ZEA mold estrogen. This is newly emerging research but stay up to date on cutting-edge findings.[i] Gut bacteria will continue to provide new and exciting discoveries and health improvement opportunities for decades to come.

But don't rely heavily on gut bacteria. Avoid ZEA mycoestrogen by preventing or avoiding mold.

Throughout the book, we've discussed various sources of mold especially including grains. Cheap coffee and cheap cocoa products should also be considered potential sources of mold.[17,18] Also check under your kitchen and bathroom sinks, refrigerator filter draft lines, under (or even inside) old refrigerators, behind walls where plumbing may have leaked, and any other damp area. Air testing is extreme but useful if you are uncertain.

---

[i] Note: I have a YouTube educational series called "Chagrin & Tonic".

Next, let's go through (*really* go through) your personal care products. Anything with perfume should be considered estrogenic, unless it specifically says "Phthalate-Free" and "Paraben-Free" (and preferably "Alkylphenol-Free" as well) or simply "Estrogenic-Free". This includes deodorant, shampoo, bar soap, and even – absolutely – laundry detergent and dryer sheets. Without "Estrogenic-Free" confirmations, you should assume that "fragrance" equals phthalates, parabens, and possibly APEs (alkylphenols). Be aggressive and err on the safe side.

If you don't have time to do your own research, you can find many of the personal care products I personally use for myself and my family on my website: *www.ajconsultingcompany.com/whatiuse*. And, once again, I have no financial connections to any of the listed items.

Next step: throw away your sunscreen if you own the cheap stuff. I happened to be a sunscreen fanatic because I absolutely need the protection, the strongest I can find. I mean the sunscreen you squeeze and a turtle-neck sweater comes out.

Probably 95% of sunblock brands contain estrogenic 4-MBC and/or BP so be vigilant. Buy something highly consumer-rated containing over 20% zinc that is devoid of 4-MBC and/or BP.

Moving on. Diminish or eliminate your processed "food" consumption. This includes fast-foods and "food" items with those massive ingredient lists and chemical names only professional chemists can pronounce. This also includes things like triangular shaped nacho corn chips that are "sprayed" with chemicals to fool our taste buds into believing we are eating a 4-course meal even as we merely eat carbs.

Buy fruits, nuts, vegetables, cheeses, and meats. Whole foods. Find a local and trusted farmer and buy directly, ideally. Also, try to obtain meat cuts that are wrapped in wax paper from a butcher (or hunter) rather than meats stewing in plastic. I'm assuming you eat meat, of course.

If you do not eat meats, you especially need to "soy vigilant".

Soy – especially soybean oil – is particularly rampant in processed "foods" and things like salad dressings. Simply be more aware of ingredient lists and avoid soy-related items.

Next, again assuming you eat meat, ask yourself what your food was eating. In other words, has your beef been eating moldy ZEA grains or atrazine herbicide? Your poultry?

Keep in mind that animals preferentially store estrogenics in fat, same as you and me, so especially hunt down good fats. It's unfortunate but you can't charcoal filter your meats and fats.

You can charcoal-filter your drinking water. DO IT. It's really a no-brainer at this point. You saw what we are dealing with in our water supply. And don't forget to use filtered water for boiling or steaming food.

Estrogenics prefer to migrate from the water in order to adhere to noodles or other items that are sitting in that water so make sure that water is "Estrogenic-Free". Sink attachment units are sufficient, here, as long as they include activated charcoal to remove hydrophobic molecules like estrogenics. I personally use the "Royal Berkey" water filter system and include the added fluoride removal filters. This is a gravity unit.

Next, be sure you aren't storing water or other liquids in plastics. Start by drinking your high-quality H2O from glass or stainless steel bottles every day, rather than from plastic bottles. If you must, filter water into plastic and then put it immediately in glass.

Again: "BPA-Free" is not sufficient. A study looking at dozens of plastic items at room temperature over a mere 24 hours found most "BPA-Free" plastics leached toxic levels of estrogenics into water.[19] That study was even done in the dark, without the estrogenic-releasing effects of UV or sunlight,[20] although the plastic products were continuously sloshed (not stationary). The research is clear. Make changes accordingly.

Except for the rare exception, I prefer glass water bottles protected by an outer shell of rubber even though I also appreciate stainless steel. Furthermore, I save tall glass bottles from San Pellegrino®, re-fill them, and bring numbers of those bottles on various adventures and trips. For babies, silicone nipples or straws are safe and good. Add these nipples or straws to glass or stainless travel bottles. Pura® Stainless is a good example and good brand to check out.

As long as we are talking about silicone, I need to mention that silicone is generally good. I am frequently asked about this. While I prefer natural wood or stainless steel, I have no issue with silicone. I'm assuming we're not talking about breast implants...

Since infants and kids are more sensitive to hormone imbalances, be ultra-vigilant on their behalf. Scrupulously avoid plastic exposures more than ever for them.

For instance, watch out for plastic baby chew-items and anything that might get chewed. Also, beware of children inhaling or breathing plastic items. Specifically, I'm thinking of play rooms littered with plastic toys and flooring or plastic crib mattresses. You may spot other major plastic intruders in your home. Carefully research crib mattresses for phthalates, parabens, and APEs, and avoid childcare facilities – daily estrogenic exposures – that have entire floors made of spongy plastic material and plastic toys as far as the eye can see. These sorts of things are terrible for the delicate hormonal balance of your children. At least include a HEPA air purifier, if you or your child must be confined in a plastic prison for some reason.

As a general rule, skin, air, and liquid exposures are the worst for estrogenic discharge. Drinking estrogenics packs them into your body, breathing estrogenics sends them into your bloodstream along with your required oxygen, and we talked about skin transfer in discussions on fat. Estrogenic transfer is more direct, on a molecular level, through all three of these modes.

Direct transfer principles apply to foods, also. Think of a steak sitting in plastic. The exterior surface is in direct contact with the plastic wrapping but not the interior of the steak. Beverages sitting in plastic, on the other hand, are constantly shifting and exposing the entire inner volume to estrogenics.

Another rule is that heating foods or liquids in plastic is far worse than storing items in plastic at room temperature. For instance, are you using a plastic colander or strainer for your boiling hot noodles? Most people do. Go stainless. Also, I appreciate outdoor survival skills but boiling eggs in plastic zipper storage bags is not cool. Again: it's fine to have short-term contact with cold plastics – I store dry food items in plastics sometimes – but heating or microwaving food or liquid directly in contact with plastics is powerfully toxifying.

For similar reasons, plastics are polluting our coffee. Think about coffee makers with all the plastic tubing, plastic coffee filter holders, k-cups, and even plastic-lined mugs for the final product. Find a ceramic coffee dripper, something stainless, or something glass like a French Press. And don't use a plastic blender with hot liquids!

I personally make coffee by boiling water to the perfect temperature using a stainless-steel pot and then I use a glass Chemex® coffee maker with a hemp filter for the actual brewing process.

For foods in contact with plastic, several additional principles apply.

First, watch out for canned food. A lot of canned foods have the inside of the can coated with plastic. This plastic is usually BPA – perfectly legal in America, of course – and it is generally even heated in some sort of pasteurization process to make the food last forever. Trader Joes apparently is a shining star compared to other major supermarkets[21] but glass is always a better choice if possible.

Another principle is that oils and fats will absorb far more estrogenics than non-fats. For instance, bacon fat in contact with plastic is far worse than steak in direct contact with plastic.

Keep in mind with fats, too, that liquids continue to be worse than solids. Oils are worse than bacon, for example, for estrogenic transfers. A common health offender is oil sitting in a plastic tub or even oil sitting in an industrial plastic bag or bucket, used for things like deep frying. Even coconut oil or MCTs (excellent and healthy fats found at high levels in coconut oil) can be compromised by storage in plastics. Frankly, for all oils and fats, room temperature is too "hot". For water, short-term room temperature storage is *probably* fine. Multi-year studies with all the proper controls will probably never be done so I'm emphasizing "probably" here.

And health issues related to "eating too much fat" undoubtedly originate from the estrogenics more so than the fats themselves. Things like phthalate should not be allowed in the same room as oils but profits are currently beating ethics in this area. Your brain is the fattiest organ in your body and it will thank you for eliminating estrogenics in fat. Don't forget that depression is 1 of *The 7 Deadly Things*.

Finally, it is worth repeating that "BPA-free" is currently meaningless. BPS, other BPA-mimicking molecules, phthalates, parabens, and APEs are just too prevalent. Be thorough and be vigilant regarding plastics.

And do I even need to remind you to avoid foods with red-food coloring? That's what I thought.

Here is another fearless quote from a science journal: "More **shocking** is the **legal amount of artificial colorants allowed** by the FDA in the foods, drugs, and cosmetics that we consume and use every day. The consuming public is largely unaware of the perilous truth behind the deceptive allure of artificial color."[22]

Since most processed foods come out looking like brown mush, the food coloring industry has a more powerful stake here than you might expect.

I can't include everything but hopefully you now are thinking like a scientist, and I can tell you, scientists are taking this stuff very seriously. So. Should. You.

Boy-Girl Numbers

Let's hit on one final principle, briefly mention something about "boys versus girls", then catch a massive tarpon fish.

Despite all the health hazards, estrogenics might *seem* to be worse for males overall. This may not be true but it's a cultural expectation.

I often hear: "Females are probably not at risk with estrogenic exposures, except maybe for the puberty issues." Or: "Women are adapted to high levels of *natural* estrogen so they're probably fine." It's a sentiment I understand. On the surface, of course, it makes sense. But it's wrong.

Essentially, this idea emerges because we all recognize natural estrogen as a *female* hormone. And estrogen mostly is. Redneck comedian Jeff Foxworthy describes his daughters, and the disproportionate numbers of daughters in his extended family, like this: "I live in the *estrogen ocean*...in the middle of the Naked Barbie Woodstock – naked Barbie's as far as the eye can see". Foxworthy is surrounded by women so he must be *inhaling* estrogen, right?

Seems legit. *Estrogenics*, therefore, must also be acceptable for women since they have such high estrogen levels. The woman's natural estrogen should overpower all the artificial stuff, right? Well, get out your estrogen-breathalyzer and let's have a quick puff.

In boys and men, estrogen is so low it is usually measured in units of "pico" grams. So far so good. As predicted, male estrogen levels are extremely low. Usually, something like 20 picograms per milliliter (pg/mL) is found in men. And, as a side note, I think it is remarkable that we can even measure such tiny amounts, since 1 picogram equals 0.000,000,000,001 grams.

But, believe it or not, women measure in the picogram range in milliliters of blood, for estrogen, as well. Depending on the time of the month, a healthy, middle-aged, woman will usually range all the way from 20 pg/mL – the *same* numbers as men – up to around 400 pg/mL. Even at the highest point, then, these female estrogen numbers are not actually sky high.

These natural estrogen numbers are incredibly low because hormones have such a massive impact on your cells. Plus, the impact lasts long, as we discussed in the beginning of the book. Generations, even.

Now: contrast those natural levels of natural estrogen (20 – 400 pg/mL) with our unnatural exposures, numbers that frequently bleed into the thousands. Women will be impacted significantly by drinking 4,000 pg/mL of any of 10 IRS estrogenic items, for instance. In other words, both women and men are massively impacted. And if you have phthalate at 4,000 pg/mL, EE2 at 4,000 pg/mL, BPA at 1,000 pg/mL, and atrazine at 6,000 pg/mL, you really have a problem! Probably a 15,000 pg/mL exposure problem or beyond, truthfully.

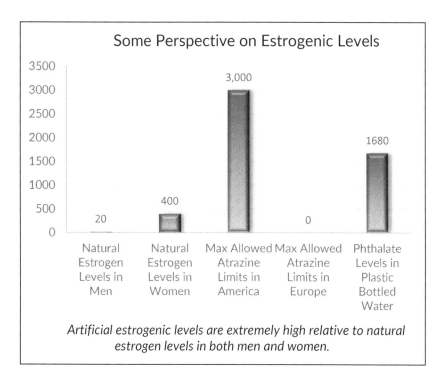

Some Perspective on Estrogenic Levels

Artificial estrogenic levels are extremely high relative to natural estrogen levels in both men and women.

That brings up one final principle called The Principle of Estrogenic Cocktails:

5.

The Principle of Estrogenic Cocktails: *Exposure to mixtures of estrogenics gives rise to many additive estrogenic effects that lead to worse health problems and "mixture effects".*

Water is the ultimate example here, because so many studies have been performed and so many find estrogenic H_2O cocktails. Just don't forget that oils, fats, meats, and other things are frequently comparable or not far behind.

A study of mixtures of 8 different estrogenics neatly demonstrates *The Principle of Estrogenic Cocktails*. Toxicity was discovered to be additive with each added estrogenic and the conclusion of this toxicity study was that "estrogenic agents are able to act together to produce *significant effects* when combined".[23]

So 4,000 ng/L of atrazine and 4,000 ng/L of EE2 is likely to equal the nasty effects that 8,000 or even 10,000 ng/L of total "estrogenic effect", effects exemplified as *The 7 Deadly Things*.

Mixture effects are massively underestimated in virtually every study on estrogenics and, even despite that fact, studies are revealing plenty of incredibly serious issues. Rising infertility of most animals on the planet comes to mind. Or our rising cancer and obesity rates. Or our rising depression rates. Allergies, too. All *The 7 Deadly Things*.

Do mixtures of estrogenics reside in our environment at such high levels as 4,000 pg/mL? Absolutely. We looked at those precise numbers in Chapter 4. And 4,000 pg/mL, by the way, is the same as saying "4,000 ng/L", in case you go back and review Chapter 4. It's the difference between human blood measurement units and environmental water measurement units but these units convert straight-up.

As I additionally mentioned in an earlier chapter, we live in a culture where, "if it is legal, it is OK". Hence, we live in an estrogenic quagmire. Be vigilant. More-so than ever. Don't look up your family tree and find out you are the sap.

Closing Keys to a Fish Tail

In 1919, the outdoorsman Zane Grey described a fishing expedition in Mexico where he hooked up with a 7-foot tarpon. Legend has it that Zane Grey would often fish some 300 days of the year, it was his "duty" as an outdoor author, but still his respect for the tarpon fish remained second to none. Grey describes his own tarpon battle experience infallibly:

> The realization dawned on me that sooner or later I would feel the strike of one of those silver tigers [the tarpon fish] and a keen, tingling thrill of excitement quivered over me. The primitive man asserted himself and I leaned forward, tense and strained with suspended breath and swelling throat.

Suddenly the strike came, so tremendous in its energy that it almost pulled me from my seat; so quick, fierce, bewildering that I could think of nothing but to hold on. Then the water split with a hissing sound to let out a great tarpon, long as a door, seemingly as wide, who shot up and up into the air. He wagged his head and shook it like a struggling wolf. When he fell back with a heavy splash, a rainbow, exquisitely beautiful and delicate, stood out of the spray, glowed, paled, and faded.

Five times he sprang toward the blue sky, and as many he plunged down with a thunderous crash. The reel screamed. The line sang. The rod, which I had thought stiff as a tree, bent like a willow wand. The silver king came up far astern and sheered to the right in a long, wide curve, leaving behind a white wake.

Then he sounded, while I watched the line with troubled eyes. But not long did he sulk. He began a series of magnificent tactics new in my experience. He stood on his tail, then on his head; he sailed like a bird; he shook himself so violently as to make a convulsive, shuffling sound; he dove, to come up covered with mud, marring his bright sides; he closed his huge gills with a slap and, most remarkable of all, he rose in the shape of a crescent, to straighten out with such marvelous power that he seemed to actually crack like a whip.[24]

This hand-to-tail combat goes on for at least another page and culminates in a broken line. Tarpon are like that; true spirit-breakers.

During random trips visiting the Florida Keys while living in Florida, Allison and I were lucky enough to witness the tarpon migration on multiple occasions. During those seasons, the tarpon would stack-up along certain shorelines and they were especially dense at a place called Robbie's, on Islamorada Key. At Robbie's, nobody was allowed to fish but you could buy a bucket of bait and hand-feed the tarpon around the docks, which we did.

The sight of all those tarpon inspired me, one day, to finally hire a fishing guide when I visited Florida from Boston.

The trip was perfect. I planned it during the tarpon migration. Invites were sent to Allison's parents, her brother, and Fishing Club President Victor. The message was simple: let's get serious and finally catch a tarpon! We all met at a nice hotel on Islamorada Key and the anticipation started to build.

The day of the guided tarpon trip finally arrived but calling it "day" is overly generous. We met the guide at 4 A.M. sharp and then buzzed across the water in total darkness where the guide piloted the boat to a "secret" spot. As soon as he slowed to a stop, we all could hear tarpon plopping around us in the darkness.

As soon as we could get a line out, one behemoth fish after another would hungrily eat live crabs from our hooks. It was amazing! Since the fish battle so violently, we could only handle one rod and one person fishing at a time. Therefore, we each took turns trying to catch a tarpon, hooking and boat-chasing. Trying. And. Trying.

What happened was these tarpon would break the line or bend or spit the hooks. We all had opportunities but nobody landed a tarpon! The entire guided adventure yielded no boat side tarpon captures, not one.

As a side bar, we did witness lunchtime for a 14-foot hammerhead shark, closer to a swimming beach than you would like to believe. The hammer came to the surface, with the dorsal fin cutting perfectly through the water, and bit a struggling tarpon exactly in half. Incidentally, this unfortunate tarpon was the one my mother-in-law had been reeling in for the past 20 minutes.

When we buzzed the boat to the spot of the hammerhead's gruesome crime, we saw blood everywhere and half of a trophy tarpon still twitching as it slowly sank. Next, we saw the big hammer wheel back around in full view and we all watched it sink teeth into the descending half-tarpon and disappear. Woah.

Overall, this total tarpon evasion was almost enough to drive me crazy. For sure, it prompted yet another trip to Florida from Boston over a full year later. This trip would finally bring closure to the tarpon dream I had now held for years.

For that adventure, Allison and I hopped on a routine flight from Boston to Fort Myers, Florida, and then stayed at a friend's house in the then brand new town of Ave Maria, Florida.

Partly to repay this family's generosity, Allison and I decided to arrange a sharking trip to our favorite beach with them. This trip was also arranged because Victor, now the captain of the Fishing Club, was able to join us. And he brought all the necessary equipment.

We arrived at the beach nearing sunset. Almost immediately, Victor hooked a 6-foot blacktip shark and the kids all took turns handling the heavy and seizuring fishing rod. The kids were able to capture that shark and, after amazing sunset photos with the shark, the family left.

Darkness crept in while Victor and I continued to fish. I gripped my fishing rod. It was strung out with a long line and a large bait at the end. The night air got damp and heavy.

Without warning, I suddenly felt the raw power of a fish I'd fought many times before but had never routed – tarpon! Victor jumped in the water, salty sea up to his waist, and he strobed the flashlight into the waves. I cranked and cranked on the reel. The fish fought valiantly but it finally gave up. It was a 40-minute battle and exactly the worthy opponent I had come to expect after all these years of close calls.

I was surprisingly quiet and calm during most of this long battle but, when I swam that exhausted tarpon up under my arms in waist-deep water, everything came out. Years of emotion exploded. I started yelling, screaming a battle cry of victory like a Super Bowl champion. In a way, this was my Super Bowl... my Fish Bowl. We took those long-coveted pictures and then released the 7-foot monster back into the black waves.

This was the life I loved, the fish I had worked so hard to catch. The outdoors, I realized, was the escape from all those unnatural burdens that always seemed to be wearing my body down. It was one last, wet, adrenaline-laced, epiphany. This was something worth fighting for, nature the way it was meant to be.

Actionable Summary on Estrogenics

THIS IS AN ACTIONABLE SUMMARY of key points from *Estrogeneration*. It includes 3 parts:

(1) the top 10 estrogenics list and where you are exposed

(2) common health problems arising from artificial estrogenics

(3) directives for diminishing your estrogenic exposures

In addition, here is a relisting of the 5 *Principles* in this book:

(1) **Principle for Evaluating Estrogenics:** *If a scientific study is favorable and positive regarding something that could be bought and sold, be wary!*

(2) **The Ideal Foods Principle:** *Try to find, use, and eat whole, unprocessed foods, from genuinely organic and naturally grown sources, preferably not stored in plastics, and raised in a healthy environment.*

(3) **The Estrogenic Effects Principle:** *If an item is estrogenic, it is likely to cause health problems that match other estrogenic items.*

(4) **The Estrogenic Epigenetic Principle:** *Estrogenic changes can be passed along to future generations via epigenetics and such inheritance can inflate these health problems.*

(5) **The Principle of Estrogenic Cocktails:** *Exposure to mixtures of estrogenics gives rise to many additive estrogenic effects that lead to worse health problems and "mixture effects".*

The Top 10 List of Estrogenics

"Estrogenics" are defined as substances that act like estrogen in your body. Through extensive research, I have found 10 major estrogenics. You are likely exposed to most of these 10 estrogenics every day. All 10 bind the estrogen receptor and mimic estrogen in your body in various ways. After that happens, your health explodes. You'll see that in *Part 2* of this Summary. Here is the Top 10 List:

Estrogenic #1.

PHYTOESTROGENS
The "Plant Estrogenics"

Phytoestrogens are plant hormones that act like estrogen in your body. They are probably the *least* concerning on this list. This does *not* mean plant estrogenics are "ok". It really just tells you how bad the other estrogenics are for your health.

So why are phytoestrogens "less bad" for you? Simple. Your gut bacteria tend to "chew-up" *some* of these nature-made plant estrogenics. This is a healthy adaptation courtesy of your probiotics. Your gut bacteria don't do so well with the artificial estrogenics but bacteria know how to break-up phyto's.

In rare instances, plant estrogenics may even act in positive ways. For example, soy might help you if your natural estrogen levels are too low. It is a natural solution to a sometimes real problem.

Generally, however, you don't want high levels of estrogenics, natural or artificial. So you want to avoid soy and flax. No plants come *remotely* close to the levels of phytoestrogen found in soy and flax. Soy and flax have literally tens of thousands of times more phytoestrogen than any other plant-foods.

Finally: you should know that lavender and marijuana are estrogenic. The estrogen levels are not terribly high, so eating them probably won't cause issues, but *breathing them in* is a different story. Many people inhale cannabis and lavender – through smoke or essential oil – which gives rise to strongly estrogenic effects. Our lungs, after all, are loaded with blood vessels near the surface. These vessels are designed to "catch" oxygens – or estrogenics – and transport them throughout our bodies in the "stream" of blood. Skin transfer is a problem here, too. Avoid lavender scented perfumes or soaps because use of these products has also been shown to cause man boobs.

Estrogenic #2.

MYCOESTROGEN [zearalenone]
The "Fungus Estrogenic"

Zearalenone [ZEA] – the fungus estrogenic – is the singular estrogenic produced by fungus. ZEA is a growing concern. *Mold*, by the way, is in the fungus family, so mold contaminations also produce "estrogenic toxins" (this is how scientists describe ZEA). Anyway, the trouble begins in damp and dark places. Usually problems arise from the massive grain-storage containers, usually on monoculture farms. Researchers around the globe are finding that fungal/mold *estrogenic* contaminations are increasingly common because mass-storage of food-grains is increasingly common. So watch out! Fungus estrogenic ends up in our food grains but also in our farm animals feed and, as a result, ZEA ends up in our grocery store meats. Even corn-fed *buffalo* meat has been found to contain fungus estrogenic ZEA!

Estrogenic #3.

ATRAZINE
The "Herbicide Estrogenic"

Atrazine is the second most common herbicide (#1 is glyphosate). Atrazine is heavily used in spraying corn and other grain crops in the Americas and China and many other food export countries. It is also a major contaminant in drinking water at *astonishingly* high levels. Well, except in countries like Europe where atrazine has been *illegal* since 2004.

Estrogenic #4.

TRICLOSAN & APEs [Alkylphenols]
The "Soap Estrogenics"

Not surprisingly, Europe has also banned the use and production of many APEs. People living in the Americas, however, can find these same APEs hidden in our cleaning products, soaps, and lubricants. Hidden. Even China has tighter regulations on APEs than America.

Triclosan is a nasty estrogenic, too, but at least triclosan makes the "active ingredient" list so you can avoid it.

What about rinsing? Doesn't washing-off soap wash-off these soap estrogenics? Nope. Maybe on a ceramic plate or a steel pot but not on your skin. Estrogenics have fat-like properties (they are "hydrophobic") so estrogenics prefer latching onto your skin rather than washing out into the water. And, like medical hormone creams, estrogenics go through your skin and into your body.

Speaking of water, APEs and Triclosan are definitely common contaminants of drinking water. Egregious water offenders.

Estrogenic #5.

BP & 4-MBC [Benzophenone & 4-Methylbenzylidene]
The "Sunscreen Estrogenics"

Here are two more "skin dippers". Cheap sunblock lotions nearly always have BP and often 4-MBC. Even "organic" sunblocks may contain BP. Oxybenzone, by the way, is a type of BP. Unfortunately, today you even need to check your *hand soaps* for BP.

For some reason, high 4-MBC levels have been found in breakfast cereal. Why is 4-MBC in breakfast cereal? I'm not sure. Strange.

Estrogenic #6.

RED NUMBERS 3 & 40
The "Artificial Red Food Color Estrogenics"

Both Red No. 40 and Red No. 3 are estrogenic.

Red No. 3 remains legal in the USA but Red No. 3 has gotten years of bad press so *food* companies hesitate to use it. They use estrogenic Red No. 40 instead. The negative Red No. 3 media press arose because the FDA *postponed* action on banning Red No. 3 more than 20 times (even after it was implicated in ADHD and other major health problems) yet despite all this, Red No. 3 was never fully banned in the USA.

Also: Red No. 40 and Red No. 3 go by many pseudonyms. I usually advise people to avoid artificial red food coloring *in general* and keep life simple. Capeesh?

Estrogenic #7.

PARABENS
The "Fragrance Estrogenics"

Parabens are found everywhere in cosmetics. They are especially hidden in the ingredient list as "fragrances". This includes your scented laundry detergent, by the way. It's amazing how persistent those cuddly paraben aromas remain in clothing from conventional laundry detergent...and how people "soak" in parabens all day long. My website lists alternatives, since you asked (*www.ajconsultingcompany.com/whatiuse*). Alternatives that work.

Does all this "topically-applied" paraben end up in your body? You bet. Another example of yet *more* estrogenic skin transfer. In fact, one study found over 90% of umbilical cords contained parabens and so did human breastmilk.

Plus, like most estrogenics, parabens are ending up in our waterways and circulating around the globe courtesy of the ocean currents. Polar bears in Northern Alaska, for instance, have been found to contain parabens. Dolphin blubber as well, parabens.

Estrogenic #8.

PHTHALATES
The "Plastic Additive Estrogenics"

Phthalates are an extremely common estrogenic plastic additive. They are not a "main ingredient" in plastic but phthalates fit into molecular "cracks" so they *transfer out* of plastic fairly easily. Just imagine tiny specks of dust or glitter in your plastic (e.g. plastic wrap on your food) and you are on the right track.

Like glitter, you cannot seem to get rid of the phthalates. Scientists find phthalates in *wild* alligator pee, for crying out loud! Researchers also find indoor *air* in California child care facilities contains phthalate levels that "exceed cancer benchmarks". Vinyl flooring and certain baby crib mattresses also contain phthalates.

And, again on the topic of "fragrances", perfumes often contain phthalates (along with the parabens). For example, pregnant women using perfume have been found to contain 167% higher *phthalate* levels than women "off the juice [perfume]". The final nail in the coffin of irony is that phthalates are often used in many medical devices. I call this "healthcareless", wouldn't you?

Estrogenic #9.

BPA & BPS [Bisphenol A & S]
The "Plastic Ingredient Estrogenics"

Rather than an "additive" like phthalates, BPA and BPS are used as "main ingredients" to make certain plastics. BPS is used in place of BPA and is equally unhealthy, so "banning" BPA can lead to problems if alternatives are bad or worse than the banned substance.

BPA has been examined in thousands of studies and is found wanting i.e. terrible for you. The moral of the story is *the more we study estrogenics, the more problematic we recognize them to be.*

Further, BPA is still being found at high levels in major drinking water sources and is still being deceptively used in certain places. For instance, BPA is often sprayed onto the insides of certain metal canned food/beverage jars (in contact with the canned food or beverage) so remain cautious.

Estrogenic #10.

EE2 [17α-Ethinylestradiol]
The "Birth Control Estrogenic"

More than 60% of married women on our planet are currently on chemical contraceptives that contain EE2. Does most of it eventually get urinated out of the human body? Yes. Does it recycle back into the drinking water? At surprisingly high levels, yes. Are we all exposed to some level of estrogenic birth control? Absolutely and sadly, yes.

Indeed, EE2 simply does not efficiently get "caught" or "captured" by the city tap water treatments. Water treatment plants are good at killing virus and bacteria but terrible at removing estrogenics. All estrogenics, actually, not just EE2. And like many estrogenics on this list, EE2 is extremely slow to degrade in the environment. I'm talking about years, here, not months.

Common Problems from Estrogenics

Ok. So now you've glimpsed the Top 10 Estrogenics and where you might find them. Let's discuss problems, starting with fat. This is a summary, so it will need to be dense. Buckle-up!

Since estrogen is made from cholesterol, it has similar properties to fats or oils. The technical term is "lipophilic" or "fat-loving". For example, estrogen mainly floats on water. Like oil. And *artificial* estrogenics, naturally, have similar characteristics to natural estrogen. Estrogenics are fat-lovers.

Furthermore, both estrogen and testosterone are derived from cholesterol. Since these "fatty substances" don't mix well with water, they travel your watery bloodstream on the same protein (called "sex hormone binging globulin" [SHBG]). Ok, now stay with me here: high levels of testosterone cause an increase in SHBG, meaning more testosterone becomes "stuck" to SHBG, riding around your blood. In other words, less testosterone is useable for your body.

Artificial *estrogenics* increase your SHBG. This further leads to less "free" testosterone in our bodies. Therefore, since men and women in first-world countries already have chronically low testosterone – a serious health concern – estrogenics compound this problem by further *lowering our free testosterone*. "Feminizing" males, according to the scientists, is a massively common side-effect from estrogenics. This causes physical changes that even include brain structural changes.

Now we circle back to fat. Because estrogenics are "fat-loving", they also are stored in fat cells. The average "age" of a human fat cell is over 1.5 years, although fat cells have been shown to "live" up to 10 years. The life of a fat cell, by the way, is the length of time that estrogenics are able to hang-out in your fat, slowly being released into your body as you burn fat stores – *if* you burn the fat stores!

To make matters worse, estrogenics are also *fattening*. Estrogenics have been shown to cause insulin resistance, weight gains – including *offspring* weight gains from estrogenic exposures during pregnancy – and what one science paper calls "diabesity". This fattening effect occurs because estrogenics "switch on" the fat-switch in our bodies, a protein called PPARγ. Mold estrogenic, ZEA, has even been used *intentionally* to fatten cattle and other food animals!

Visualize this: while artificial estrogenic usage has been rising, American obesity has been rising in parallel. In 1990, US obesity was around 10%; in the year 2000, it was around 20%. What about 2010? You guessed it: 30%. Meanwhile, unlike America, Europe's obesity rates are under control. Here's the key: remembering that Europe banned many of these artificial estrogenics.

Next, increased rates of depression are linked to estrogenics from the Top 10 List, including higher suicide rates. This appears to be directly caused by estrogenics but is hard to scientifically prove. Depression from estrogenic exposures may be related to the fattening effects of estrogenics, for example, rather than direct neurological changes.

Speaking of growth, estrogenics cause certain cancer cells to grow. Birth control EE2, for instance, is clearly associated with breast cancer, various liver tumors, and cervical cancer. Soy? Also associated with breast cancer promotion. Prostate cancer is another common one found in studies of most estrogenics. To make matters worse, studies are now beginning to come out showing that estrogenic cancers can be "epigenetic" and these increased cancer risks are likely to be passed on to our kids (and grandkids) from *our* estrogenic exposures. Obesity and even cancer are being discovered to potentially be passed along to future generations as well. Not good. It makes me wonder what other bad environmental substances cause epigenetic inheritance (Future book? Absolutely!).

Immune system dysfunctions are another major estrogenic issue. ZEA (fungus/mold estrogenic), for instance, is openly referred to by scientists as "immunotoxic". Heck, BPA and phthalates are too! EE2 from birth control hints at similar problems, as do food dyes, and other estrogenics have clear studies showing immune system derangements.

In addition, people frequently seem to have a variety of immune-related skin problems when consuming *dairy* (for example, eczema inflammation). Think about this: standard industrial dairy is highly *estrogenic*. Milk is stored in plastics that leach estrogenics. The estrogenics include phthalates, APEs, and parabens. The cows are eating grains, such as corn, that often has mycoestrogen (fungus/mold estrogen) plus estrogenic atrazine (weed-killer). All these factors are probably why drinking whole milk was found to *lower testosterone* in men within one hour. Certain scientists blame this effect on the high levels of *cow estrogen* in milk but artificial estrogenics are likely playing a major role too.

Wait...milk has "high levels of cow estrogen", too? Yes, absolutely. According to researchers, farmers are milking *very* pregnant cows and mixing that "cow estrogen milk" with all the other milk. Yay, technology. Either way, estrogenics disrupt immune cells, leading to higher rates of allergies, skin problems, and many other chronic health problems related to immune system dysfunction.

At this point and due to estrogenics, we've seen (1) decreases in testosterone as well as increases in (2) fat, (3) depression, (4) certain cancers, and (5) immune system dysfunctions. We also need to include (6) blood clots as well as (7) major fertility problems. I call these *The 7 Deadly Things* associated with estrogenics and you may recognize that these are *all currently on the rise* in our most medically, technologically, and chemically advanced nations. Our health is on the decline, folks, and estrogenics are at least partly to blame!

Now, I don't want to gloss past infertility. The fact that estrogenics are causing infertility is probably the most alarming problem. The newest evidence clearly shows that single estrogenic exposures *in parents* can lead to future offspring – including grandchildren – to become infertile. This "infertility inheritance" is due to epigenetics, or "marks" on top of our DNA. In fact, and in my own opinion, the field of "epigenetics" will be the most revolutionary in the near future, within scientific fields. Epigenetics is most likely to see the biggest breakthroughs in medical science since it is theoretically possible to change epigenetic "marks" quickly. Sequencing epigenetics, like sequencing DNA, will also see major innovation as it becomes cheap, robotic, and accessible. Will it come in time for you or your family? I'm not sure. Don't wait around. Cut-off your estrogenic exposures today!

Directives for Avoiding Estrogenics

You may notice that I don't generally use the phrase "eliminate estrogenics". If polar bears in Northern Alaska are unable to completely eliminate estrogenics you probably are too. Drastically *diminishing* estrogenics, on the other hand, is an attainable goal. Diminishing estrogenics is a long-term solution to many of our chronic health problems, ideally for *prevention* of *The 7 Deadly Things*.

Realize this process may take years, since estrogenics store in fat cells for years. If you carry excess fat, losing weight can help squeeze out estrogenics from your fat cells but remember: losing weight is also much more achievable when you seriously diminish your estrogenic exposures. They act as a "fat-switch", remember?

So, first of all, stop eating soy and flax. Just stop. Soy protein even has far more estrogenic load than you should be consuming, male or female. Soy anything. Move away from the lavender beauty products, too.

Next, in terms of your brain and especially your children's brains, I'm a huge fan of DHA (a good fat found in fish oil and a major component in our brain). Start babies on DHA in the womb and, after the babies are weaned (breast milk has DHA if the mother is supplementing), spoon-feed toddlers the DHA oil. Just use DHA from something other than flax! Avoid flax.

Moldy grains can be avoided by avoiding grains in general, depending on how serious you are about your health and how serious you are about estrogenic avoidance. Avoiding grains is brutally difficult. I know because I do it. If you are on the fences about whether or not to avoid grains, consider the chronic illnesses that may run in your family. Do you see illnesses that fit *The 7 Deadly Things*? Furthermore, unlike Europe, consider that American farmers also spray those "amber waves of grain" with heavy atrazine loads. Add that to the list of why grains are usually unhealthy. From what I've seen, avoiding grains truly benefits an astonishing number of people. And, sadly, corn should be also considered a "grain".

What about mass-produced "feedlot" corn-fed animals? Extremely estrogenic. We investigate the actual numbers in the book. And like humans (and whales, etc.), farm animals also store estrogenics in their fat. This means foods like bacon are important to buy from more traditional farm sources. In general, can and should you buy local, pasture-raised meats? Can and should you have it packaged in wax paper rather than plastics? You already know the answers.

Next: buy shampoos and body soaps free of Red No. 40 (I can't believe I need to say this!). Also, be sure they are free of BP and APEs. No triclosan, either! You should not be rubbing these things onto your skin. Plus, be more careful with the "fragrances". Fragrances are *major* sources of clandestine estrogenics; nasty estrogenics like parabens and phthalates. On a similar note, if you or your family are regular sunscreen users like Yours Truly, be sure to use something with zinc and avoid BP and 4-MBC. Simple.

Once again, my website *www.ajconsultingcompany.com/whatiuse* has specific products (I am not receiving any financial benefits from them).

Plastics are hard to completely avoid but do what you can. Since things like vinyl flooring and crib mattresses are giving off detectable amounts of estrogenic phthalate "exhaust", you need to heighten your awareness regarding potential estrogenic sources in your overall home environment. I simply cannot list everything so use your best judgement.

Regarding plastics and foods, certainly don't heat anything in plastic. This includes coffee by the way. I personally boil water and use a Chemex® pot. I also roast my own beans so I am a total coffee snob. I suggest you don't even stir hot liquids or foods with plastic items. This includes things like plastic spoons or plastic spatula turners. Use silicone.

Next, use glass for food storage whenever possible and heat foods in glass/ceramic bowls and plates. Glass/ceramic, silicone, and stainless steel are all generally smart choices. I use stainless sippy cups and re-use glass San Pellegrino® bottles for a traveling supply of water.

Finally, a word about water. I get asked about drinking water filtration all the time and for some reason there seems to be mass confusion. EE2, parabens, phthalates, atrazine, BPA, and other estrogenics are clearly in most our *drinking* water supply. Again, we go through the staggering details in the book. Fortunately, you will remove almost every estrogenic molecule from your water if your water filter has "activated charcoal". Change the filter as recommended and it is that simple. Good luck and I hope you can start to erase your "estrogenic history" today!

Acknowledgements

All my editors indelibly stamped this book with their own unique flavors. Not surprisingly, my good friends Karen and Joe Kelly deserve special recognition for their thorough and detailed editing work. Joe Kelly also conceived the sub title for this book. In addition, the early-readings from Allison Jay (of course!), my parents, Allison's parents, Juan Carmona, Christian and Darcie Nielson, Peter and Helen Syski, Caitlin Jay, Dave Englestad, and Tim Drake are all profoundly appreciated. Finally, I want to thank Matthew Vicinanzo for the incredible title "Estrogeneration". Genius.

References

Introduction

1. Forouzanfar, M. H., Foreman, K. J., Delossantos, A. M., Lozano, R., Lopez, A. D., Murray, C. J., and Naghavi, M. (2011) Breast and cervical cancer in 187 countries between 1980 and 2010: a systematic analysis. *Lancet* **378**, 1461-1484

Chapter 1

1. Braekevelt, E., Lau, B. P., Tague, B., Popovic, S., and Tittlemier, S. A. (2011) Effect of cooking on concentrations of beta-estradiol and metabolites in model matrices and beef. *J Agric Food Chem* **59**, 915-920

2. Benita, Y., Cao, Z., Giallourakis, C., Li, C., Gardet, A., and Xavier, R. J. (2010) Gene enrichment profiles reveal T-cell development, differentiation, and lineage-specific transcription factors including ZBTB25 as a novel NF-AT repressor. *Blood* http://xavierlab2.mgh.harvard.edu/EnrichmentProfiler/index.html **115**, 5376-5384

3. www.ajconsultingcompany.com/estrogenics.

Chapter 2

1. Ohinata, K., Agui, S., and Yoshikawa, M. (2007) Soymorphins, novel mu opioid peptides derived from soy beta-conglycinin beta-subunit, have anxiolytic activities. *Biosci Biotechnol Biochem* **71**, 2618-2621

2. Thompson, L. U., Boucher, B. A., Liu, Z., Cotterchio, M., and Kreiger, N. (2006) Phytoestrogen content of foods consumed in Canada, including isoflavones, lignans, and coumestan. *Nutr Cancer* **54**, 184-201

3. Lee, S. Y., Oh, S. M., and Chung, K. H. (2006) Estrogenic effects of marijuana smoke condensate and cannabinoid compounds. *Toxicol Appl Pharmacol* **214**, 270-278

4.   Diaz, A., Luque, L., Badar, Z., Kornic, S., and Danon, M. (2016) Prepubertal gynecomastia and chronic lavender exposure: report of three cases. *J Pediatr Endocrinol Metab* **29**, 103-107

5.   Henley, D. V., Lipson, N., Korach, K. S., and Bloch, C. A. (2007) Prepubertal gynecomastia linked to lavender and tea tree oils. *N Engl J Med* **356**, 479-485

6.   Adlercreutz, H., Hockerstedt, K., Bannwart, C., Bloigu, S., Hamalainen, E., Fotsis, T., and Ollus, A. (1987) Effect of dietary components, including lignans and phytoestrogens, on enterohepatic circulation and liver metabolism of estrogens and on sex hormone binding globulin (SHBG). *J Steroid Biochem* **27**, 1135-1144

7.   Lampe, J. W., Atkinson, C., and Hullar, M. A. (2006) Assessing exposure to lignans and their metabolites in humans. *J AOAC Int* **89**, 1174-1181

8.   Lamblin, F., Hano, C., Fliniaux, O., Mesnard, F., Fliniaux, M. A., and Laine, E. (2008) [Interest of lignans in prevention and treatment of cancers]. *Med Sci (Paris)* **24**, 511-519

9.   Adolphe, J. L., Whiting, S. J., Juurlink, B. H., Thorpe, L. U., and Alcorn, J. (2010) Health effects with consumption of the flax lignan secoisolariciresinol diglucoside. *Br J Nutr* **103**, 929-938

10.   Peterson, J., Dwyer, J., Adlercreutz, H., Scalbert, A., Jacques, P., and McCullough, M. L. (2010) Dietary lignans: physiology and potential for cardiovascular disease risk reduction. *Nutr Rev* **68**, 571-603

11.   Bakos, K., Kovacs, R., Staszny, A., Sipos, D. K., Urbanyi, B., Muller, F., Csenki, Z., and Kovacs, B. (2013) Developmental toxicity and estrogenic potency of zearalenone in zebrafish (Danio rerio). *Aquat Toxicol* **136-137**, 13-21

12.   Mazumder, P. M., and Sasmal, D. (2001) Mycotoxins - limits and regulations. *Anc Sci Life* **20**, 1-19

13.   Lee, H. J., and Ryu, D. (2015) Advances in Mycotoxin Research: Public Health Perspectives. *J Food Sci* **80**, T2970-2983

14.   Nations, F. a. A. O. o. t. U. (2003) Worldwide regulations for mycotoxins in food and feed in 2003.

15. J. Fink-Gremmels, H. M. (2007) Clinical effects and biochemical mechanisms associated with exposure to the mycoestrogen zearalenone. *Animal Feed Science and Technology* **137**, 326-341

16. Coe, J. E., Ishak, K. G., Ward, J. M., and Ross, M. J. (1992) Tamoxifen prevents induction of hepatic neoplasia by zeranol, an estrogenic food contaminant. *Proc Natl Acad Sci USA* **89**, 1085-1089

17. Kriszt, R., Winkler, Z., Polyak, A., Kuti, D., Molnar, C., Hrabovszky, E., Kallo, I., Szoke, Z., Ferenczi, S., and Kovacs, K. J. (2015) Xenoestrogens Ethinyl Estradiol and Zearalenone Cause Precocious Puberty in Female Rats via Central Kisspeptin Signaling. *Endocrinology* **156**, 3996-4007

18. Massart, F., Meucci, V., Saggese, G., and Soldani, G. (2008) High growth rate of girls with precocious puberty exposed to estrogenic mycotoxins. *J Pediatr* **152**, 690-695, 695 e691

19. Vasatkova, A., Krizova, S., Krystofova, O., Adam, V., Zeman, L., Beklova, M., and Kizek, R. (2009) Effect of naturally mouldy wheat or fungi administration on metallothioneins level in brain tissues of rats. *Neuro Endocrinol Lett* **30 Suppl 1**, 163-168

20. Zheng, W., Pan, S., Wang, G., Wang, Y. J., Liu, Q., Gu, J., Yuan, Y., Liu, X. Z., Liu, Z. P., and Bian, J. C. (2016) Zearalenone impairs the male reproductive system functions via inducing structural and functional alterations of sertoli cells. *Environ Toxicol Pharmacol* **42**, 146-155

21. Zinedine, A., Soriano, J. M., Molto, J. C., and Manes, J. (2007) Review on the toxicity, occurrence, metabolism, detoxification, regulations and intake of zearalenone: an oestrogenic mycotoxin. *Food Chem Toxicol* **45**, 1-18

22. Cortinovis, C., Pizzo, F., Spicer, L. J., and Caloni, F. (2013) Fusarium mycotoxins: effects on reproductive function in domestic animals--a review. *Theriogenology* **80**, 557-564

23. Leung, M. C., Diaz-Llano, G., and Smith, T. K. (2006) Mycotoxins in pet food: a review on worldwide prevalence and preventative strategies. *J Agric Food Chem* **54**, 9623-9635

24. Boermans, H. J., and Leung, M. C. (2007) Mycotoxins and the pet food industry: toxicological evidence and risk assessment. *Int J Food Microbiol* **119**, 95-102

25. Pazaiti, A., Kontos, M., and Fentiman, I. S. (2012) ZEN and the art of breast health maintenance. *Int J Clin Pract* **66**, 28-36

26. Eldridge, J. C., Stevens, J. T., and Breckenridge, C. B. (2008) Atrazine interaction with estrogen expression systems. *Rev Environ Contam Toxicol* **196**, 147-160

27. Wilce, R. (2012) Atrazine: A Molecular Bull in a China Shop: http://www.prwatch.org/news/2012/02/11263/atrazine-molecular-bull-china-shop.

28. (2015) EPA Forced to Study Impact of Atrazine and Glyphosate on US Endangered Species: http://sustainablepulse.com/2015/06/28/epa-forced-to-study-impact-of-atrazine-and-glyphosate-on-us-endangered-species/.

29. Greenlee, A. R., Ellis, T. M., and Berg, R. L. (2004) Low-dose agrochemicals and lawn-care pesticides induce developmental toxicity in murine preimplantation embryos. *Environ Health Perspect* **112**, 703-709

30. Lubinsky, M. (2012) Hypothesis: Estrogen related thrombosis explains the pathogenesis and epidemiology of gastroschisis. *Am J Med Genet A* **158A**, 808-811

31. Yuan, M., Bai, M. Z., Huang, X. F., Zhang, Y., Liu, J., Hu, M. H., Zheng, W. Q., and Jin, F. (2015) Preimplantation Exposure to Bisphenol A and Triclosan May Lead to Implantation Failure in Humans. *Biomed Res Int* **2015**, 184845

32. Lu, Z., and Gan, J. (2014) Analysis, toxicity, occurrence and biodegradation of nonylphenol isomers: a review. *Environ Int* **73**, 334-345

33. Soto, A. M., Justicia, H., Wray, J. W., and Sonnenschein, C. (1991) p-Nonyl-phenol: an estrogenic xenobiotic released from "modified" polystyrene. *Environ Health Perspect* **92**, 167-173

34. Watanabe, H., Suzuki, A., Goto, M., Lubahn, D. B., Handa, H., and Iguchi, T. (2004) Tissue-specific estrogenic and non-estrogenic effects of a xenoestrogen, nonylphenol. *J Mol Endocrinol* **33**, 243-252

35. (2011) China Adds Nonylphenols to Restricted Substances List: https://chemicalwatch.com/6300/china-adds-nonylphenols-to-restricted-substances-list.

36. Soares, A., Guieysse, B., Jefferson, B., Cartmell, E., and Lester, J. N. (2008) Nonylphenol in the environment: a critical review on occurrence, fate, toxicity and treatment in wastewaters. *Environ Int* **34**, 1033-1049

37. (2016) Commission Implementing Decision (EU) 2016/110 of 27 January 2016 not approving triclosan as an existing active substance for use in biocidal products for product-type 1. *Official Journal of the European Union*

38. (2016) Safety and Effectiveness of Consumer Antiseptics; Topical Antimicrobial Drug Products for Over-the-Counter Human Use. *Federal Register* **81**

39. Wang, X., Chen, X., Feng, X., Chang, F., Chen, M., Xia, Y., and Chen, L. (2015) Triclosan causes spontaneous abortion accompanied by decline of estrogen sulfotransferase activity in humans and mice. *Sci Rep* **5**, 18252

40. Baer, A., and Mayer, G. (2012) Comparative anatomy of slime glands in onychophora (velvet worms). *J Morphol* **273**, 1079-1088

41. Puy-Azurmendi, E., Olivares, A., Vallejo, A., Ortiz-Zarragoitia, M., Pina, B., Zuloaga, O., and Cajaraville, M. P. (2014) Estrogenic effects of nonylphenol and octylphenol isomers in vitro by recombinant yeast assay (RYA) and in vivo with early life stages of zebrafish. *Sci Total Environ* **466-467**, 1-10

42. Huang, Y. F., Wang, P. W., Huang, L. W., Yang, W., Yu, C. J., Yang, S. H., Chiu, H. H., and Chen, M. L. (2014) Nonylphenol in pregnant women and their matching fetuses: placental transfer and potential risks of infants. *Environ Res* **134**, 143-148

43. Bechi, N., Ietta, F., Romagnoli, R., Jantra, S., Cencini, M., Galassi, G., Serchi, T., Corsi, I., Focardi, S., and Paulesu, L. (2010) Environmental levels of para-nonylphenol are able to affect cytokine secretion in human placenta. *Environ Health Perspect* **118**, 427-431

44. Kim, S., and Choi, K. (2014) Occurrences, toxicities, and ecological risks of benzophenone-3, a common component of organic sunscreen products: a mini-review. *Environ Int* **70**, 143-157

45. Hamann, I., Schmutzler, C, Kirschmeyer, P, Jarry, H, Köhrle, J. (2006) 4-methylbenzylidene-camphor (4MBC) causes pituitary effects comparable to hypothyroidism. *Endocrine Abstracts* **11**

46. Jimenez-Diaz, I., Molina-Molina, J. M., Zafra-Gomez, A., Ballesteros, O., Navalon, A., Real, M., Saenz, J. M., Fernandez, M. F., and Olea, N. (2013) Simultaneous determination of the UV-filters benzyl salicylate, phenyl salicylate, octyl salicylate, homosalate, 3-(4-methylbenzylidene) camphor and 3-benzylidene camphor in human placental tissue by LC-MS/MS. Assessment of their in vitro endocrine activity. *J Chromatogr B Analyt Technol Biomed Life Sci* **936**, 80-87

47. Coronado, M., De Haro, H., Deng, X., Rempel, M. A., Lavado, R., and Schlenk, D. (2008) Estrogenic activity and reproductive effects of the UV-filter oxybenzone (2-hydroxy-4-methoxyphenyl-methanone) in fish. *Aquat Toxicol* **90**, 182-187

48. Brunk, D. (2014) Benzophenone named 2014 contact allergen of the year. *skinandallergynews.com*

49. (2015) Commision Regulation (EU) 2015/1298 of 28 July 2015 amending Annexes II and VI to Regulation (EC) No 1223/2009 of the European Parliament and of the Council on cosmetic products.

50. (1997) Photoprotective/cosmetic compositions comprising at least one solid organic sunscreen compound and salicylate solvents therefor

51. Kunisue, T., Chen, Z., Buck Louis, G. M., Sundaram, R., Hediger, M. L., Sun, L., and Kannan, K. (2012) Urinary concentrations of benzophenone-type UV filters in U.S. women and their association with endometriosis. *Environ Sci Technol* **46**, 4624-4632

52. Batada, A., and Jacobson, M. F. (2016) Prevalence of Artificial Food Colors in Grocery Store Products Marketed to Children. *Clin Pediatr (Phila)* **55**, 1113-1119

53. Arnold, L. E., Lofthouse, N., and Hurt, E. (2012) Artificial food colors and attention-deficit/hyperactivity symptoms: conclusions to dye for. *Neurotherapeutics* **9**, 599-609

54. Dees, C., Askari, M., Garrett, S., Gehrs, K., Henley, D., and Ardies, C. M. (1997) Estrogenic and DNA-damaging activity of Red No. 3 in human breast cancer cells. *Environ Health Perspect* **105 Suppl 3**, 625-632

55. el-Yousef, M. K., and Manier, D. H. (1974) Letter: Estrogen effects on phenothiazine derivative blood levels. *JAMA* **228**, 827-828

56. (2008) Modernising the rules on food additives and labelling of azo dyes, http://www.europarl.europa.eu/sides/getDoc.do?language=en&type=IM-PRESS&reference=20080707IPR33563. *Eeropean Parliament Plenary Sessions*

57. (2016) Food labelling and packaging, https://www.gov.uk/food-labelling-and-packaging/food-and-drink-warnings.

58. http://www.ukfoodguide.net/e129.htm.

59. http://www.foodcolor.com/enumbers.

60. http://www.feingold.org/Research/PDFstudies/List-of-Colorants.pdf.

61. (2011) Scientific Opinion on the re-evaluation of Erythrosine (E 127) as a food additive, https://www.efsa.europa.eu/en/efsajournal/pub/1854. *EFSA Panel on Food Additives and Nutrient Sources Added to Food*

62. Greger, M. (2015) Red Dye No. 3 and Thyroid Cancer: http://nutritionfacts.org/2015/04/30/coloring-to-dye-for-dangers-of-red-no-3/.

63. Yankell, S. L., and Loux, J. J. (1977) Acute toxicity testing of erythrosine and sodium fluorescein in mice and rats. *J Periodontol* **48**, 228-231

64. Mailman, R. B., Ferris, R. M., Tang, F. L., Vogel, R. A., Kilts, C. D., Lipton, M. A., Smith, D. A., Mueller, R. A., and Breese, G. R. (1980) Erythrosine (Red No. 3) and its nonspecific biochemical actions: what relation to behavioral changes? *Science* **207**, 535-537

65.   Mailman, R. B., and Lewis, M. H. (1983) Food additives and childhood hyperactivity. *ASDC J Dent Child* **50**, 283-286

66.   McCann, D., Barrett, A., Cooper, A., Crumpler, D., Dalen, L., Grimshaw, K., Kitchin, E., Lok, K., Porteous, L., Prince, E., Sonuga-Barke, E., Warner, J. O., and Stevenson, J. (2007) Food additives and hyperactive behaviour in 3-year-old and 8/9-year-old children in the community: a randomised, double-blinded, placebo-controlled trial. *Lancet* **370**, 1560-1567

67.   (1990) FDA Limits Red Dye No. 3: http://www.nytimes.com/1990/01/30/science/fda-limits-red-dye-no-3.html.

68.   (2015) Color additive status list, http://www.fda.gov/ForIndustry/ColorAdditives/ColorAdditive Inventories/ucm106626.htm. *FDA*

69.   Golden, R., Gandy, J., and Vollmer, G. (2005) A review of the endocrine activity of parabens and implications for potential risks to human health. *Crit Rev Toxicol* **35**, 435-458

70.   Kim, S. M., Jung, E. M., An, B. S., Hwang, I., Vo, T. T., Kim, S. R., Lee, S. M., Choi, K. C., and Jeung, E. B. (2012) Additional effects of bisphenol A and paraben on the induction of calbindin-D(9K) and progesterone receptor via an estrogen receptor pathway in rat pituitary GH3 cells. *J Physiol Pharmacol* **63**, 445-455

71.   (2014) EU Bans Five Parabens, Restricts Triclosan in Cosmetics: https://chemicalwatch.com/19141/eu-bans-five-parabens-restricts-triclosan-in-cosmetics.

72.   Aker, A. M., Watkins, D. J., Johns, L. E., Ferguson, K. K., Soldin, O. P., Anzalota Del Toro, L. V., Alshawabkeh, A. N., Cordero, J. F., and Meeker, J. D. (2016) Phenols and parabens in relation to reproductive and thyroid hormones in pregnant women. *Environ Res* **151**, 30-37

73.   Hegazy, H. G., Ali, E. H., and Elgoly, A. H. (2015) Interplay between pro-inflammatory cytokines and brain oxidative stress biomarkers: evidence of parallels between butyl paraben intoxication and the valproic acid brain physiopathology in autism rat model. *Cytokine* **71**, 173-180

74. Ali, E. H., and Elgoly, A. H. (2013) Combined prenatal and postnatal butyl paraben exposure produces autism-like symptoms in offspring: comparison with valproic acid autistic model. *Pharmacol Biochem Behav* **111**, 102-110

75. Kawaguchi, M., Morohoshi, K., Imai, H., Morita, M., Kato, N., and Himi, T. (2010) Maternal exposure to isobutyl-paraben impairs social recognition in adult female rats. *Exp Anim* **59**, 631-635

76. Kawaguchi, M., Irie, K., Morohoshi, K., Watanabe, G., Taya, K., Morita, M., Kondo, Y., Imai, H., and Himi, T. (2009) Maternal isobutyl-paraben exposure alters anxiety and passive avoidance test performance in adult male rats. *Neurosci Res* **65**, 136-140

77. Serrano, S. E., Braun, J., Trasande, L., Dills, R., and Sathyanarayana, S. (2014) Phthalates and diet: a review of the food monitoring and epidemiology data. *Environ Health* **13**, 43

78. Liang, Y., and Xu, Y. (2014) Emission of phthalates and phthalate alternatives from vinyl flooring and crib mattress covers: the influence of temperature. *Environ Sci Technol* **48**, 14228-14237

79. Moreira, M. A., Andre, L. C., and Cardeal, Z. L. (2014) Analysis of phthalate migration to food simulants in plastic containers during microwave operations. *Int J Environ Res Public Health* **11**, 507-526

80. Chou, K., and Wright, R. O. (2006) Phthalates in food and medical devices. *J Med Toxicol* **2**, 126-135

81. Al-Saleh, I., and Elkhatib, R. (2016) Screening of phthalate esters in 47 branded perfumes. *Environ Sci Pollut Res Int* **23**, 455-468

82. Harris, C. A., Henttu, P., Parker, M. G., and Sumpter, J. P. (1997) The estrogenic activity of phthalate esters in vitro. *Environ Health Perspect* **105**, 802-811

83. Chen, F. P., and Chien, M. H. (2014) Lower concentrations of phthalates induce proliferation in human breast cancer cells. *Climacteric* **17**, 377-384

84. Maradonna, F., Evangelisti, M., Gioacchini, G., Migliarini, B., Olivotto, I., and Carnevali, O. (2013) Assay of vtg, ERs and PPARs as endpoint for the rapid in vitro screening of the harmful effect of Di-(2-ethylhexyl)-phthalate (DEHP) and phthalic acid (PA) in zebrafish primary hepatocyte cultures. *Toxicol In Vitro* **27**, 84-91

85.   (2015) Amending Annex II to Directive 2011/65/EU of the European Parliament and of the Council as regards the list of restricted substances , http://ec.europa.eu/transparency/regdoc/rep/3/2015/EN/3-2015-2067-EN-F1-1.PDF.

86.   Denmark yields to EU pressure and scraps phthalate ban, http://cphpost.dk/news/international/denmark-yields-to-eu-pressure-and-scraps-phthalate-ban.html. *CPH Post Online*

87.   FDA: http://www.fda.gov/Cosmetics/ProductsIngredients/Ingredients/ucm128250.htm.

88.   US Consumer Product Safety Commission: https://www.cpsc.gov/Business--Manufacturing/Business-Education/Business-Guidance/Phthalates-Information.

89.   Worland, J. (2015) The strange connection between saunas and longevity. *Time Magazine*

90.   Crinnion, W. J. (2010) Toxic effects of the easily avoidable phthalates and parabens. *Altern Med Rev* **15**, 190-196

91.   Tasker, R. C., and Sharpe, R. M. (2016) Dealing with phthalates in medical devices: a case of primum non nocere (first do no harm)? *Intensive Care Med* **42**, 602-604

92.   Wojtowicz, A. K., Szychowski, K. A., Wnuk, A., and Kajta, M. (2016) Dibutyl Phthalate (DBP)-Induced Apoptosis and Neurotoxicity are Mediated via the Aryl Hydrocarbon Receptor (AhR) but not by Estrogen Receptor Alpha (ERalpha), Estrogen Receptor Beta (ERbeta), or Peroxisome Proliferator-Activated Receptor Gamma (PPARgamma) in Mouse Cortical Neurons. *Neurotox Res*

93.   Ponsonby, A. L., Symeonides, C., Vuillermin, P., Mueller, J., Sly, P. D., and Saffery, R. (2016) Epigenetic regulation of neurodevelopmental genes in response to in utero exposure to phthalate plastic chemicals: How can we delineate causal effects? *Neurotoxicology* **55**, 92-101

94.   Huang, H. B., Pan, W. H., Chang, J. W., Chiang, H. C., Guo, Y. L., Jaakkola, J. J., and Huang, P. C. (2016) Does exposure to phthalates influence thyroid function and growth hormone

homeostasis? The Taiwan Environmental Survey for Toxicants (TEST) 2013. *Environ Res* **153**, 63-72

95.   Latini, G., Dipaola, L., Andreassi, M. G., Rocchiccioli, S., Massaro, M., and Picano, E. (2016) Interaction between Ionizing Radiation and Phthalates: An Unrecognized Risk for Human Health? *Mini Rev Med Chem*

96.   Chen, D., Kannan, K., Tan, H., Zheng, Z., Feng, Y. L., Wu, Y., and Widelka, M. (2016) Bisphenol Analogues Other Than BPA: Environmental Occurrence, Human Exposure, and Toxicity-A Review. *Environ Sci Technol* **50**, 5438-5453

97.   Dupont, J., White, P. J., Johnston, K. M., Heggtveit, H. A., McDonald, B. E., Grundy, S. M., and Bonanome, A. (1989) Food safety and health effects of canola oil. *J Am Coll Nutr* **8**, 360-375

98.   Dreher, M. L., and Davenport, A. J. (2013) Hass avocado composition and potential health effects. *Crit Rev Food Sci Nutr* **53**, 738-750

99.   Mailman, D., and Rose, C. (1990) Binding and solubility of oleic acid to laboratory materials: a possible artifact. *Life Sci* **47**, 1737-1744

100.   Sun, F., Kang, L., Xiang, X., Li, H., Luo, X., Luo, R., Lu, C., and Peng, X. (2016) Recent advances and progress in the detection of bisphenol A. *Anal Bioanal Chem* **408**, 6913-6927

101.   Legislatures, N. C. o. S. NCSL policy update: state restrictions on bisphenol a (BPA) in consumer products, http://www.ncsl.org/research/environment-and-natural-resources/policy-update-on-state-restrictions-on-bisphenol-a.aspx.

102.   Harrington, R. (2010) Denmark and France maintain bisphenol A ban, http://www.foodqualitynews.com/Regulation-and-safety/Denmark-and-France-maintain-bisphenol-A-ban.

103.   EFSA. (2015) No consumer health risk from bisphenol A exposure, https://www.efsa.europa.eu/en/press/news/150121.

104.   FSN. (2015) Denmark's national food institute says Europe's BPA safe levels need work,

http://www.foodsafetynews.com/2015/02/denmarks-national-food-institute-says-europes-bpa-safe-levels-need-work/.

105. Ejaredar, M., Lee, Y., Roberts, D. J., Sauve, R., and Dewey, D. (2016) Bisphenol A exposure and children's behavior: A systematic review. *J Expo Sci Environ Epidemiol*

106. Engler-Chiurazzi, E. B., Brown, C. M., Povroznik, J. M., and Simpkins, J. W. (2016) Estrogens as neuroprotectants: Estrogenic actions in the context of cognitive aging and brain injury. *Prog Neurobiol*

107. Tan, L., Wang, S., Wang, Y., He, M., and Liu, D. (2015) Bisphenol A exposure accelerated the aging process in the nematode Caenorhabditis elegans. *Toxicol Lett* **235**, 75-83

108. Liu, T., Li, Y., Zhao, X., Zhang, M., and Gu, W. (2014) Ethylparaben affects lifespan, fecundity, and the expression levels of ERR, EcR and YPR in Drosophila melanogaster. *J Insect Physiol* **71**, 1-7

109. Christin-Maitre, S. (2013) History of oral contraceptive drugs and their use worldwide. *Best Pract Res Clin Endocrinol Metab* **27**, 3-12

110. Institute, G. (2016) Minor's access to contraceptive services, https://www.guttmacher.org/state-policy/explore/minors-access-contraceptive-services.

111. www.ajconsultingcompany.com/ee2_drug_labels.html.

Chapter 3

1. Tillekeratne, L. M., Sherette, A., Fulmer, J. A., Hupe, L., Hupe, D., Gabbara, S., Peliska, J. A., and Hudson, R. A. (2002) Differential inhibition of polymerase and strand-transfer activities of HIV-1 reverse transcriptase. *Bioorg Med Chem Lett* **12**, 525-528

2. Angell, M. (2005) The Truth about the Drug Companies : How They Deceive Us and What to Do about It. *Random House Trade Paperback Ed.*

3. Ak, N., Koo, H. C., Hamid Jan, J. M., Mohd Nasir, M. T., Tan, S. Y., Appukutty, M., Nurliyana, A. R., Thielecke, F., Hopkins, S., Ong, M. K., Ning, C., and Tee, E. S. (2015) Whole Grain Intakes in the Diets Of Malaysian Children and Adolescents--Findings from the MyBreakfast Study. *PLoS One* **10**, e0138247

4. Nestle, M. Food Politics Blog, Conflicts-of-Interest: http://www.foodpolitics.com/tag/conflicts-of-interest/.

5. Ge, J. H., and Chang, B. (2006) [Estrogenic activities of parabens]. *Wei Sheng Yan Jiu* **35**, 650-652

6. Ross, G. (2006) A perspective on the safety of cosmetic products: a position paper of the American Council on Science and Health. *Int J Toxicol* **25**, 269-277

7. Gobry, P.-E. (2016) Big Science is Broken: http://theweek.com/articles/618141/big-science-broken.

8. Wilson, W. A. (2016) Scientific Regress: http://www.firstthings.com/article/2016/05/scientific-regress.

9. Lindsay, S. H., and Claywell, L. G. (1999) Considering soy: its estrogenic effects may protect women. *J Obstet Gynecol Neonatal Nurs* **28**, 21-24

10. Shurtleff, W., Aoyagi, A. (2013) History of Tofu and Tofu Products: Extensively Annotated Bibliography and Sourcebook. *Soyinfo Center*

11. Soyinfo Center Website Mission: http://www.soyinfocenter.com/index.php.

12. Pawlowski, J. W., Martin, B. R., McCabe, G. P., McCabe, L., Jackson, G. S., Peacock, M., Barnes, S., and Weaver, C. M. (2015) Impact of equol-producing capacity and soy-isoflavone profiles of supplements on bone calcium retention in postmenopausal women: a randomized crossover trial. *Am J Clin Nutr* **102**, 695-703

13. (2015) Add Soy to Your Diet, but Don't Subtract Other Healthy Foods. http://www.health.harvard.edu/staying-healthy/add-soy-to-your-diet-but-dont-subtract-other-healthy-foods

14. Isidori, M., Lavorgna, M., Palumbo, M., Piccioli, V., and Parrella, A. (2007) Influence of alkylphenols and trace elements in toxic, genotoxic, and endocrine disruption activity of wastewater treatment plants. *Environ Toxicol Chem* **26**, 1686-1694

15. Doerge, D. R., and Sheehan, D. M. (2002) Goitrogenic and estrogenic activity of soy isoflavones. *Environ Health Perspect* **110 Suppl 3**, 349-353

16. Hydovitz, J. D. (1960) Occurrence of goiter in an infant on a soy diet. *N Engl J Med* **262**, 351-353

17. Ripp, J. A. (1961) Soybean-induced goiter. *Am J Dis Child* **102**, 106-109

18. Liener, I. E., and Seto, T. A. (1955) Nonspecific effect of soybean hemagglutinin on tumor growth. *Cancer Res* **15**, 407-409

19. D'Adamo, C. R., and Sahin, A. (2014) Soy foods and supplementation: a review of commonly perceived health benefits and risks. *Altern Ther Health Med* **20 Suppl 1**, 39-51

Chapter 4

1. MN Dept of Health, Statewide Safe-Eating Guidelines for Fish: http://www.health.state.mn.us/divs/eh/fish/eating/kidmom/index.html.

2. Zota, A. R., Phillips, C. A., and Mitro, S. D. (2016) Recent Fast Food Consumption and Bisphenol A and Phthalates Exposures among the U.S. Population in NHANES, 2003-2010. *Environ Health Perspect*

3. Santos, E. A., Cruz, C., Carraschi, S. P., Marques Silva, J. R., Grossi Botelho, R., Velini, E. D., and Pitelli, R. A. (2015) Atrazine levels in the Jaboticabal water stream (Sao Paulo State, Brazil) and its toxicological effects on the pacu fish Piaractus mesopotamicus. *Arh Hig Rada Toksikol* **66**, 73-82

4. Blanco, F., Almeida, SDB, Matallo, MB (2013) Herbicide — Soil Interactions, Applied to Maize Crop Under Brazilian Conditions. *Agricultural and Biological Sciences: Herbicides - Current Research and Case Studies in Use*

5. Jin, R., and Ke, J. (2002) Impact of atrazine disposal on the water resources of the Yang river in Zhangjiakou area in China. *Bull Environ Contam Toxicol* **68**, 893-900

6. Gu, J. G., Fan, Y., and Gu, J. D. (2003) Biodegradability of Atrazine, Cyanazine and Dicamba under methanogenic condition in three soils of China. *Chemosphere* **52**, 1515-1521

7. Biello, D. (2010) How Fast Can Microbes Clean Up the Gulf Oil Spill? . *Scientific American*

8. Sousa, A. S., Duavi, W. C., Cavalcante, R. M., Milhome, M. A., and do Nascimento, R. F. (2016) Estimated Levels of Environmental

Contamination and Health Risk Assessment for Herbicides and Insecticides in Surface Water of Ceara, Brazil. *Bull Environ Contam Toxicol* **96**, 90-95

9. ATSDR, A. f. T. S. D. R. (2003) Public Health Statement for Atrazine.

10. Smalling, K. L., Reeves, R., Muths, E., Vandever, M., Battaglin, W. A., Hladik, M. L., and Pierce, C. L. (2015) Pesticide concentrations in frog tissue and wetland habitats in a landscape dominated by agriculture. *Sci Total Environ* **502**, 80-90

11. Thurman, E. M., Bastian, K. C., and Mollhagen, T. (2000) Occurrence of cotton herbicides and insecticides in playa lakes of the High Plains of West Texas. *Sci Total Environ* **248**, 189-200

12. Kalkhoff, S. J., Lee, K. E., Porter, S. D., Terrio, P. J., and Thurman, E. M. (2003) Herbicides and herbicide degradation products in Upper Midwest agricultural streams during August base-flow conditions. *J Environ Qual* **32**, 1025-1035

13. Staniszewska, M., Nehring, I., and Mudrak-Cegiolka, S. (2016) Changes of concentrations and possibility of accumulation of bisphenol A and alkylphenols, depending on biomass and composition, in zooplankton of the Southern Baltic (Gulf of Gdansk). *Environ Pollut* **213**, 489-501

14. Mortazavi, S., Bakhtiari, A. R., Sari, A. E., Bahramifar, N., and Rahbarizade, F. (2012) Phenolic endocrine disrupting chemicals (EDCs) in Anzali Wetland, Iran: elevated concentrations of 4-nonylphenol, octhylphenol and bisphenol A. *Mar Pollut Bull* **64**, 1067-1073

15. Hamlin, H. J., Marciano, K., and Downs, C. A. (2015) Migration of nonylphenol from food-grade plastic is toxic to the coral reef fish species Pseudochromis fridmani. *Chemosphere* **139**, 223-228

16. Kawahata, H., Ohta, H., Inoue, M., and Suzuki, A. (2004) Endocrine disrupter nonylphenol and bisphenol A contamination in Okinawa and Ishigaki Islands, Japan--within coral reefs and adjacent river mouths. *Chemosphere* **55**, 1519-1527

17. Net, S., Sempere, R., Delmont, A., Paluselli, A., and Ouddane, B. (2015) Occurrence, fate, behavior and ecotoxicological state of

phthalates in different environmental matrices. *Environ Sci Technol* **49**, 4019-4035

18.   North, M. L., Takaro, T. K., Diamond, M. L., and Ellis, A. K. (2014) Effects of phthalates on the development and expression of allergic disease and asthma. *Ann Allergy Asthma Immunol* **112**, 496-502

19.   Liang, Y., and Xu, Y. (2014) Emission of phthalates and phthalate alternatives from vinyl flooring and crib mattress covers: the influence of temperature. *Environ Sci Technol* **48**, 14228-14237

20.   Wan, Y., Xue, J., and Kannan, K. (2015) Occurrence of benzophenone-3 in indoor air from Albany, New York, USA, and its implications for inhalation exposure. *Sci Total Environ* **537**, 304-308

21.   (2013) Danish Ministry of the Environment, Environmental Protection Agency: Survey of Parabens, Part of the LOUS-Review, Project No. 1474.

22.   Xue, J., Sasaki, N., Elangovan, M., Diamond, G., and Kannan, K. (2015) Elevated Accumulation of Parabens and their Metabolites in Marine Mammals from the United States Coastal Waters. *Environ Sci Technol* **49**, 12071-12079

23.   Hammer, J., Kraak, M. H., and Parsons, J. R. (2012) Plastics in the marine environment: the dark side of a modern gift. *Rev Environ Contam Toxicol* **220**, 1-44

24.   Zhang, L. P., Wang, X. H., Ya, M. L., Wu, Y. L., Li, Y. Y., and Zhang, Z. L. (2014) Levels of endocrine disrupting compounds in South China Sea. *Mar Pollut Bull* **85**, 628-633

25.   Wang, G., Ma, P., Zhang, Q., Lewis, J., Lacey, M., Furukawa, Y., O'Reilly, S. E., Meaux, S., McLachlan, J., and Zhang, S. (2012) Endocrine disrupting chemicals in New Orleans surface waters and Mississippi Sound sediments. *J Environ Monit* **14**, 1353-1364

26.   Mosquin, P., Whitmore, R. W., and Chen, W. (2012) Estimation of upper centile concentrations using historical atrazine monitoring data from community water systems. *J Environ Qual* **41**, 834-844

27.   Mela, M., Guiloski, I. C., Doria, H. B., Randi, M. A., de Oliveira Ribeiro, C. A., Pereira, L., Maraschi, A. C., Prodocimo, V., Freire,

C. A., and Silva de Assis, H. C. (2013) Effects of the herbicide atrazine in neotropical catfish (Rhamdia quelen). *Ecotoxicol Environ Saf* **93**, 13-21

28. Rowell, C., Kuiper, N., and Preud'Homme, H. (2016) Is container type the biggest predictor of trace element and BPA leaching from drinking water bottles? *Food Chem* **202**, 88-93

29. Stiles, R., Yang, I., Lippincott, R. L., Murphy, E., and Buckley, B. (2008) Measurement of drinking water contaminants by solid phase microextraction initially quantified in source water samples by the USGS. *Environ Sci Technol* **42**, 2976-2981

30. Klecka, G., Persoon, C., and Currie, R. (2010) Chemicals of emerging concern in the Great Lakes Basin: an analysis of environmental exposures. *Rev Environ Contam Toxicol* **207**, 1-93

31. Otero, P., Saha, S. K., Moane, S., Barron, J., Clancy, G., and Murray, P. (2015) Improved method for rapid detection of phthalates in bottled water by gas chromatography-mass spectrometry. *J Chromatogr B Analyt Technol Biomed Life Sci* **997**, 229-235

32. Oehlmann, J., Schulte-Oehlmann, U., Kloas, W., Jagnytsch, O., Lutz, I., Kusk, K. O., Wollenberger, L., Santos, E. M., Paull, G. C., Van Look, K. J., and Tyler, C. R. (2009) A critical analysis of the biological impacts of plasticizers on wildlife. *Philos Trans R Soc Lond B Biol Sci* **364**, 2047-2062

33. Kang, J. H., and Kondo, F. (2002) Bisphenol A migration from cans containing coffee and caffeine. *Food Addit Contam* **19**, 886-890

34. Li, Z., Xiang, X., Li, M., Ma, Y., Wang, J., and Liu, X. (2015) Occurrence and risk assessment of pharmaceuticals and personal care products and endocrine disrupting chemicals in reclaimed water and receiving groundwater in China. *Ecotoxicol Environ Saf* **119**, 74-80

35. Parkinson, J. (2015) Five numbers that sum up China's one-child policy: http://www.bbc.com/news/magazine-34666440.

36. Jarosova, B., Filip, J., Hilscherova, K., Tucek, J., Simek, Z., Giesy, J. P., Zboril, R., and Blaha, L. (2015) Can zero-valent iron

nanoparticles remove waterborne estrogens? *J Environ Manage* **150**, 387-392

37. Yang, Y., Cao, X., Zhang, M., and Wang, J. (2015) Occurrence and distribution of endocrine-disrupting compounds in the Honghu Lake and East Dongting Lake along the Central Yangtze River, China. *Environ Sci Pollut Res Int* **22**, 17644-17652

38. Ma, T., Wan, X., Huang, Q., Wang, Z., and Liu, J. (2005) Biomarker responses and reproductive toxicity of the effluent from a Chinese large sewage treatment plant in Japanese medaka (Oryzias latipes). *Chemosphere* **59**, 281-288

39. Zuo, Y., Zhang, K., and Zhou, S. (2013) Determination of estrogenic steroids and microbial and photochemical degradation of 17alpha-ethinylestradiol (EE2) in lake surface water, a case study. *Environ Sci Process Impacts* **15**, 1529-1535

40. Zuo, Y., Zhang, K., and Deng, Y. (2006) Occurrence and photochemical degradation of 17alpha-ethinylestradiol in Acushnet River Estuary. *Chemosphere* **63**, 1583-1590

41. Kostich, M., Flick, R., and Martinson, J. (2013) Comparing predicted estrogen concentrations with measurements in US waters. *Environ Pollut* **178**, 271-277

42. Sabik, H., Gagne, F., Blaise, C., Marcogliese, D. J., and Jeannot, R. (2003) Occurrence of alkylphenol polyethoxylates in the St. Lawrence River and their bioconcentration by mussels (Elliptio complanata). *Chemosphere* **51**, 349-356

43. Berchier, C. E., Slot, D. E., Haps, S., and Van der Weijden, G. A. (2008) The efficacy of dental floss in addition to a toothbrush on plaque and parameters of gingival inflammation: a systematic review. *Int J Dent Hyg* **6**, 265-279

44. Puy-Azurmendi, E., Ortiz-Zarragoitia, M., Kuster, M., Martinez, E., Guillamon, M., Dominguez, C., Serrano, T., Barbero, M. C., Alda, M. L., Bayona, J. M., Barcelo, D., and Cajaraville, M. P. (2010) An integrated study of endocrine disruptors in sediments and reproduction-related parameters in bivalve molluscs from the Biosphere's Reserve of Urdaibai (Bay of Biscay). *Mar Environ Res* **69 Suppl**, S63-66

45.   Pojana, G., Gomiero, A., Jonkers, N., and Marcomini, A. (2007) Natural and synthetic endocrine disrupting compounds (EDCs) in water, sediment and biota of a coastal lagoon. *Environ Int* **33**, 929-936

46.   Staniszewska, M., Falkowska, L., Grabowski, P., Kwasniak, J., Mudrak-Cegiolka, S., Reindl, A. R., Sokolowski, A., Szumilo, E., and Zgrundo, A. (2014) Bisphenol A, 4-tert-octylphenol, and 4-nonylphenol in the Gulf of Gdansk (Southern Baltic). *Arch Environ Contam Toxicol* **67**, 335-347

47.   (2003) NRDC Sues EPA for Failing to Protect Endangered Wildlife   from   Herbicide: https://www.nrdc.org/media/2003/030820.

48.   Andrew, M. N., Dunstan, R. H., O'Connor, W. A., Van Zwieten, L., Nixon, B., and MacFarlane, G. R. (2008) Effects of 4-nonylphenol and 17alpha-ethynylestradiol exposure in the Sydney rock oyster, Saccostrea glomerata: Vitellogenin induction and gonadal development. *Aquat Toxicol* **88**, 39-47

49.   Leonard, J. A., Cope, W. G., Barnhart, M. C., and Bringolf, R. B. (2014) Metabolomic, behavioral, and reproductive effects of the synthetic estrogen 17 alpha-ethinylestradiol on the unionid mussel Lampsilis fasciola. *Aquat Toxicol* **150**, 103-116

50.   Heil, T. P., and Lindsay, R. C. (1990) Environmental and industrial factors relating to flavor tainting of fish in the upper Wisconsin river. *J Environ Sci Health B* **25**, 527-552

51.   Priac, A., Morin-Crini, N, Druart, C, Gavoille, S, Bradu, C, Lagarrigue, C, Torri, G, Winterton, P, Crini, G. (2014) Alkylphenol and alkylphenol polyethoxylates in water and wastewater: A review of options for their elimination. *Arabian Journal of Chemistry* http://dx.doi.org/10.1016/j.arabjc.2014.05.011

52.   Liedtke, A., Schonenberger, R., Eggen, R. I., and Suter, M. J. (2009) Internal exposure of whitefish (Coregonus lavaretus) to estrogens. *Aquat Toxicol* **93**, 158-165

53.   Miranda, A. L., Roche, H., Randi, M. A., Menezes, M. L., and Ribeiro, C. A. (2008) Bioaccumulation of chlorinated pesticides and PCBs in the tropical freshwater fish Hoplias malabaricus:

histopathological, physiological, and immunological findings. *Environ Int* **34**, 939-949

54. Brock, J. W., Bell, J. M., and Guillette, L. J., Jr. (2016) Urinary Phthalate Metabolites in American Alligators (Alligator mississippiensis) from Selected Florida Wetlands. *Arch Environ Contam Toxicol*

55. Franke, A. A., Halm, B. M., Custer, L. J., Tatsumura, Y., and Hebshi, S. (2006) Isoflavones in breastfed infants after mothers consume soy. *Am J Clin Nutr* **84**, 406-413

56. Arbuckle, T. E., Fisher, M., MacPherson, S., Lang, C., Provencher, G., LeBlanc, A., Hauser, R., Feeley, M., Ayotte, P., Neisa, A., Ramsay, T., and Tawagi, G. (2016) Maternal and early life exposure to phthalates: The Plastics and Personal-care Products use in Pregnancy (P4) study. *Sci Total Environ* **551-552**, 344-356

57. Kilic, M., and Lindsay, R. C. (2005) Distribution of conjugates of alkylphenols in milk from different ruminant species. *J Dairy Sci* **88**, 7-12

58. Fierens, T., Van Holderbeke, M., Willems, H., De Henauw, S., and Sioen, I. (2013) Transfer of eight phthalates through the milk chain--a case study. *Environ Int* **51**, 1-7

59. Liao, C., Liu, F., and Kannan, K. (2013) Occurrence of and dietary exposure to parabens in foodstuffs from the United States. *Environ Sci Technol* **47**, 3918-3925

60. Muldoon, M. T., and Stanker, L. H. (1997) Molecularly imprinted solid phase extraction of atrazine from beef liver extracts. *Anal Chem* **69**, 803-808

61. Curren, M., King, J. (2001) Using Hot Water as a Solvent to Analyze Atrazine in Meat: http://agresearchmag.ars.usda.gov/2001/oct/meat/.

62. Peighambarzadeh, S., Safi, S., Shahtaheri, S., Javanbakht, M., and Rahimi Forushani, A. (2011) Presence of atrazine in the biological samples of cattle and its consequence adversity in human health. *Iran J Public Health* **40**, 112-121

63. Kocasari, F. S., Mor, F., Oguz, M. N., and Oguz, F. K. (2013) Occurrence of mycotoxins in feed samples in Burdur Province, Turkey. *Environ Monit Assess* **185**, 4943-4949

64. Jovaisiene, J., Bakutis, B., Baliukoniene, V., and Gerulis, G. (2016) Fusarium and Aspergillus mycotoxins effects on dairy cow health, performance and the efficacy of Anti-Mycotoxin Additive. *Pol J Vet Sci* **19**, 79-87

65. Becker-Algeri, T. A., Castagnaro, D., de Bortoli, K., de Souza, C., Drunkler, D. A., and Badiale-Furlong, E. (2016) Mycotoxins in Bovine Milk and Dairy Products: A Review. *J Food Sci* **81**, R544-552

66. Jay, A. G., and Hamilton, J. A. (2016) The enigmatic membrane fatty acid transporter CD36: New insights into fatty acid binding and their effects on uptake of oxidized LDL. *Prostaglandins Leukot Essent Fatty Acids*

67. Jay, A. G., and Hamilton, J. A. (2016) Disorder Amidst Membrane Order: Standardizing Laurdan Generalized Polarization and Membrane Fluidity Terms. *J Fluoresc*

68. Prelusky, D. B., Scott, P. M., Trenholm, H. L., and Lawrence, G. A. (1990) Minimal transmission of zearalenone to milk of dairy cows. *J Environ Sci Health B* **25**, 87-103

69. Witte, C., Hooser, S. (2003) The presence, effect, and diagnosis of zearalenone in dairy cattle: https://www.addl.purdue.edu/newsletters/2003/winter/zearal onenone.shtml. *Purdue University*

70. Hsieh, M., Chen, H, Chang, J, She, W, Chou, C. (2013) Electrochemical Detection of Zeranol and Zearalenone Metabolic Analogs in Meats and Grains by Screen-Plated Carbon-Plated Disposable Electrodes *Food and Nutrition Sciences* **4**, 31-38

71. Mahmoudi, R. (2014) Occurrence of zearalenone in raw animal origin food produced in north-west of Iran. *Journal of Food Quality and Hazards Control* **1**, 25-28

72. Khan, S. U., and Foster, T. S. (1976) Residues of atrazine (2-chloro-4-ethylamino-6-isopropylamino-s-triazine)and its metabolities in chicken tissues. *J Agric Food Chem* **24**, 768-771

73. Tsumura, Y., Ishimitsu, S., Kaihara, A., Yoshii, K., Nakamura, Y., and Tonogai, Y. (2001) Di(2-ethylhexyl) phthalate contamination

of retail packed lunches caused by PVC gloves used in the preparation of foods. *Food Addit Contam* **18**, 569-579

74.   Stephany, R. W. (2010) Hormonal growth promoting agents in food producing animals. *Handb Exp Pharmacol*, 355-367

75.   Wang, L., Asimakopoulos, A. G., and Kannan, K. (2015) Accumulation of 19 environmental phenolic and xenobiotic heterocyclic aromatic compounds in human adipose tissue. *Environ Int* **78**, 45-50

Chapter 5

1.   Api, A. M. (2001) Toxicological profile of diethyl phthalate: a vehicle for fragrance and cosmetic ingredients. *Food Chem Toxicol* **39**, 97-108

2.   Crinnion, W. J. (2010) Toxic effects of the easily avoidable phthalates and parabens. *Altern Med Rev* **15**, 190-196

3.   Li, W., Shi, Y., Gao, L., Liu, J., and Cai, Y. (2015) Occurrence and human exposure of parabens and their chlorinated derivatives in swimming pools. *Environ Sci Pollut Res Int* **22**, 17987-17997

4.   Karpuzoglu, E., Holladay, S. D., and Gogal, R. M., Jr. (2013) Parabens: potential impact of low-affinity estrogen receptor binding chemicals on human health. *J Toxicol Environ Health B Crit Rev* **16**, 321-335

5.   Pycke, B. F., Geer, L. A., Dalloul, M., Abulafia, O., and Halden, R. U. (2015) Maternal and fetal exposure to parabens in a multiethnic urban U.S. population. *Environ Int* **84**, 193-200

6.   Guerre, P. (2015) Fusariotoxins in Avian Species: Toxicokinetics, Metabolism and Persistence in Tissues. *Toxins (Basel)* **7**, 2289-2305

7.   Suen, J. L., Hung, C. H., Yu, H. S., and Huang, S. K. (2012) Alkylphenols--potential modulators of the allergic response. *Kaohsiung J Med Sci* **28**, S43-48

8.   Kim, S., and Choi, K. (2014) Occurrences, toxicities, and ecological risks of benzophenone-3, a common component of organic sunscreen products: a mini-review. *Environ Int* **70**, 143-157

9.   Wang, L., Asimakopoulos, A. G., and Kannan, K. (2015) Accumulation of 19 environmental phenolic and xenobiotic

heterocyclic aromatic compounds in human adipose tissue. *Environ Int* **78**, 45-50

10. Gunasekaran, N., Long, L. E., Dawson, B. L., Hansen, G. H., Richardson, D. P., Li, K. M., Arnold, J. C., and McGregor, I. S. (2009) Reintoxication: the release of fat-stored delta(9)-tetrahydrocannabinol (THC) into blood is enhanced by food deprivation or ACTH exposure. *Br J Pharmacol* **158**, 1330-1337

11. Drummer, O. H. (2004) Postmortem toxicology of drugs of abuse. *Forensic Sci Int* **142**, 101-113

12. Arner, P., Bernard, S., Salehpour, M., Possnert, G., Liebl, J., Steier, P., Buchholz, B. A., Eriksson, M., Arner, E., Hauner, H., Skurk, T., Ryden, M., Frayn, K. N., and Spalding, K. L. (2011) Dynamics of human adipose lipid turnover in health and metabolic disease. *Nature* **478**, 110-113

13. Langin, D. (2011) In and out: adipose tissue lipid turnover in obesity and dyslipidemia. *Cell Metab* **14**, 569-570

14. Spalding, K. L., Arner, E., Westermark, P. O., Bernard, S., Buchholz, B. A., Bergmann, O., Blomqvist, L., Hoffstedt, J., Naslund, E., Britton, T., Concha, H., Hassan, M., Ryden, M., Frisen, J., and Arner, P. (2008) Dynamics of fat cell turnover in humans. *Nature* **453**, 783-787

15. Kane, J. (2012) Health costs: how the U.S. compares with other countries, http://www.pbs.org/newshour/rundown/health-costs-how-the-us-compares-with-other-countries/. *PBS NewsHour*

16. Lim, S., Ahn, S. Y., Song, I. C., Chung, M. H., Jang, H. C., Park, K. S., Lee, K. U., Pak, Y. K., and Lee, H. K. (2009) Chronic exposure to the herbicide, atrazine, causes mitochondrial dysfunction and insulin resistance. *PLoS One* **4**, e5186

17. Cao, J., Echelberger, R., Liu, M., Sluzas, E., McCaffrey, K., Buckley, B., and Patisaul, H. B. (2015) Soy but not bisphenol A (BPA) or the phytoestrogen genistin alters developmental weight gain and food intake in pregnant rats and their offspring. *Reprod Toxicol* **58**, 282-294

18. Vafeiadi, M., Roumeliotaki, T., Myridakis, A., Chalkiadaki, G., Fthenou, E., Dermitzaki, E., Karachaliou, M., Sarri, K., Vassilaki,

M., Stephanou, E. G., Kogevinas, M., and Chatzi, L. (2016) Association of early life exposure to bisphenol A with obesity and cardiometabolic traits in childhood. *Environ Res* **146**, 379-387

19. Li, J., Wang, Y., Fang, F., Chen, D., Gao, Y., Liu, J., Gao, R., Wang, J., and Xiao, H. (2016) Bisphenol A disrupts glucose transport and neurophysiological role of IR/IRS/AKT/GSK3beta axis in the brain of male mice. *Environ Toxicol Pharmacol* **43**, 7-12

20. Berg, J., Tymockzko, JL, Stryer, L. (2005) Biochemistry. *New York: WH Freeman* **Each Organ Has a Unique Metabolic Profile**, 30.32

21. Bertoli, S., Leone, A., and Battezzati, A. (2015) Human Bisphenol A Exposure and the "Diabesity Phenotype". *Dose Response*

22. Pazaiti, A., Kontos, M., and Fentiman, I. S. (2012) ZEN and the art of breast health maintenance. *Int J Clin Pract* **66**, 28-36

23. Choi, J., Eom, J., Kim, J., Lee, S., and Kim, Y. (2014) Association between some endocrine-disrupting chemicals and childhood obesity in biological samples of young girls: a cross-sectional study. *Environ Toxicol Pharmacol* **38**, 51-57

24. Pearle, L., Katrandjian, O, Cuomo, C. (2011) FDA to review safety issues surrounding leading birth control pill Yaz: http://abcnews.go.com/Health/fda-discuss-safety-issues-surrounding-leading-birth-control/story?id=15099220.

25. Pereira-Fernandes, A., Demaegdt, H., Vandermeiren, K., Hectors, T. L., Jorens, P. G., Blust, R., and Vanparys, C. (2013) Evaluation of a screening system for obesogenic compounds: screening of endocrine disrupting compounds and evaluation of the PPAR dependency of the effect. *PLoS One* **8**, e77481

26. Cromie, W. (2002) Scientists get straight skinny on fat cells: single path found that leads to fat production: http://news.harvard.edu/gazette/2002/01.17/01-fatcells.html. *Harvard University Gazette*

27. Haleem, D. J. (2015) Drug Targets for Obesity and Depression: From Serotonin to Leptin. *Curr Drug Targets*

28. Hannaford, P. C., Iversen, L., Macfarlane, T. V., Elliott, A. M., Angus, V., and Lee, A. J. (2010) Mortality among contraceptive pill users: cohort evidence from Royal College of General Practitioners' Oral Contraception Study. *BMJ* **340**, c927

29.   Doshi, P. (2013) Influenza: marketing vaccine by marketing disease. *BMJ* **346**, f3037

30.   Merriott, D. (2016) Factors associated with the farmer suicide crisis in India. *J Epidemiol Glob Health*

31.   Kennedy, J., and King, L. (2014) The political economy of farmers' suicides in India: indebted cash-crop farmers with marginal landholdings explain state-level variation in suicide rates. *Global Health* **10**, 16

32.   Aggarwal, S. (2015) Suicide in India. *Br Med Bull* **114**, 127-134

33.   Ackerman, F., Whited, M., and Knight, P. (2014) Would banning atrazine benefit farmers? *Int J Occup Environ Health* **20**, 61-70

34.   Aslam, M., Alam, M, Rais, S. (2013) Detection of atrazine and simazine in ground water of Delhi using high performance liquid chormatography with ultraviolet detector. *Current World Environment* **8**, 323-329

35.   Pathak, R., Dikshit, AK,. (2012) Atrazine and its use *International Journal of Research in Chemistry and Environment* **2**, 1-6

36.   Tinelli, A., Menis, T., Brotto, F., Tinelli, R., and Tinelli, F. G. (2003) [Depression, menopause and hormonal replacement therapy (HRT)]. *Minerva Ginecol* **55**, 221-231

37.   Kok, L., Kreijkamp-Kaspers, S., Grobbee, D. E., Lampe, J. W., and van der Schouw, Y. T. (2005) A randomized, placebo-controlled trial on the effects of soy protein containing isoflavones on quality of life in postmenopausal women. *Menopause* **12**, 56-62

38.   Shiue, I. (2015) Urinary heavy metals, phthalates and polyaromatic hydrocarbons independent of health events are associated with adult depression: USA NHANES, 2011-2012. *Environ Sci Pollut Res Int* **22**, 17095-17103

39.   Kim, K. N., Choi, Y. H., Lim, Y. H., and Hong, Y. C. (2016) Urinary phthalate metabolites and depression in an elderly population: National Health and Nutrition Examination Survey 2005-2012. *Environ Res* **145**, 61-67

40.   Ejaredar, M., Lee, Y., Roberts, D. J., Sauve, R., and Dewey, D. (2016) Bisphenol A exposure and children's behavior: A systematic review. *J Expo Sci Environ Epidemiol*

41.   Ribeiro-Varandas, E., Pereira, H. S., Viegas, W., and Delgado, M. (2016) Bisphenol A alters transcript levels of biomarker genes for Major Depressive Disorder in vascular endothelial cells and colon cancer cells. *Chemosphere* **153**, 75-77

42.   Gahr, M., Freudenmann, R. W., Connemann, B. J., Kolle, M. A., and Schonfeldt-Lecuona, C. (2014) Rapid relapse in depression following initialization of oral contraception with ethinyl estradiol and chlormadinone acetate. *Gen Hosp Psychiatry* **36**, 230 e231-232

43.   Rumsey, T. S., Tyrrell, H. F., Dinius, D. A., Moe, P. W., and Cross, H. R. (1981) Effect of diethylstilbestrol on tissue gain and carcass merit of feedlot beef steers. *J Anim Sci* **53**, 589-600

44.   O'Reilly, E. J., Mirzaei, F., Forman, M. R., and Ascherio, A. (2010) Diethylstilbestrol exposure in utero and depression in women. *Am J Epidemiol* **171**, 876-882

Chapter 6

1.   Cooke, B. M., Breedlove, S. M., and Jordan, C. L. (2003) Both estrogen receptors and androgen receptors contribute to testosterone-induced changes in the morphology of the medial amygdala and sexual arousal in male rats. *Horm Behav* **43**, 336-346

2.   Losecaat Vermeer, A. B., Riecansky, I., and Eisenegger, C. (2016) Competition, testosterone, and adult neurobehavioral plasticity. *Prog Brain Res* **229**, 213-238

3.   www.ajconsultingcompany.com/thesis.

4.   Cieri, R., Churchill, SE, Franciscus, RG, Tan, J, Hare, B. (2014) Craniofacial feminization, social tolerance, and the origins of behavioral modernity. *Current Anthropology* **55**

5.   Carlsen, E., Giwercman, A., Keiding, N., and Skakkebaek, N. E. (1992) Evidence for decreasing quality of semen during past 50 years. *BMJ* **305**, 609-613

6.   Bachmann, G., Bancroft, J., Braunstein, G., Burger, H., Davis, S., Dennerstein, L., Goldstein, I., Guay, A., Leiblum, S., Lobo, R., Notelovitz, M., Rosen, R., Sarrel, P., Sherwin, B., Simon, J., Simpson, E., Shifren, J., Spark, R., Traish, A., and Princeton. (2002) Female androgen insufficiency: the Princeton consensus

statement on definition, classification, and assessment. *Fertil Steril* **77**, 660-665

7. Vesper, H. W., Wang, Y., Vidal, M., Botelho, J. C., and Caudill, S. P. (2015) Serum Total Testosterone Concentrations in the US Household Population from the NHANES 2011-2012 Study Population. *Clin Chem* **61**, 1495-1504

8. Rohr, U. D. (2002) The impact of testosterone imbalance on depression and women's health. *Maturitas* **41 Suppl 1**, S25-46

9. Hidaka, B. H. (2012) Depression as a disease of modernity: explanations for increasing prevalence. *J Affect Disord* **140**, 205-214

10. Maruyama, K., Oshima, T., and Ohyama, K. (2010) Exposure to exogenous estrogen through intake of commercial milk produced from pregnant cows. *Pediatr Int* **52**, 33-38

11. Bernardino, R. L., Alves, M. G., Silva, J., Barros, A., Ferraz, L., Sousa, M., Sa, R., and Oliveira, P. F. (2016) Expression of Estrogen Receptors Alpha (ER-alpha), Beta (ER-beta), and G Protein-Coupled Receptor 30 (GPR30) in Testicular Tissue of Men with Klinefelter Syndrome. *Horm Metab Res*

12. Yiu, K. W., Lee, C. K., Kwok, K. C., and Cheung, N. H. (2014) Measuring the kinetics of the binding of xenoestrogens and estrogen receptor alpha by fluorescence polarization. *Environ Sci Technol* **48**, 11591-11599

13. Dindyal, S. (2003) The sperm count has been decreasing steadily for many years in Western industrialized countries: Is there an endocrine basis for this decrease? *The Internet Journal of Urology* **2**

14. Gopalakrishnan, S., Cheung, N. K., Yip, B. W., and Au, D. W. (2013) Medaka fish exhibits longevity gender gap, a natural drop in estrogen and telomere shortening during aging: a unique model for studying sex-dependent longevity. *Front Zool* **10**, 78

15. Chiabotto, P., Costante, L., and de Sanctis, C. (2006) Premature thelarche and environmental pollutants. *Minerva Med* **97**, 277-285

16. Krysiak, R., Szkrobka, W., Kowalska, B., and Okopien, B. (2014) [Precocious puberty in boys]. *Przegl Lek* **71**, 549-558

17.   Ibanez, L., Diaz, R., Lopez-Bermejo, A., and Marcos, M. V. (2009) Clinical spectrum of premature pubarche: links to metabolic syndrome and ovarian hyperandrogenism. *Rev Endocr Metab Disord* **10**, 63-76

18.   Walsh, N. (2013) Effects of Early Puberty in Girls Persist as Adults. *MedPage Today, Endocrinology*

19.   Kim, Y. R., Jung, E. M., Choi, K. C., and Jeung, E. B. (2012) Synergistic effects of octylphenol and isobutyl paraben on the expression of calbindin-D(9)k in GH3 rat pituitary cells. *Int J Mol Med* **29**, 294-302

20.   Lee, Y., and Styne, D. (2013) Influences on the onset and tempo of puberty in human beings and implications for adolescent psychological development. *Horm Behav* **64**, 250-261

21.   Roy, J. R., Chakraborty, S., and Chakraborty, T. R. (2009) Estrogen-like endocrine disrupting chemicals affecting puberty in humans--a review. *Med Sci Monit* **15**, RA137-145

22.   Willoughby, K. N., Sarkar, A. J., Boyadjieva, N. I., and Sarkar, D. K. (2005) Neonatally administered tert-octylphenol affects onset of puberty and reproductive development in female rats. *Endocrine* **26**, 161-168

23.   Fortes, E. M., Malerba, M. I., Luchini, P. D., Sugawara, E. K., Sumodjo, L., Ribeiro Neto, L. M., and Verreschi, I. T. (2007) [High intake of phytoestrogens and precocious thelarche: case report with a possible correlation]. *Arq Bras Endocrinol Metabol* **51**, 500-503

24.   Mortenson, T. (2006) The state of American manhood. *Postsecondary Education Opportunity*

25.   Rocheleau, M. (2016) On campus, women outnumber men more than ever. *The Boston Globe*

26.   Wallerson, R. (2014) Youth participation weakens in basketball, football, baseball, soccer: http://www.wsj.com/articles/SB10001424052702303519404 579350892629229918. *The Wall Street Journal*

27.   Arbuckle, T. E., Fisher, M., MacPherson, S., Lang, C., Provencher, G., LeBlanc, A., Hauser, R., Feeley, M., Ayotte, P., Neisa, A., Ramsay, T., and Tawagi, G. (2016) Maternal and early life

exposure to phthalates: The Plastics and Personal-care Products use in Pregnancy (P4) study. *Sci Total Environ* **551-552**, 344-356

28. Meyer, K., and Korz, V. (2013) Estrogen receptor alpha functions in the regulation of motivation and spatial cognition in young male rats. *PLoS One* **8**, e79303

29. Meyer, K., and Korz, V. (2013) Age dependent differences in the regulation of hippocampal steroid hormones and receptor genes: relations to motivation and cognition in male rats. *Horm Behav* **63**, 376-384

30. Jarque, S., Quiros, L., Grimalt, J. O., Gallego, E., Catalan, J., Lackner, R., and Pina, B. (2015) Background fish feminization effects in European remote sites. *Sci Rep* **5**, 11292

31. Jandegian, C. M., Deem, S. L., Bhandari, R. K., Holliday, C. M., Nicks, D., Rosenfeld, C. S., Selcer, K. W., Tillitt, D. E., Vom Saal, F. S., Velez-Rivera, V., Yang, Y., and Holliday, D. K. (2015) Developmental exposure to bisphenol A (BPA) alters sexual differentiation in painted turtles (Chrysemys picta). *Gen Comp Endocrinol* **216**, 77-85

32. Kang, L. N., Wang, Y., and Han, X. D. (2003) [Effects of nonylphenol on the reproductive system of male animals]. *Zhonghua Nan Ke Xue* **9**, 539-542

33. Hayes, T. B., Anderson, L. L., Beasley, V. R., de Solla, S. R., Iguchi, T., Ingraham, H., Kestemont, P., Kniewald, J., Kniewald, Z., Langlois, V. S., Luque, E. H., McCoy, K. A., Munoz-de-Toro, M., Oka, T., Oliveira, C. A., Orton, F., Ruby, S., Suzawa, M., Tavera-Mendoza, L. E., Trudeau, V. L., Victor-Costa, A. B., and Willingham, E. (2011) Demasculinization and feminization of male gonads by atrazine: consistent effects across vertebrate classes. *J Steroid Biochem Mol Biol* **127**, 64-73

34. Lioy, P. J., Hauser, R., Gennings, C., Koch, H. M., Mirkes, P. E., Schwetz, B. A., and Kortenkamp, A. (2015) Assessment of phthalates/phthalate alternatives in children's toys and childcare articles: Review of the report including conclusions and recommendation of the Chronic Hazard Advisory Panel of the Consumer Product Safety Commission. *J Expo Sci Environ Epidemiol* **25**, 343-353

35. Liu, X., Nie, S., Yu, Q., Wang, X., Huang, D., and Xie, M. (2016) Downregulation of steroid hormone receptor expression and activation of cell signal transduction pathways induced by a chiral nonylphenol isomer in mouse sertoli TM4 cells. *Environ Toxicol*

36. Jimenez-Diaz, I., Molina-Molina, J. M., Zafra-Gomez, A., Ballesteros, O., Navalon, A., Real, M., Saenz, J. M., Fernandez, M. F., and Olea, N. (2013) Simultaneous determination of the UV-filters benzyl salicylate, phenyl salicylate, octyl salicylate, homosalate, 3-(4-methylbenzylidene) camphor and 3-benzylidene camphor in human placental tissue by LC-MS/MS. Assessment of their in vitro endocrine activity. *J Chromatogr B Analyt Technol Biomed Life Sci* **936**, 80-87

Chapter 7

1. Luster, M. I., Hayes, H. T., Korach, K., Tucker, A. N., Dean, J. H., Greenlee, W. F., and Boorman, G. A. (1984) Estrogen immunosuppression is regulated through estrogenic responses in the thymus. *J Immunol* **133**, 110-116

2. Walker, S. E. (2011) Estrogen and autoimmune disease. *Clin Rev Allergy Immunol* **40**, 60-65

3. Walker, S. E., Besch-Williford, C. L., and Keisler, D. H. (1994) Accelerated deaths from systemic lupus erythematosus in NZB x NZW F1 mice treated with the testosterone-blocking drug flutamide. *J Lab Clin Med* **124**, 401-407

4. Hueza, I. M., Raspantini, P. C., Raspantini, L. E., Latorre, A. O., and Gorniak, S. L. (2014) Zearalenone, an estrogenic mycotoxin, is an immunotoxic compound. *Toxins (Basel)* **6**, 1080-1095

5. Morahan, P. S., Bradley, S. G., Munson, A. E., Duke, S., Fromtling, R. A., and Marciano-Cabral, F. (1984) Immunotoxic effects of diethylstilbestrol on host resistance: comparison with cyclophosphamide. *J Leukoc Biol* **35**, 329-341

6. Luebke, R. W., Chen, D. H., Dietert, R., Yang, Y., King, M., Luster, M. I., and Immunotoxicology, W. (2006) The comparative immunotoxicity of five selected compounds following developmental or adult exposure. *J Toxicol Environ Health B Crit Rev* **9**, 1-26

7. AAAAI, A. A. o. A., Asthma, & Immunology. Allergy Statistics: http://www.aaaai.org/about-aaaai/newsroom/allergy-statistics. And Figure: Fortune. 2010 Jul 26;162(2):14. When allergies attack. It's not just you. Allergies are increasing nationwide--and so is the impact on the work place. Lindner M.

8. Tuohy, P. G. (2003) Soy infant formula and phytoestrogens. *J Paediatr Child Health* **39**, 401-405

9. Abbes, S., Ben Salah-Abbes, J., Sharafi, H., Oueslati, R., and Noghabi, K. A. (2013) Lactobacillus paracasei BEJ01 prevents immunotoxic effects during chronic zearalenone exposure in Balb/c mice. *Immunopharmacol Immunotoxicol* **35**, 341-348

10. Robinson, L., and Miller, R. (2015) The Impact of Bisphenol A and Phthalates on Allergy, Asthma, and Immune Function: a Review of Latest Findings. *Curr Environ Health Rep* **2**, 379-387

11. Rowe, A. M., Brundage, K. M., and Barnett, J. B. (2008) Developmental immunotoxicity of atrazine in rodents. *Basic Clin Pharmacol Toxicol* **102**, 139-145

12. Rooney, A. A., Matulka, R. A., and Luebke, R. W. (2003) Developmental atrazine exposure suppresses immune function in male, but not female Sprague-Dawley rats. *Toxicol Sci* **76**, 366-375

13. Filby, A. L., Neuparth, T., Thorpe, K. L., Owen, R., Galloway, T. S., and Tyler, C. R. (2007) Health impacts of estrogens in the environment, considering complex mixture effects. *Environ Health Perspect* **115**, 1704-1710

14. Vojdani, A., and Vojdani, C. (2015) Immune reactivity to food coloring. *Altern Ther Health Med* **21 Suppl 1**, 52-62

15. Suen, J. L., Hung, C. H., Yu, H. S., and Huang, S. K. (2012) Alkylphenols--potential modulators of the allergic response. *Kaohsiung J Med Sci* **28**, S43-48

16. Peterson, J., Dwyer, J., Adlercreutz, H., Scalbert, A., Jacques, P., and McCullough, M. L. (2010) Dietary lignans: physiology and potential for cardiovascular disease risk reduction. *Nutr Rev* **68**, 571-603

17. Prince, M., Glueck, C. J., Shah, P., Kumar, A., Goldenberg, M., Rothschild, M., Motayar, N., Jetty, V., Lee, K., and Wang, P.

(2016) Hospitalization for pulmonary embolism associated with antecedent testosterone or estrogen therapy in patients found to have familial and acquired thrombophilia. *BMC Hematol* **16**, 6

18.   Kuhnel, L., and Heinrichs, C. (1984) [Clinical course study in thrombophilia]. *Folia Haematol Int Mag Klin Morphol Blutforsch* **111**, 519-527

19.   Snir, M., Cohen, S., Ben-Sira, I., and Buckman, G. (1985) Retinal manifestations of thrombotic thrombocytopenic purpura (TTP) following use of contraceptive treatment. *Ann Ophthalmol* **17**, 109-112

20.   www.ajconsultingcompany.com/ee2_drug_labels.html.

21.   Covin, R. B., Rich, N. L., and Aysola, A. (2004) Upper-extremity deep venous thrombosis complicating whole-blood donation. *Transfusion* **44**, 586-590

22.   Danschutter, D., Braet, F., Van Gyseghem, E., Hachimi-Idrissi, S., Van Bruwaene, B., Moloney-Harmon, P., and Huyghens, L. (2007) Di-(2-ethylhexyl)phthalate and deep venous thrombosis in children: a clinical and experimental analysis. *Pediatrics* **119**, e742-753

23.   Guimaraes, J., and Azevedo, E. (2005) Phytoestrogens as a risk factor for cerebral sinus thrombosis. *Cerebrovasc Dis* **20**, 137-138

24.   Mullin, R. (2014) Tufts study finds big rise in cost of drug development: http://cen.acs.org/articles/92/web/2014/11/Tufts-Study-Finds-Big-Rise.html.

25.   Angell, M. (2005) The Truth about the Drug Companies : How They Deceive Us and What to Do about It. *Random House Trade Paperback Ed.*

26.   Taggart, K. H. a. K. (2013) Above the law: America's worse charities: http://www.cnn.com/2013/06/13/us/worst-charities/   and   http://www.tampabay.com/americas-worst-charities/.

27.   Kandoth, C., McLellan, M. D., Vandin, F., Ye, K., Niu, B., Lu, C., Xie, M., Zhang, Q., McMichael, J. F., Wyczalkowski, M. A., Leiserson, M. D., Miller, C. A., Welch, J. S., Walter, M. J., Wendl, M. C., Ley, T. J., Wilson, R. K., Raphael, B. J., and Ding, L. (2013)

Mutational landscape and significance across 12 major cancer types. *Nature* **502**, 333-339

28.   Boland, C. R., and Ricciardiello, L. (1999) How many mutations does it take to make a tumor? *Proc Natl Acad Sci U S A* **96**, 14675-14677

29.   Merz, W. E. (2004) [Hormone replacement therapy and the risk of developing breast cancer]. *MMW Fortschr Med* **146**, 26-28, 30

30.   Forouzanfar, M. H., Foreman, K. J., Delossantos, A. M., Lozano, R., Lopez, A. D., Murray, C. J., and Naghavi, M. (2011) Breast and cervical cancer in 187 countries between 1980 and 2010: a systematic analysis. *Lancet* **378**, 1461-1484

31.   Havrilesky, L. J., Moorman, P. G., Lowery, W. J., Gierisch, J. M., Coeytaux, R. R., Urrutia, R. P., Dinan, M., McBroom, A. J., Hasselblad, V., Sanders, G. D., and Myers, E. R. (2013) Oral contraceptive pills as primary prevention for ovarian cancer: a systematic review and meta-analysis. *Obstet Gynecol* **122**, 139-147

32.   Hatzipetros, I., Gocze, P. M., and Farkas, B. (2013) Oral contraceptive pills as primary prevention for ovarian cancer: a systematic review and meta-analysis. *Obstet Gynecol* **122**, 1114

33.   Collaborative Group on Hormonal Factors in Breast, C. (1996) Breast cancer and hormonal contraceptives: collaborative reanalysis of individual data on 53 297 women with breast cancer and 100 239 women without breast cancer from 54 epidemiological studies. *Lancet* **347**, 1713-1727

34.   Heinemann, L. A., Weimann, A., Gerken, G., Thiel, C., Schlaud, M., and DoMinh, T. (1998) Modern oral contraceptive use and benign liver tumors: the German Benign Liver Tumor Case-Control Study. *Eur J Contracept Reprod Health Care* **3**, 194-200

35.   Farrell, S. C. a. G. (2007) Adverse effects of hormones and hormone antagonists on the liver. *Drug-Induced Liver Disease*, 707-722

36.   La Vecchia, C., and Boccia, S. (2014) Oral contraceptives, human papillomavirus and cervical cancer. *Eur J Cancer Prev* **23**, 110-112

37.   Marasas, W. F., van Rensburg, S. J., and Mirocha, C. J. (1979) Incidence of Fusarium species and the mycotoxins,

deoxynivalenol and zearalenone, in corn produced in esophageal cancer areas in Transkei. *J Agric Food Chem* **27**, 1108-1112

38. Hsia, C. C., Wu, J. L., Lu, X. Q., and Li, Y. S. (1988) Natural occurrence and clastogenic effects of nivalenol, deoxynivalenol, 3-acetyl-deoxynivalenol, 15-acetyl-deoxynivalenol, and zearalenone in corn from a high-risk area of esophageal cancer. *Cancer Detect Prev* **13**, 79-86

39. Belhassen, H., Jimenez-Diaz, I., Arrebola, J. P., Ghali, R., Ghorbel, H., Olea, N., and Hedili, A. (2015) Zearalenone and its metabolites in urine and breast cancer risk: a case-control study in Tunisia. *Chemosphere* **128**, 1-6

40. Jowa, L., and Howd, R. (2011) Should atrazine and related chlorotriazines be considered carcinogenic for human health risk assessment? *J Environ Sci Health C Environ Carcinog Ecotoxicol Rev* **29**, 91-144

41. Hu, K., Tian, Y., Du, Y., Huang, L., Chen, J., Li, N., Liu, W., Liang, Z., and Zhao, L. (2016) Atrazine promotes RM1 prostate cancer cell proliferation by activating STAT3 signaling. *Int J Oncol* **48**, 2166-2174

42. Varinska, L., Gal, P., Mojzisova, G., Mirossay, L., and Mojzis, J. (2015) Soy and breast cancer: focus on angiogenesis. *Int J Mol Sci* **16**, 11728-11749

43. Takagi, A., Kano, M., and Kaga, C. (2015) Possibility of breast cancer prevention: use of soy isoflavones and fermented soy beverage produced using probiotics. *Int J Mol Sci* **16**, 10907-10920

44. Johnson, K. A., Vemuri, S., Alsahafi, S., Castillo, R., and Cheriyath, V. (2016) Glycone-rich Soy Isoflavone Extracts Promote Estrogen Receptor Positive Breast Cancer Cell Growth. *Nutr Cancer* **68**, 622-633

45. Park, M. A., Hwang, K. A., Lee, H. R., Yi, B. R., Jeung, E. B., and Choi, K. C. (2013) Benzophenone-1 stimulated the growth of BG-1 ovarian cancer cells by cell cycle regulation via an estrogen receptor alpha-mediated signaling pathway in cellular and xenograft mouse models. *Toxicology* **305**, 41-48

46. Kim, S. H., Hwang, K. A., Shim, S. M., and Choi, K. C. (2015) Growth and migration of LNCaP prostate cancer cells are promoted by triclosan and benzophenone-1 via an androgen receptor signaling pathway. *Environ Toxicol Pharmacol* **39**, 568-576

47. In, S. J., Kim, S. H., Go, R. E., Hwang, K. A., and Choi, K. C. (2015) Benzophenone-1 and nonylphenol stimulated MCF-7 breast cancer growth by regulating cell cycle and metastasis-related genes via an estrogen receptor alpha-dependent pathway. *J Toxicol Environ Health A* **78**, 492-505

48. Shin, S., Go, R. E., Kim, C. W., Hwang, K. A., Nam, K. H., and Choi, K. C. (2016) Effect of benzophenone-1 and octylphenol on the regulation of epithelial-mesenchymal transition via an estrogen receptor-dependent pathway in estrogen receptor expressing ovarian cancer cells. *Food Chem Toxicol* **93**, 58-65

49. Piskounova, E., Agathocleous, M., Murphy, M. M., Hu, Z., Huddlestun, S. E., Zhao, Z., Leitch, A. M., Johnson, T. M., DeBerardinis, R. J., and Morrison, S. J. (2015) Oxidative stress inhibits distant metastasis by human melanoma cells. *Nature* **527**, 186-191

50. (1994) The effect of vitamin E and beta carotene on the incidence of lung cancer and other cancers in male smokers. The Alpha-Tocopherol, Beta Carotene Cancer Prevention Study Group. *N Engl J Med* **330**, 1029-1035

51. Klann, A., Levy, G., Lutz, I., Muller, C., Kloas, W., and Hildebrandt, J. P. (2005) Estrogen-like effects of ultraviolet screen 3-(4-methylbenzylidene)-camphor (Eusolex 6300) on cell proliferation and gene induction in mammalian and amphibian cells. *Environ Res* **97**, 274-281

52. Lagakos, S., and Mosteller, F. (1981) A case study of statistics in the regulatory process: the FD&C Red No. 40 experiments. *J Natl Cancer Inst* **66**, 197-212

53. Darbre, P. D., and Harvey, P. W. (2014) Parabens can enable hallmarks and characteristics of cancer in human breast epithelial cells: a review of the literature with reference to new exposure data and regulatory status. *J Appl Toxicol* **34**, 925-938

54.   Crinnion, W. J. (2010) Toxic effects of the easily avoidable phthalates and parabens. *Altern Med Rev* **15**, 190-196

55.   Sajid, M., Basheer, C., Narasimhan, K., Choolani, M., and Lee, H. K. (2015) Application of microwave-assisted micro-solid-phase extraction for determination of parabens in human ovarian cancer tissues. *J Chromatogr B Analyt Technol Biomed Life Sci* **1000**, 192-198

56.   Chen, F. P., and Chien, M. H. (2014) Lower concentrations of phthalates induce proliferation in human breast cancer cells. *Climacteric* **17**, 377-384

57.   Hruba, E., Pernicova, Z., Palkova, L., Soucek, K., Vondracek, J., and Machala, M. (2014) Phthalates deregulate cell proliferation, but not neuroendocrine transdifferentiation, in human LNCaP prostate cancer cell model. *Folia Biol (Praha)* **60 Suppl 1**, 56-61

58.   Paulose, T., Speroni, L., Sonnenschein, C., and Soto, A. M. (2015) Estrogens in the wrong place at the wrong time: Fetal BPA exposure and mammary cancer. *Reprod Toxicol* **54**, 58-65

59.   Fillon, M. (2012) Getting it right: BPA and the difficulty proving environmental cancer risks. *J Natl Cancer Inst* **104**, 652-655

60.   Amaro, A. A., Esposito, A. I., Mirisola, V., Mehilli, A., Rosano, C., Noonan, D. M., Albini, A., Pfeffer, U., and Angelini, G. (2014) Endocrine disruptor agent nonyl phenol exerts an estrogen-like transcriptional activity on estrogen receptor positive breast cancer cells. *Curr Med Chem* **21**, 630-640

61.   Speirs, V., and Shaaban, A. M. (2009) The rising incidence of male breast cancer. *Breast Cancer Res Treat* **115**, 429-430

62.   Ajj, H., Chesnel, A., Pinel, S., Plenat, F., Flament, S., and Dumond, H. (2013) An alkylphenol mix promotes seminoma derived cell proliferation through an ERalpha36-mediated mechanism. *PLoS One* **8**, e61758

Chapter 8

1.   Stein, Z., and Susser, M. (1975) The Dutch famine, 1944-1945, and the reproductive process. I. Effects on six indices at birth. *Pediatr Res* **9**, 70-76

2. Pembrey, M. (1996) Imprinting and transgenerational modulation of gene expression; human growth as a model. *Acta Genet Med Gemellol (Roma)* **45**, 111-125

3. Heijmans, B. T., Tobi, E. W., Stein, A. D., Putter, H., Blauw, G. J., Susser, E. S., Slagboom, P. E., and Lumey, L. H. (2008) Persistent epigenetic differences associated with prenatal exposure to famine in humans. *Proc Natl Acad Sci U S A* **105**, 17046-17049

4. Whitelaw, E. (2006) Epigenetics: sins of the fathers, and their fathers. *Eur J Hum Genet* **14**, 131-132

5. Lane, M., Zander-Fox, D. L., Robker, R. L., and McPherson, N. O. (2015) Peri-conception parental obesity, reproductive health, and transgenerational impacts. *Trends Endocrinol Metab* **26**, 84-90

6. McLachlan, J. A. (2016) Environmental signaling: from environmental estrogens to endocrine-disrupting chemicals and beyond. *Andrology* **4**, 684-694

7. Wei, Y., Yang, C. R., Wei, Y. P., Zhao, Z. A., Hou, Y., Schatten, H., and Sun, Q. Y. (2014) Paternally induced transgenerational inheritance of susceptibility to diabetes in mammals. *Proc Natl Acad Sci U S A* **111**, 1873-1878

8. Hughes, V. (2014) Epigenetics: The sins of the father. *Nature* **507**, 22-24

9. Cheng, R. Y., Hockman, T., Crawford, E., Anderson, L. M., and Shiao, Y. H. (2004) Epigenetic and gene expression changes related to transgenerational carcinogenesis. *Mol Carcinog* **40**, 1-11

10. Tsuda, S., Murakami, M., Matsusaka, N., Kano, K., Taniguchi, K., and Sasaki, Y. F. (2001) DNA damage induced by red food dyes orally administered to pregnant and male mice. *Toxicol Sci* **61**, 92-99

11. Gadzala-Kopciuch, R., Cendrowski, K., Cesarz, A., Kielbasa, P., and Buszewski, B. (2011) Determination of zearalenone and its metabolites in endometrial cancer by coupled separation techniques. *Anal Bioanal Chem* **401**, 2069-2078

12. Rafique, S., Thomas, J. S., Sproul, D., and Bickmore, W. A. (2015) Estrogen-induced chromatin decondensation and nuclear re-

organization linked to regional epigenetic regulation in breast cancer. *Genome Biol* **16**, 145

13. Newbold, R. R., Padilla-Banks, E., and Jefferson, W. N. (2006) Adverse effects of the model environmental estrogen diethylstilbestrol are transmitted to subsequent generations. *Endocrinology* **147**, S11-17

14. Singh, S., and Li, S. S. (2012) Epigenetic effects of environmental chemicals bisphenol A and phthalates. *Int J Mol Sci* **13**, 10143-10153

Chapter 9

1. Schultz, I. R., Skillman, A., Nicolas, J. M., Cyr, D. G., and Nagler, J. J. (2003) Short-term exposure to 17 alpha-ethynylestradiol decreases the fertility of sexually maturing male rainbow trout (Oncorhynchus mykiss). *Environ Toxicol Chem* **22**, 1272-1280

2. Nash, J. P., Kime, D. E., Van der Ven, L. T., Wester, P. W., Brion, F., Maack, G., Stahlschmidt-Allner, P., and Tyler, C. R. (2004) Long-term exposure to environmental concentrations of the pharmaceutical ethynylestradiol causes reproductive failure in fish. *Environ Health Perspect* **112**, 1725-1733

3. Hatef, A., Alavi, S. M., Milla, S., Kristan, J., Golshan, M., Fontaine, P., and Linhart, O. (2012) Anti-androgen vinclozolin impairs sperm quality and steroidogenesis in goldfish. *Aquat Toxicol* **122-123**, 181-187

4. Chang, K., Kurtz, H. J., and Mirocha, C. J. (1979) Effects of the mycotoxin zearalenone on swine reproduction. *Am J Vet Res* **40**, 1260-1267

5. Yazdanpanah, H., Zarghi, A., Shafaati, A. R., Foroutan, S. M., Aboul-Fathi, F., Khoddam, A., and Nazari, F. (2012) Exposure assessment of the tehran population (iran) to zearalenone mycotoxin. *Iran J Pharm Res* **11**, 251-256

6. Greenlee, A. R., Ellis, T. M., and Berg, R. L. (2004) Low-dose agrochemicals and lawn-care pesticides induce developmental toxicity in murine preimplantation embryos. *Environ Health Perspect* **112**, 703-709

7. Wang, X., Chen, X., Feng, X., Chang, F., Chen, M., Xia, Y., and Chen, L. (2015) Triclosan causes spontaneous abortion

accompanied by decline of estrogen sulfotransferase activity in humans and mice. *Sci Rep* **5**, 18252

8. Kay, V. R., Chambers, C., and Foster, W. G. (2013) Reproductive and developmental effects of phthalate diesters in females. *Crit Rev Toxicol* **43**, 200-219

9. Giahi, L., Mohammadmoradi, S., Javidan, A., and Sadeghi, M. R. (2016) Nutritional modifications in male infertility: a systematic review covering 2 decades. *Nutr Rev* **74**, 118-130

10. Chen, M., Tang, R., Fu, G., Xu, B., Zhu, P., Qiao, S., Chen, X., Xu, B., Qin, Y., Lu, C., Hang, B., Xia, Y., and Wang, X. (2013) Association of exposure to phenols and idiopathic male infertility. *J Hazard Mater* **250-251**, 115-121

11. Iwase, T., Sano, F., Murakami, T., and Inazawa, K. (1995) Male reproductive toxicity of ethinylestradiol associated with 4 weeks daily dosing prior to mating in rats. *J Toxicol Sci* **20**, 265-279

12. Rahman, M. S., Kwon, W. S., Lee, J. S., Yoon, S. J., Ryu, B. Y., and Pang, M. G. (2015) Bisphenol-A affects male fertility via fertility-related proteins in spermatozoa. *Sci Rep* **5**, 9169

13. Association, N. S. S. a. P. (2016) Dog sperm quality decline is blamed on pet food chemicals. *New Scientist*

14. Guillette, L. J., Jr., and Moore, B. C. (2006) Environmental contaminants, fertility, and multioocytic follicles: a lesson from wildlife? *Semin Reprod Med* **24**, 134-141

15. Bhandari, R. K., vom Saal, F. S., and Tillitt, D. E. (2015) Transgenerational effects from early developmental exposures to bisphenol A or 17alpha-ethinylestradiol in medaka, Oryzias latipes. *Sci Rep* **5**, 9303

16. Schwindt, A., et al. (2014) An environmental oestrogen disrupts fish population dynamics through direct and transgenerational effects on survival and fecundity. *Journal of Applied Ecology* **51**

17. Corrales, J., Thornton, C., White, M., and Willett, K. L. (2014) Multigenerational effects of benzo[a]pyrene exposure on survival and developmental deformities in zebrafish larvae. *Aquat Toxicol* **148**, 16-26

18. Kharat, I., and Saatcioglu, F. (1996) Antiestrogenic effects of 2,3,7,8-tetrachlorodibenzo-p-dioxin are mediated by direct

transcriptional interference with the liganded estrogen receptor. Cross-talk between aryl hydrocarbon- and estrogen-mediated signaling. *J Biol Chem* **271**, 10533-10537

19. Baker, T. R., Peterson, R. E., and Heideman, W. (2014) Using zebrafish as a model system for studying the transgenerational effects of dioxin. *Toxicol Sci* **138**, 403-411

20. Tournaire, M., Epelboin, S., Devouche, E., Viot, G., Le Bidois, J., Cabau, A., Dunbavand, A., and Levadou, A. (2016) Adverse health effects in children of women exposed in utero to diethylstilbestrol (DES). *Therapie* **71**, 395-404

21. Reed, C. E., and Fenton, S. E. (2013) Exposure to diethylstilbestrol during sensitive life stages: a legacy of heritable health effects. *Birth Defects Res C Embryo Today* **99**, 134-146

22. Manikkam, M., Tracey, R., Guerrero-Bosagna, C., and Skinner, M. K. (2013) Plastics derived endocrine disruptors (BPA, DEHP and DBP) induce epigenetic transgenerational inheritance of obesity, reproductive disease and sperm epimutations. *PLoS One* **8**, e55387

Chapter 10

1. Society, A. C. (2016) Known and probable human carcinogens.

2. Kim, K. N., Lee, M. R., Choi, Y. H., Hwang, H., Oh, S. Y., Park, C., and Hong, Y. C. (2016) Association between phthalate exposure and lower handgrip strength in an elderly population: a repeated-measures study. *Environ Health* **15**, 93

3. He, F., Chen, J. (2013) Consumption of soybean, soy foods, soy isoflavones and breast cancer incidence: Differences between Chinese women and women in Western countries and possible mechanisms *Food Science and Human Wellness* **2**, 146-161

4. Reeves, R. (2012) Why soybean oil is called vegetable oil. *Health and Nutrition Newsletter: SoyConnection by the United Soybean Board*

5. Pearson, C. (2015) The app that could be a 99 percent effective form of birth control. http://www.huffingtonpost.com/2015/01/15/contraceptive-app-natural-cycles_n_6472642.html

6.   Rea, W. J., Pan, Y., and Griffiths, B. (2009) The treatment of patients with mycotoxin-induced disease. *Toxicol Ind Health* **25**, 711-714

7.   Worland, J. (2015) The strange connection between saunas and longevity. *Time Magazine*

8.   Yen, T. H., Lin-Tan, D. T., and Lin, J. L. (2011) Food safety involving ingestion of foods and beverages prepared with phthalate-plasticizer-containing clouding agents. *J Formos Med Assoc* **110**, 671-684

9.   Rustagi, N., Pradhan, S. K., and Singh, R. (2011) Public health impact of plastics: An overview. *Indian J Occup Environ Med* **15**, 100-103

10.   http://www.ajconsultingcompany.com/plans.html.

11.   de Lemos, M. L., Hamata, L., and Vu, T. (2005) Leaching of diethylhexyl phthalate from polyvinyl chloride materials into etoposide intravenous solutions. *J Oncol Pharm Pract* **11**, 155-157

12.   Lewis, R. (1999) Vinyl chloride and polyvinyl chloride. *Occup Med* **14**, 719-742

13.   Ohno, K., Azuma, Y., Date, K., Nakano, S., Kobayashi, T., Nagao, Y., and Yamada, T. (2003) Evaluation of styrene oligomers eluted from polystyrene for estrogenicity in estrogen receptor binding assay, reporter gene assay, and uterotrophic assay. *Food Chem Toxicol* **41**, 131-141

14.   Mooney, A., Ward, P. G., and O'Connor, K. E. (2006) Microbial degradation of styrene: biochemistry, molecular genetics, and perspectives for biotechnological applications. *Appl Microbiol Biotechnol* **72**, 1-10

15.   Yang, C. Z., Yaniger, S. I., Jordan, V. C., Klein, D. J., and Bittner, G. D. (2011) Most plastic products release estrogenic chemicals: a potential health problem that can be solved. *Environ Health Perspect* **119**, 989-996

16.   Kissin, Y., et al. (2008) Ziegler-Natta catalysts for propylene polymerization: Chemistry of reactions leading to the formation of active centers. *Journal of Molecular Catalysis A: Chemical* **287**, 45-52

17. de Fatima Rezende, E., Borges, J. G., Cirillo, M. A., Prado, G., Paiva, L. C., and Batista, L. R. (2013) Ochratoxigenic fungi associated with green coffee beans (Coffea arabica L.) in conventional and organic cultivation in Brazil. *Braz J Microbiol* **44**, 377-384

18. Copetti, M. V., Iamanaka, B. T., Pitt, J. I., and Taniwaki, M. H. (2014) Fungi and mycotoxins in cocoa: from farm to chocolate. *Int J Food Microbiol* **178**, 13-20

19. Lithner, D., Nordensvan, I., and Dave, G. (2012) Comparative acute toxicity of leachates from plastic products made of polypropylene, polyethylene, PVC, acrylonitrile-butadiene-styrene, and epoxy to Daphnia magna. *Environ Sci Pollut Res Int* **19**, 1763-1772

20. Bejgarn, S., MacLeod, M., Bogdal, C., and Breitholtz, M. (2015) Toxicity of leachate from weathering plastics: An exploratory screening study with Nitocra spinipes. *Chemosphere* **132**, 114-119

21. Jones, A. Consumer Alert: Toxic Hormone-Disrupting Chemical BPA is Leaching from Food Can Liners: https://www.organicconsumers.org/news/consumer-alert-toxic-hormone-disrupting-chemical-bpa-leaching-food-can-liners. *Terrain Magazine*

22. Vojdani, A., and Vojdani, C. (2015) Immune reactivity to food coloring. *Altern Ther Health Med* **21 Suppl 1**, 52-62

23. Silva, E., Rajapakse, N., and Kortenkamp, A. (2002) Something from "nothing"--eight weak estrogenic chemicals combined at concentrations below NOECs produce significant mixture effects. *Environ Sci Technol* **36**, 1751-1756

24. Grey, Z. (1919) Tales of Fishes. *The Derrydale Press, Lanham, Maryland*

Index

Made in the USA
Columbia, SC
19 July 2018